THIS NEW WORLD

The Civilization of Latin America

By William Lytle Schurz

THIS NEW WORLD

THE CIVILIZATION OF LATIN AMERICA

by

William Lytle Schurz

illustrations by

Carl Folke Sahlin

A Dutton  *Paperback*

NEW YORK

E. P. DUTTON & CO., INC.

This paperback edition of

"THIS NEW WORLD"

First published 1964 by E. P. Dutton & Co., Inc.
All rights reserved. Printed in the U.S.A.

Copyright, 1954, by William Lytle Schurz

Published simultaneously in Canada by Clarke, Irwin
and Company Limited, Toronto and Vancouver.

SBN 0-525-47137-5

TO THE

STUDENTS AND GRADUATES

OF THE

AMERICAN INSTITUTE FOR FOREIGN TRADE

"As I noted the many great and strange things that are to be seen in this new world of the Indies, there came upon me a strong desire to write an account of some of them, as well those which I had seen with my own eyes as those which I had heard of from persons of good repute."

Pedro de Cieza de León, conqueror, and chronicler of the conquest, of Peru.

ACKNOWLEDGMENT

Most of those who have helped me to write this book—stout Cortés and Bernal Díaz; Gonzalo de Oviedo and Antonio de Herrera, the royal chroniclers; Garcilaso, the Spanish Inca, and Cieza de León; Fathers Acosta and Vázquez de Espinosa; diligent Richard Hakluyt and that literate buccaneer, William Dampier; John Stephens and Captain Basil Hall; and all their companions who put their story to paper—are long since dead. To their ghosts, swapping yarns on some adventurers' Olympus, my deepest gratitude.

WILLIAM LYTLE SCHURZ, distinguished historian, journalist, and former State Department official, was born in South Lebanon, Ohio. He was educated at Oberlin College and at the University of California, with two years of research work in the Archives of the Indies at Seville, Spain. He taught Latin American history at the University of Michigan and lectured in history at four other universities. As diplomat, journalist, explorer, commercial agent, export manager of a large manufacturing firm, and economic adviser to a Latin-American government, he acquired a comprehensive knowledge of Latin-American affairs. Dr. Schurz also taught for many years at the American Institute for Foreign Trade in Phoenix, Arizona. He died in 1962. In addition to *This New World,* Dr. Schurz was the author of *The Manila Galleon* (1939), *Latin America: A Descriptive Survey* (second revised edition, 1963), *American Foreign Affairs* (1959), and *Brazil: The Infinite Country* (1961).

THIS NEW WORLD: *The Civilization of Latin America* was first published in 1954.

CONTENTS

A NOTE ON PRONUNCIATION

This book contains many Spanish and Portuguese words. The author believes that the reader unfamiliar with the sound of these languages will derive some reward and satisfaction from the feeling that he is mentally pronouncing these words with a reasonable degree of correctness. For this purpose, there follows a brief, tabulated guide to the approximate pronunciation of both languages.

Letter	Spanish	Portuguese
a	m*a*no: like *a* in "f*a*ther"	*a*ba: like *a* in "f*a*ther"
e	p*e*so: like *e* in "f*e*te"	p*é*: like *e* in "l*e*t"
i	l*i*sta: like *i* in "mach*i*ne"	*i*da: like *i* in "mach*i*ne"
o	c*o*mo: like *o* in "n*o*te"	t*o*da: like *o* in "n*o*te"
u	m*u*la: like *oo* in "b*oo*t" (never like *u* in "*u*se")	m*u*la: like *oo* in "b*oo*t" (never like *u* in "*u*se")
		All Portuguese vowels become nasalized (air stream passing through mouth and nose at same time) either when marked with a til (∼) as in p*a*o, p*o*e: or when followed by an *n* or *m*: c*o*nto, c*a*mpo. If the -*m* is final in the word or the *n* is found in the final combination -*ns*, nasalization of the vowel is indicated but neither the *m* nor *n* is pronounced: viag*em*, viag*ens*.
c	*c*ine: like *s* in "*s*ing" before *e* or *i*	*c*ima: like *s* in "*s*ing" before *e* or *i*
c	*c*afé: like *c* and *k* in "*c*a*k*e" before *a, o, u*	*c*afé: like *c* and *k* in "*c*a*k*e" before *a, o, u*
ç		a*ç*o: like *s* in "*s*ing"
ch		*ch*á: like *sh* in "*sh*e"
g	*g*ente: somewhat like *h* in "be*h*ind" before *e* or *i*	*g*êlo: like *z* in "a*z*ure" before *e* or *i*
g	*g*ato: like *g* in "*g*ate" before *a, o, u*	*g*ato: like *g* in "*g*ate" before *a, o, u*
gu	*gu*ia: like *g* in "*g*ate" before *e, i* (the letter *u* is silent)	*gu*ia: like *g* in "*g*ate" before *e, i*

xii # A NOTE ON PRONUNCIATION

Letter	Spanish	Portuguese
h	*h*ora: not pronounced as in "*h*our"	*h*ora: not pronounced as in "*h*our"
j	*j*ota: somewhat like *h* in "be*h*ind"	*j*ôgo: like *z* in "a*z*ure"
ll	*ll*ave: like *y* in "*y*es"	
lh		ve*lh*o: like *lli* in "mi*lli*on"
ñ	ca*ñ*o: like *ny* in "ca*ny*on"	
nh		u*nh*a: like *ny* in "ca*ny*on"
qu	*Qu*ito: like *k* in "*k*ite" (the letter *u* is silent)	*qu*eimo: like *k* in "*k*ite" before *e* or *i*
		*qu*ota: like *qu* in "*qu*ite" before *a* or *o*
s	Jo*s*é: like *ss* in "ki*ss*" (never like *s* in "po*s*e")	ca*s*a: like *s* in "po*s*e" between vowels: in all other cases like *ss* in "ki*ss*": *s*i, pa*ss*o
z	*z*aga: like *ss* in "ki*ss*"	*z*êlo: like *z* in "do*z*e"

The diacritic (¨) over *ü* in Spanish or Portuguese indicates that the letter *u* is pronounced. The diacritic (´) in Spanish and (´) and (ˆ) in Portuguese indicate word stress.

All letters not listed in the above table are pronounced similarly in Spanish, Portuguese, and English.

THIS NEW WORLD

The Civilization of Latin America

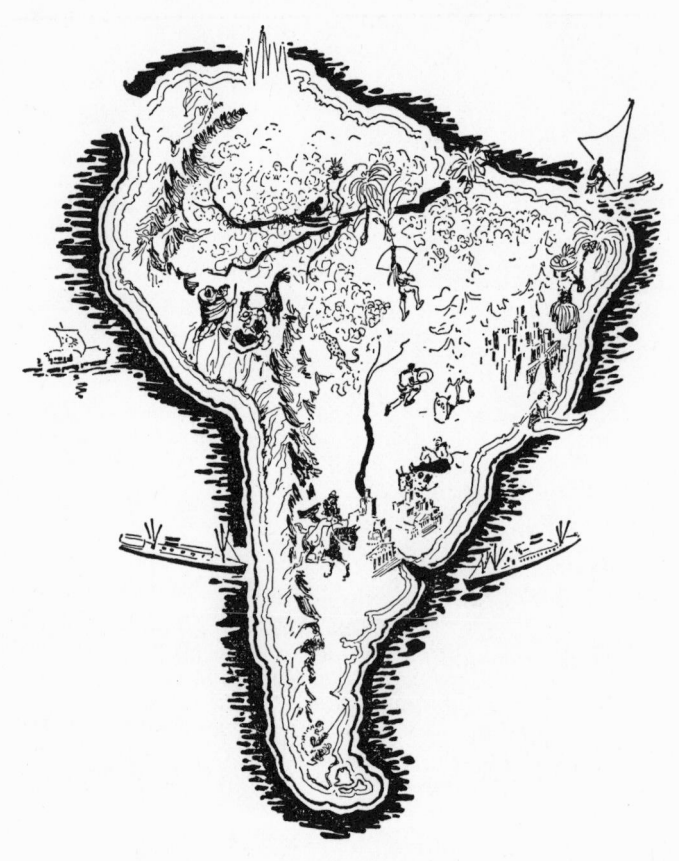

Chapter I
THE ENVIRONMENT

PEOPLE WHO leave the country of their birth for another tend to judge their new environment in the familiar terms of their old habitat. The Spaniards who went to the New World left behind them a hard and niggardly land. The heart of the country was an almost treeless plateau, burnt by a relentless sun in the summer, and chilled in winter by frigid winds from off the gaunt mountains which everywhere break the surface of the Castilian Tableland. Most Spaniards had always lived in the sight of mountains, and they felt strangely disoriented when the horizon became a straight line before them. For the mountains provided fixed and permanent bearings for their comings and goings, and anchors in the landscape for their vision. The face of nature in Spain, though generally forbidding and inhospitable to the foreigner, was on a scale that did not dwarf the egos of those who grew up in view of its stern profile. Spiritually, the rugged setting of their lives seemed of their own stature and measure, and some of the rocky quality of the mountains had entered into their souls and their bodies, just as today one may see peasants in Aragón and Old Castile who appear to be of a piece with the very land about them. The Spaniards who conquered and settled the Indies lived on friendly terms with their mountains, but expected little of them beyond protection in time of danger. For they knew their way about the defiles and the moors, and sometimes they built their towns on the tops of the hills, as they did at Sepúlveda and Soria. And in the Middle Ages, when Spaniard fought Spaniard and both fought the Moslem, they crowned the jutting promontories with castles like those of Almansa and Peñafiel and Segovia.[1] The austerity of the Spanish earth is portrayed in the backgrounds used by painters from El Greco to Zuloaga.

Around the rim of the Iberian peninsula, nature is more benign. Though the mountains come down to the sea in many places and for long distances, the country sometimes opens out into expanses of plain, as in the *vega* of Valencia, the wide coastal strip between Alicante and Cartagena, the lower valley of the Guadalquivir, and, above all, in the western side of Portugal. While the parts of Spain that border on the Atlantic, like the Asturias and the Basque Provinces, are mountainous, they are much greener than the arid highlands of Castile and Aragón. So is the hill country of Portugal. On the protected Spanish riviera, along the warm Levantine coast, the prevailing vegetation changes and there are orange groves and forests of date palms and fields of sugar cane.

This was the physical background, whose memories Spaniards and Portuguese carried with them to the Indies, but which had long been parcel of the fiber of the race. In the New World, they were to find few replicas of their homeland, and when they did they clung to them with a nostalgic attachment. But for the most part, nature was on an infinitely greater scale than in the peninsula. Everything—mountains, rivers, forests, plains, and swamps—was larger. And the moods of nature were more violent and unpredictable, for in its fury it sometimes exploded in earthquakes and hurricanes and the eruption of volcanoes.

First impressions of the New World were of ecstasy and wonderment. The discoverers marveled at the luxuriance and variety of the vegetation, and the pleasing lay of the land as they sailed among the Antilles. Columbus, an adopted Spaniard, went into raptures at the sights and sounds of Hispaniola.[2] "The nightingale was singing," he said, "and other small birds as they do in that month in Spain. . . . It was the greatest delight in the world." He called the island "Little Spain," because—by some obvious strain on his imagination—the rich plains of the Cibao reminded him, at least by their "fertility, of the lands of Castile." He rhapsodized even more about Cuba, and called it "the loveliest island that eyes have ever seen," an endorsement which the Tourist Department of the Cuban Republic has made the most of. Peter Martyr, the Italian friar who lived at the Spanish court, learned much of the idyllic isles from Columbus and his companions. Probably writing in the harsh Castilian winter, he meditated on the attractions of Hispaniola: "What greater happiness could one wish in this world than to live in a country where such wonders are to be seen and enjoyed? Is there a more agreeable existence than that one leads in a country where one is not forced to shut himself in narrow rooms to escape cold that chills or heat that suffocates? A land where it is not necessary to load the body with heavy clothing in winter, or to toast one's legs at a continual fire, a practice which ages people in the twinkling of an eye, exhausts their force, and provokes a thousand different maladies." [3] However, he was concerned lest "the perfumes and soft odors of these countrys" might contribute to idleness and effeminacy and luxurious living.

As the Spaniards penetrated into the interior of the continent, the face of the New World changed. Sometimes they met nature at its worst. Often they had to push their way to a firm foothold on the solid earth—the *Tierra Firme*—through mangrove and other swamps that fringed the coasts.[4] Beyond the screen of swamp that was neither land nor sea, but a separate element compounded of both, there often lay hundreds of miles of rain forest and trackless mountains, such as Francisco César crossed on his painful way up to the Cundinamarca Plateau of Colombia and Cortés encountered on his long journey from Mexico to Honduras.

But in Mexico Cortés had found a land to his liking. There was much about it that reminded him, and other Spaniards, of Spain. So he wrote to the Emperor Charles: "From what I have seen and understood concerning the similarity between this country and Spain, in its fertility, its size, its climate, and in many other features of it, it seemed to me the most suitable name for this country would be New Spain of the Ocean Sea, and this in the name of Your Majesty I have christened it." [5] "The Anonymous Conqueror" commented in a like strain: "The land of New Spain is similar to Spain, and the hills, valleys, and plains are nearly of the same manner, except that the mountains are more terrible and rugged." [6] And he added that the fields in Mexico were "most agreeable." Here was, indeed, a favored land.

In the southern hemisphere, too, the Spaniards were always searching for a land that would cure their homesickness. Of the region about Quito, Cieza de León wrote that "the country is very pleasant, and particularly resembles Spain in its pastures and its climate." [7] Of the Riobamba country farther down the plateau, he said that "its beautiful plains are very similar to those of Spain in climate, in the flowers and grasses, and in other things." [8]

It was in the vale of Chile, at the southern end of the long trail of conquest, that the Spaniards found the promised land from which there was no return or desire to return. Here on the far edge of the world, between the mighty wall of the Andes and the Pacific, was the Ultima Thule of the great Spanish dream. Pedro de Valdivia, the conqueror, called it "the best piece of land there is in the world . . . very healthful, most fertile and pleasant, and with a very fine climate." It was a land "of much contentment" and its air was a "delight." [9] There was little gold to be found and the Indians were very belligerent, but it was a good country for men to live their lives in and it was worth fighting to hold. Of it Father Acosta wrote: "The Countrie which doth most resemble Spaine, and the regions of Europe, in all the West Indies, is the realme of Chile, which is without the generall rule of these other Provinces, being seated without the burning Zone, and the Tropicke of Capricorne. This land of itself is coole and fertile, and brings forth all kinds of fruites that be in Spaine; it yeeldes great aboundance of bread and wine, and aboundes in pastures and cattell. The aire is wholesome and cleere, and its temperature betwixt heate and colde." [10]

BRAZIL

As it was with the conquests of Spain, so was it with Brazil, once the Portuguese began to take a serious interest in the vast colony which they neglected for so long. The lush greenery of tropic shores was no novelty to them, as it was to the Spaniards. For their ships had long followed the west African coasts and were now to break into the seas to the eastward as far as the Pacific, before they turned their attention to the "Land of Parrots." It is worth noting that Duarte Coelho, the *donatario* of Pernambuco and most successful of the original colonists of Brazil, had experience with a similar environment in the East. In fact, their recent African and Asiatic background was to be of great service to the Portuguese in creating the remarkable rural society of northern Brazil, for they were already familiar with the tropical conditions which they found in the New World.

After they had undertaken its settlement and development, the Portuguese appreciated the charm of the country. Thus, Pero de Magalhaes wrote that it was "the most suitable of all the provinces of America for mankind, because usually the air is good and the soil most fertile, and [the land] is of the most delightful and pleasant appearance to the human sight." [11] The famous Jesuit, Father Anchieta, said: "All Brazil is a fresh-blooming garden and shady grove, and throughout the year there is not to be seen a barren tree or plant. The woods appear to touch the clouds, the trees are of marvelous size, and there is a great variety of species. Many of them yield good fruit, and the thing that gives them a special charm is the many beautiful birds of every sort that are to be seen in them and whose song is in no wise inferior to that of the nightingales, linnets, and canaries of Portugal. These birds create such a harmony that one who passes that way is impelled to praise the Lord, and the groves are so cool and fresh that the pretty little artificial ones of Portugal cannot compare with them." [12] And he adds that "the eye never tires of all this changing splendor." To Father Pitta, Brazil was "an earthly paradise" and nowhere on earth was "the dawn more beautiful." [13] Hans Staden, the nostalgic German, said: "It is a pleasant country to look at: the trees are always green, but there is no wood like our wood, and"—as though they were a part of the landscape— "the savages go naked." [14]

The three major manifestations of nature which the Spaniard or the Portuguese found in the new continent were the Andes, the Amazon jungle, and the Argentine pampa. He liked none of the three. He lost the mastery of his own body in the high Andes. In the jungle he was cramped by the trees, awed by the rivers, and beaten by the rains. The pampa was too empty. The high mountains gave rise to nervous tensions that he could not control. The rain forest induced melancholy. On the pampa, he feared that his mind might become a blank in the endless void, or if he indulged in thinking, his thoughts were likely to be aimless or to run in circles. All three dwarfed his individuality and took away something of his feeling of importance. So he avoided them for lesser lands that were more congenial to his Hispanic spirit—for lands which he might dominate or with which he might live on equal terms. It was this problem of which Humboldt wrote: "In the Old World, nations and the distinctions of their civilizations form the principal point in the picture; in the New World, man and his production almost disappear amidst the stupendous display of wild and gigantic nature." [15]

THE ANDES

The Spaniard always felt a stranger in the high Andes. But to the subject of the Inca, the Cordillera was home and he never left its heights without regret and risk to his health. Whenever, for economic or political reasons, the Incas resettled the peoples of their empire, they were careful not to move a group to a different zone of altitude than that to which it was long habituated. Through millenia, the Indian had become adjusted, biologically and spiritually, to the locale. His barrel-like chest, with its abnormal lung space, was the resultant of an evolution that came to compensate for the lack of oxygen in the rarefied atmosphere. The llama carried his burdens and provided companionship in the silent wastes of the plateau. Its wool furnished the clothing that protected him against the cold, and its pelt a bed for him to lie on at night. Its dung was often his only fuel. The coca was an anodyne that eased his hunger and his weariness and the pain in his body. The sun warmed him after the chill of the night and drew the numbness of the dawn out of his limbs. The solstices marked the seasons for him. And the beneficent sun was the principal object of his worship. With terraces and irrigation canals he changed the face of the mountains and adapted their hostile topography to his uses. The great peaks, like Illimani and Sorata and Huascarán, that towered above the general level of the *altiplano,* were untouchable abodes of spirits, to be regarded with awe and veneration. These, and every other feature of the landscape—the bleak and melancholy *páramos,* the fruitful valleys between the ranges, the wide floor of the plateau of the Collao, the icy rivers from off the snow beds, the lake with its holy island and its majestic backdrop—were all familiar and acceptable to him as the eternal setting of his brief life.

To the Spaniard, the high Andes could never be home. They were to him at best a boardinghouse in a vast mining camp. And it was only the lure of the mines that could draw him for long from lower altitudes. Only the Basques and the Asturians were willing to establish themselves for relatively long periods in such dreary places as Potosí, Castrovirreina, or Oruro. Even they had retreats at lower levels, as at Chuquisaca or La Plata and Cocha-bamba, where they tended to spend most of their time, and to which they ultimately withdrew to enjoy their riches in comfort. The warm-blooded Andalusians avoided the *altiplano*, and only the offer of some lucrative post of the viceroyalty could generally induce a Castilian to leave the coast for a spell among the condors.

The struggle for adjustment to the physical environment of the high sierra was too difficult for the Spaniard. The conquerors, like those who came after them, often suffered bitterly from the cold of the heights. "They went on carelessly," wrote Cieza de León of Pizarro's soldiers in their pursuit of Almagro, "without their tents to protect them from the heavy falls of snow, and they could not endure the cold. . . . It was only by a lucky chance that they were not all frozen to death." Pizarro's men were also attacked by *soroche* or "mountain sickness." "They were attacked by giddiness," says Cieza; "the disease so affected them that they vomited, staggered, and threw down their arms." [16] These are a few of the familiar symptoms of one of the most disagreeable of ailments, which is caused by the imbalance of bodily and atmos-pheric pressures in high altitudes, aggravated by the deficiency of oxygen for breathing. The newcomer of the sierra is also likely to suffer from acute nervous tensions. The turbulent life of Potosí during its bonanza times was not only the natural condition of a rich mining camp; the abnormally high altitude, almost three miles above the sea, predisposed tempers to irritability and quar-relsomeness, that broke out occasionally in aimless and riotous violence. Another handicap of life in the high Andes was male sterility. [17] It was a long time before Spanish babies were con-ceived and born in Potosí, and longer still before any of those who were born survived the hazards of infancy in the cradle of the forbidding "Imperial City." These factors continue to be a deterrent to the increase of white inhabitants in the higher levels of the Andean plateaus, where the population remains overwhelm-ingly Indian or mestizo.

Below, at about 9,000 feet in tropical latitudes, there begins a zone in which it is possible to lead something like a normal physical existence. The strain on the heart and lungs is consider-ably lessened, and, except at night, one can keep warm without great effort. At this general level are such important old cities as Cuzco, and Cochabamba, and Quito and Bogotá, and many lesser towns, where Spaniards settled and lived with comfort and satisfaction—and progeny.

Except in the lower-lying islands of the Antilles, and the temperate south of the continent, the Spaniard showed a predilection for the lands that lie between 3,000 and 7,000 feet altitude. Mexico City and Arequipa are a little above this zone, and Santiago and San Salvador are below its level. But within this belt lie most of the major cities of Mexico and Colombia; the capitals of Guatemala, Honduras, Costa Rica, and Venezuela; and many other cities of Spanish America. Here in the mid-zone of the *tierra templada* the Spaniard found a temperate climate that stimulated, instead of numbing or debilitating him, and gave him a feeling of bodily well-being free from the threat of either soroche or malaria. And here would grow the crops and other plants with which he was familiar in Spain. Moreover, in these altitudes the mountains were of a size which he could measure and comprehend and with which he could associate on terms of equality.

Mexico is as mountainous as Spain. Though the mountains are the traditional—and illusory—source of its mineral wealth, the vast majority of its people have always made their living from agriculture. It has not been a good and bountiful living that they have made, for the violent and dramatic landscape holds within its recesses little good earth for farming.[18] Most of the population is crowded into the series of intermount basins of the great central plateau, where the sparse arable land is concentrated. But the race between human fecundity and exhaustion of the soil has forced the republic to initiate a series of irrigation works in the northern part of the country in order to increase the precarious food supply of the nation. Over the plateau the rains are highly seasonal and their uncertainty is responsible for much of the fatalism of the Mexican people, to whom the threat of hunger has always been present as it has in Spain.

The mountains that cut up the country into pockets and wall off one valley or basin from another have encouraged the isolation and immobility of communities which were originally founded on racial differences and fixed by the inertia of centuries. In its efforts to inculcate a national spirit in the people, the government of the republic has had to contend with this deep-seated localism whose roots are both ethnic and topographic. Only a minority of the population has benefited from the railroads and highways and airplanes which have revolutionized transportation in this rugged land. The majority still clings to its villages as it did before the Spaniards came, indifferent to the pleas of the capital to integrate themselves into the larger community of Mexico. In the north the country opens out and vistas are wider. The inhabitants are more venturesome and anxious about what lies beyond the horizon, and they move about more. But even here the western ranges of the Sierra Madre, with their deep gorges, form an almost impossible barrier to travel between the interior and the states that border the Pacific.

As such things go in South America, the highlands of Brazil can scarcely be called mountains. Yet much of this vast and rugged plateau lies above an altitude of four thousand feet. It is this circumstance which explains the temperate climate of a large part of the country that would otherwise be as tropical as the corresponding latitudes of Africa. In São Paulo it is a rolling tableland that falls toward the west and invites man to the heart of the continent, as it did the early *Bandeirantes* who penetrated the far interior into the basins of the Paraguay and the Madeira. The lay of the rivers that flow into the upper Paraná afforded natural roads into the Matto Grosso hinterland for the venturesome Paulistas. Most of Minas Geraes has a true mountainous character, and the majority of its people, who live in the valleys between the sierras or ranges, have the cautious and conservative qualities of mountaineers. It has always been the source of most of Brazil's mineral wealth—gold and diamonds, iron and manganese, mica and quartz crystal—though it is agriculture which has fixed the mass of Mineiros in their upland habitat.

THE PAMPA

The Argentine Pampa is a vast plain reaching westward from the Atlantic coast and the Paraná River to the rise of the continental floor that first signals the nearness of the Andes. To the north it circles the Córdoba Hills, to end at the foot of the mountains that come down out of Bolivia or merges farther east in the forested lowlands of the Argentine Chaco. To the south beyond the Rio Negro it gives way to the wind-swept steppes of Patagonia. The lush Mesopotamian lands between the Paraná and the Uruguay are a continuation of the Pampa, but with local characteristics of their own. Beneath its grassy surface lies probably the richest soil on earth. For hundreds of miles there is no break in its flatness and no natural landmarks by which men could get their bearings.

The first Spaniards penetrated this topographic void from four directions: from the shores of the Plata estuary; by the high passes on the side of Chile that led into the attractive piedmont country of Cuyo; from the Charcas plateau of Upper Peru; and down-river from the Indianized colony in Paraguay. From the beginning the immensity of its trackless interior daunted them, and they clung to its edges, where there were mountains or rivers or ocean to give them some sense of identity with the familiar world they knew.[19] They were daunted also by the fierce Indians who shared its wastes with that lesser kin of the llama, the guanaco; the burrowing viscacha, and the emu or New World ostrich. These animals were joined early by horses and cattle, which flourished and increased prodigiously in the wild state as they spread deep into the Pampa. Acquisition of the horse revolutionized transportation among the Indians of the Pampa, who found in it a means of dominating their still pedestrian enemies, and an effective device for surprise attacks on the isolated settlements of the Spaniards. It was not until the Indian was either merged with the blood of the Spaniard in a slow process of miscegenation or pushed off the land by military force in the middle of the last century that it became possible for the white man to occupy and develop the Pampa. In the long interim he remained a lonely intruder in an environment that was alien to all his memories and traditions and antipathetic to the innermost longings of his Spanish soul. And when he finally became reconciled to his habitat he was no longer a Spaniard, but a creature of the Pampa, and no Castilian would have found kinship in him. For in the three centuries between Juan de Garay and Martín Fierro he had undergone a very deep metamorphosis.[20]

To the Gaucho, who was the end product of this evolutionary process, the Pampa was all *"paja y cielo,"* or grass and sky.[21] An Argentine of our time described it as a world without direction or landmarks or dimensions.[22] He called the first Spaniards who entered it *"señores de nada"*—lords of nothingness, of a boundless vacuum, where the sight of a guanaco or an ostrich must sometimes have brought a sense of reality, of *this*-worldliness. Here man was pitted against the infinity of space. When at last the Pampa was fenced and there were closed gates in the barbed-wire boundaries of the *estancias,* it had become a finite and measurable thing, and the Gaucho knew then that his day was done.

W. H. Hudson describes the transformation which took place in those who peopled the Pampa.[23] "The first colonists," he said, "came from a land where the people are accustomed to sit in the shade of trees, where corn (i.e., wheat) and wine and oil are supposed to be necessaries, and where there is salad in the garden. Naturally they made gardens and planted trees, both for shade and fruit, wherever they built themselves a house on the pampas, and no doubt for two or three generations they tried to live as people live in Spain, in the rural districts. But now the main business of their lives was cattle raising, and as the cattle roamed at will over the vast plains and were more like wild than domestic animals, it was a life on horseback. They could no longer dig or plow the earth or protect their crops from insects and birds and their own animals. They gave up their oil and wine and bread, and lived on flesh alone. They sat in the shade and ate the fruit of trees planted by their fathers or their great-grandfathers until the trees died of old age, or were blown down or killed by the cattle, and there was no more shade and fruit.

"It thus came about that the Spanish colonists on the pampas declined from the state of an agricultural people to that of an exclusively pastoral and hunting one, and later, when the Spanish yoke, as it was called, was shaken off, the incessant throat-cutting wars of the various factions, which were like the wars of 'crows and pies,' except that knives were used instead of beaks, confirmed and sunk them deeper in their wild and barbarious manner of life."

This was the "barbarism" which Domingo Faustino Sarmiento contrasted with the "civilization" of the Argentine capitol.[24] Horsebound, the Gaucho was of a race of centaurs, awkward and uneasy on foot; taciturn and suspicious, but with his own code and character, that included a primitive dignity of bearing and an Arab hospitality for the stray wayfarer who threw himself on his mercy; a restless wanderer and a congenital anarch, resentful of all bonds or controls, whether of state or family or church; shaggy, uncouth and unkempt, and scornful of the finery and fripperies of city dwellers; carnivorous, but sober in his drinking, his excesses in half-raw meat compensated by his addiction to maté; his senses of sight and sound hyperdeveloped, with ears attuned to silence and the eyes of hawks; his leisure spent in relaxing like a tired dog under the lean-to of a cabin or in the shade of an *ombu* tree, in swapping reminiscences with his kind in some lone *pulpería* on the trail, in rough games on horseback, or, when in a rare lyrical mood, in the laborious improvisation of mournful and monotonous verses to the twanging of a guitar; his love a casual affair of the epidermis; his home the saddle.

He had departed far from the original pattern of his Spanish ancestors, who tried to farm the Pampa as they would a field in Estremadura. Through the succeeding generations the Pampa had gradually molded him to *its* pattern.[25] As he came to terms with the inflexible demands of the land, so he compromised, unwittingly and involuntarily, with his enemy, the Indian. He borrowed the Indian's craft and his ways, and he borrowed his women. For the "china" who bore his children and kept house for him while he rode the plains was of the stock of the Tehuelche or the Cachiquel or the Guaraní.

The Gaucho passed out with the longhorns and the open range.[26] He had no place in the new era of the *Sociedad Rural* and the great *estancieros* or ranchers. So he became only a picturesque anachronism and a part of the folklore and legendry of Argentina. In a more sophisticated age there grew up a nostalgic literature about him. Cesáreo Bernaldo de Quirós portrayed him in his flaming canvasses and, more realistically, Francisco Molina Campos caricatures his gaucheries and rustic gallantries.

THE LLANOS

In the hinterland of the Spanish Main is another area similar in its general topography to the Argentine Pampa. This is the Llanos of Venezuela and Colombia, which cover much of the upper basin of the Orinoco, particularly the lands about the Apure and the Arauca. Like the Pampa, it is as Humboldt described it, "a sea of grass," but broken along the river courses by low trees and scrub. As the early Spaniards who tramped aimlessly across its wastes in search of El Dorado found to their sorrow, it is not well suited to human existence. It would be impossible to build a civilized society in such an environment. The climate is excessively tropical and insects find in it an ideal habitat. For much of the year the plains are parched and cracked by the sun as the rains cease. During the rest of the year vast reaches of the country become a shallow ocean, like the Bolivian plains of the Beni. The intermediate season is a time of mud and malaria before the wide sloughs and bogs disappear from the water-logged landscape.

The Llanos have long been the seat of a primitive cattle industry. Like the half-wild animals they tend, the *llaneros* are a gaunt breed. They are good horsemen, and as lancers they performed a valuable service to both sides in the Wars of Independence. Later political chieftains have often found it easy to recruit an irregular cavalry from their ranks. Since the horizon of the Llanos lacks the long lure of the Pampa, they are not given to wandering so far afield as did the Gaucho, who was an inveterate nomad. Their minds run in much the same simple grooves of thought and emotion as did the Gaucho's and their daily life is as crude. The egos of both are dwarfed by the immensity of their physical world. Whereas the Gaucho gave way to the encroachments of Sarmiento's "civilization," the llanero remains little changed in the stagnant backlands of the two republics. The relative inaccessibility of the Llanos, the superior attractiveness of living conditions in the highlands, and the obsession of Venezuela with oil have combined to leave him undisturbed in his isolation and backwardness.[27]

The Llanos are the scene of the *Doña Bárbara* of Rómulo Gallegos, one of the most famous of Latin American novels. In the atavistic musings of Santos Luzardo, the young aristocrat who has returned to the ancestral lands of his family, Gallegos expresses the character and moods of the Llanos and their people. He writes of the llanero's "struggle against Nature, against the insalubrity that is annihilating the race, against flood and drouth which dispute the earth between them, against the wilderness that is a barrier to civilization." As for the denizen of this inhospitable locale, he says of the contradictions of his temperament: "In the face of life, he is indomitable and long-suffering, indolent and tireless; in combat, impulsive and wary; before his superior, undisciplined and loyal; with his friend, suspicious and unselfish; with woman, passionate and rough; with himself, a creature of the senses and temperate. In conversation, he is sardonic and ingenuous, incredulous and superstitious. He is both gay and melancholy, a realist and a weaver of fantasies. Afoot, he is humble; on horseback, he is proud."

The Jungle

The last areas to be settled in Latin America have been the rain forests. Most of them are still a demographic vacuum, and after four centuries the Amazon Selva has fewer inhabitants than the island of Puerto Rico. Except to the chronic nomad, the devoted missionary, or the renegade from society, there was little inducement to abandon the settled lands in the mountains or along the coasts for those sterile wastes until the rubber boom of the early nineteen hundreds introduced a major profit motive into the jungle.

The Amazon Valley is the most extensive wooded area in the world. To the north, it merges into the basin of the Orinoco, and to the south, beyond a low and imperceptible divide, into the lands about the headwaters of the Platine system of rivers. There are other rain forests in Latin America—in southern Mexico and on the coastal plains of Central America, and in the drenched Chocó country of Colombia, thence south along the Pacific to the edge of the Peruvian desert, and, far to the east, in parts of the Brazilian states of Bahia and Espiritu Santo bordering on the Atlantic. But neither alone nor in the aggregate do they compare in size with the vast expanse of the Amazon jungle and the contiguous watersheds of the Orinoco and the Paraguay.

Spaniards and Portuguese early penetrated into the dark recesses. They did not like what they found well enough to wish to stay or to come again. They found no gold in nugget or temple wall, though they searched far and wide for El Dorado or the phantom city whose wealth was to dwarf Cuzco and Tenochtitlán. For the endless discomfort and weariness, the Amazonia offered no compensation that appealed to them. Cortés and Jiménez de Quesada made long and painful forays into its depths, and Gonzalo Pizarro and Francisco de Orellana came and went on their parted ways. So did many lesser and as disillusioned men of the Conquest. Pedro de Teixeira went upriver to claim the country and its waters for Portugal. But until Father Acuña came down out of the Andes in 1639, no one had a good word to say for the land of the Amazons. The Jesuit priest even praised the climate, though a "little moon ray" gave him headaches, and, but for "the plague of mosquitoes," he considered the land a "paradise." The members of his order who founded the missions on the upper Marañón were to be the first Europeans to establish themselves in the Amazon Valley. The *Bandeirantes* of São Paulo crossed the divide into the basin of the Madeira on their legendary treks, but they found little to hold them in the distant wilderness. Moreover, like most of the nameless men who later followed the courses of the rivers in search of rubber, they left no records of their travels. It was not until after the great Humboldt entered the valley through the Cassiquiare Canal from the Orinoco that literate men told the story of Amazonia to the world. Since then a distinguished group of scientists, explorers, and observers have written of its natural wonders. Among them have been the American naval officers, Herndon and Gibbon; Bates, the English naturalist; Agassiz and Wallace; Orton and Heath and Church; Spix and Martius, the Germans; the Coudreaus; General Rondon, the famous head of the Brazilian Indian Service; the encyclopedic Frenchman, Paul Le Cointe; the Brazilians, Euclydes da Cunha and José Verissimo; Theodore Roosevelt and Leo Miller; Dickey and Hanson and Tomlinson (author of *The Sea and the Jungle*). In the meantime, from Belem at the mouth of "The River" Portuguese entered the valley in increasing numbers during the eighteenth century in search of Indian slaves and other products of the jungle. The thin infiltration continued into the following century, and new settlements grew up on the rivers, but it was not until the beginning of this century that the migration assumed considerable proportions. Even then, so vast was the scene of the occupation that, as the human stream trickled into a thousand channels, the wilderness closed in behind them and seemed almost as empty as ever.

It was an environment that only the bold and adventurous or the physically conditioned would freely choose as home. Of the newcomers, the Portuguese fared much better than the Spaniard, and here, as elsewhere in the tropics, he showed a remarkable facility for adjustment to strange and trying conditions. The Spaniard, who had always lived in open country, shunned the jungle as though it was a green prison. When he did try to live in the tropics, he insisted on dragging along with him too much of his culture that was entirely unsuited to the milieu. On the other hand, the Portuguese was ready to discard such of his mores as served no useful purpose. In the Amazonia, the Negro, whose ancestors were familiar with a similar environment in equatorial Africa, was in his element. In fact, he seemed more at home in the jungle than was the Indian, who never became entirely adapted to the habitat in which he had lived for so long. In the end, it was a mixture of the three—Portuguese, Negro, and Indian—that proved to be best suited to the peculiar demands of life in the rain forest. The triple hybrid was hardy and resistant and free from nostalgia, unlike the Indian, who appeared eternally and vaguely homesick for some ancestral land of which he had lost all memory. On the other hand, the mixed-breed was as much an integral part of the locale as the *habitant* was in the Canadian woods.

The basic ecological facts of the Amazonia are the rivers and the jungle and the rains and the heat. There are times when all four seem to be one and the same and not separate elements, in a primeval and formless cosmos, in which man has no place.

The rivers are the roads, but where the currents are strong the going may be much harder in one direction than in the other. People travel on them in steamers and launches, and on rafts, and in all manner of boats, but mostly in dugout canoes. But whatever the craft, whenever man would go from one place to another he generally goes by water. His canoe may be lost in the immensity of the swirling river or he may steer it skilfully through the rapids, where basalt hills cut across the course. He is a good boatman, especially if there is much Indian blood in him, for the Indian shuns the forest for the open river, whose ways he understands. One of the most interesting of the rivermen is the pilot who guides the *gaiolas*, or flat-bottomed steamers, from Belem and Manaos. He knows the secrets and the caprices of his river —the shifting sand bars, the covered reefs, the currents and eddies in its course, its sudden rises and falls, which can leave a steamer at anchor stranded high on a bank between night and morning. He can read the language of the sunlight on the water, and where everything looks alike to the stranger the landmarks on the shore are familiar to him, whether by day or in the dark of the moon.

If the river is transportation, it is also food. For the Amazonian rivers are rich in fish. On some of them, like the Branco, turtles abound and their flesh and eggs have long been a staple diet of the river people. Also, unlike the deceptive brooks in the jungle, whose clear water may have been contaminated by vegetable poisons, one can always drink with confidence from the rivers.

Life on the banks of the rivers is more comfortable, too, than in the jungle, particularly where the banks are high as they often are and for long distances. Many of the Amazonian towns have fine sites, as do Santarem at the mouth of the Tapajoz, Obidos, and Teffé, where Bates, the naturalist, lived for many years. It is cooler by the river and at night a refreshing breeze may blow off it over the land. The open vista over the river, sometimes deep and wide, as at Santarem, offers the spirit a comforting release from the overwhelming pressure of the forest to the rear. Then, too, the river forms a link with the world outside, so that the feeling of isolation is lessened, and the individual retains some sense of communion with his fellow men. Even the Seringueiro at the headwaters of the little rivers knows that he is not hopelessly alone, and that the rivers eventually lead to cities where people ride in cars on tires whose rubber may come from the trees he bleeds in his far corner of the great forest. The rivers induce restlessness, too, and the nomadic character of the Amazonian population, which is reluctant to fix its habitat in one place, is a product of the invitation to movement which the flowing highway offers.

The Amazon dwarfs all other rivers of the world. To the Indians of the Tupi race, it was the Paranáguassú, "The Great River"; to the Portuguese, it was the Rio-Mar, or "River-Sea," "The Mediterranean of South America." [28] But no hyperbole could give a true idea of its magnitude and power—of the relentless yellow flood that drains half a continent in its area of heaviest rainfall, finally to discolor the Atlantic for over two hundred miles offshore. It is so vast that one name does not suffice for all of it. Below the mouth of the Negro, it is the true Amazon. Thence, to the border of Peru it is the Solimôes, or River of the Solomons. In the Peruvian section, to its source in the Andes, it is the Marañón. It is no wonder that men tend to be awestruck and humble in its presence, for it embodies a continuous dynamic force such as exists nowhere else in nature.

To H. M. Tomlinson, to whom the Amazonia held something of "astronomy's amplitudes," the river itself was "a monstrous Tree," with an infinity of ramifying watercourses that fed its channels.[29] Some of the major tributaries of the Amazon, like the Madeira and the Negro, the Purús and the Juruá, the Tapajoz and the Tocantíns-Araguaya, are in themselves among the great rivers of the world. Yet, in spite of the deceptive monotony of the Amazonia—a sameness that is more apparent than real—the rivers have personalities of their own that communicate a special mood to those who live upon them or frequent them. They vary in their coloring. The Negro, like the Jutahý and other secondary streams, is as black as though it originated in some cosmic ink-well that was diluted on the way by its paler branches. The meandering Purús and Juruá are yellow rivers, like the master stream itself. The Tapajoz and the Xingú and the Tocantíns-Araguaya, which come down off the central plateau of Brazil and for a long way flow between rocky hills, where rapids are frequent in their course, are clear rivers pleasing to the eye.

Some of the rivers have channels as clear-cut as the Ohio's, where they have found their final and natural beds. Others, like the lower Japurá or the confused waterways of the triangle between the lower Madeira and the Amazon, are tangled and labyrinthine mazes. The Amazon itself flows through a single channel only at the deep Obidos gap. Though there may be a single main channel, on either side there are side channels, or *paranás,* connected by cross canals, or *furos.* During the season of high water, when the snows in the Andes are melting, the River-Sea spreads over the wide flood plain between the high flanks of the *terra firme* to north and south. The amphibian inhabitants who customarily live on the flats of the *varzea* then retire to the higher ground or roost in their houses that are built on stilts, until the flood subsides to leave their waterlogged world coated deep with mud and debris.

Though the process never ceases, during the time of the annual deluge the river attacks with primeval violence the land through which it flows. Sometimes it tears great pieces of the earth loose from their moorings and carries them downstream as floating islands, often complete with trees, in whose branches monkeys or birds may sit. On the way, the island may be broken up or find a refuge in some eddy of the flood, where it is attached again to the precarious land. At night one may occasionally hear the thunderous noise made by the falling banks of the river as they are undermined for long distances by the relentless flood. Meanwhile, out beyond the gaping mouth that opens between the mainland of Macapá and the island of Marajó the mighty river builds up in a final effort other and vaster islands in the sea. Only in mid-ocean is man made to feel so small and inconsequential as in this moving chaos of water and earth.

On the other hand, there are many long stretches along the rivers, where the water is under control and men are at ease in its presence. On the attractive Tapajoz, for example, there are wide sandy beaches and pleasant benches of habitable land, and on the Branco the sandy *praias* extend for miles along its banks. For long distances there may be high palisadelike bluffs above the river, from whose top there is a fine vista over the far expanse of open water. And sometimes, as on the Trombetas and the Maués, there are reaches of quiet water with clean islands in midstream. Of another kind, in contrast to the riotous vegetation of the rain forest in the flood plains, is the dead landscape of the mournful islands which dot the wide expanse of black water in the Boiossú Channel of the Negro above Manaos.

There are two kinds of jungle, that of *terra firme*, or the high ground, and that of the *varzea*, or flood-plain. The former is often open, with little undergrowth so that one may walk about in it without difficulty. The trees are predominantly of hardwood. Overhead there is a curtain through which the sun does not penetrate to the floor of the forest, except where there is a small *clairière*, or natural clearing. The *matto da varzea*, or lowland forest, represents the jungle at its worst, and those who write of the "green hell" have it in mind. It consists of dense and matted vegetation, in which palms and *cecropias* and other soft wood trees prevail, mixed with a thick undergrowth and vines, through which only hard machete work can cut a way.

In the jungle one has at worst a feeling of wonderment and admiration at the barbaric wealth of its plant life, of the pulsating and burgeoning vitality of tropical nature. Tomlinson wrote of the "luscious and generative earth," [30] and Bates, the naturalist, had brief moments of elation or ecstasty in his favored corners of the wilderness. But the mood of the rain forest is not a happy one. It is never hospitable or generous, and in its depths one can very easily starve or die of thirst or lose one's way hopelessly. "It is too dark and silent to be gay," Paul Le Cointe wrote; "it shelters too many 'vermine' to be agreeable; it produces on the traveller an impression of vague sadness, of uneasiness, a sort of oppressiveness that causes him to utter a sigh of contentment and a cry of joy when chance leads him to some *campinarana*, or open space, or when he reaches the sunny shore of some river." [31] Of the sinister and menacing face of the jungle that always keeps men instinctively on their guard against its seductions, Tomlinson wrote after a walk in the forest near Manaos: "We went on, and no words we could think of when we woke tell what we felt when we looked into those long silent aisles of the house without a name; for we knew something was there; but there was no telling what the thing would be like when it showed." [32] As night closes down over the jungle, man's feeling of helplessness is intensified. The dusk is a particularly oppressive time, as the normal gloom deepens into complete darkness. And whereas the jungle is silent during the day, except for the occasional call of a bird or the hum of insects, it comes to life at night. The larger animals are on the prowl and sometimes one may hear the screams of their prey, mingled with strange and unidentifiable sounds. Added to the normal accompaniments of a night in the jungle, the added incidence of a tropical storm can be a terrifying experience to any but the most seasoned jungle dweller.

The fauna, large and small, of the Amazonia account for much of its special flavor. The only large Carnivora are the jaguar, of which the black specimens have a particularly sinister appearance, and the puma, which is known locally as a "lion." Neither is aggressive, but with the lesser predatory cats which roam the woods at night they add much to the stage effects of the jungle after dark. The night is often ushered in by the infernal howling of the *guaribas* in the treetops. These large and intractable red monkeys are appropriately known to science as *Mycestes beelzebub*. Heard overhead in the impending tropical dusk, their roar is probably the most bloodcurdling sound in nature.

Among other features of the jungle symphony are the shrill chatter of the smaller monkeys; the plaintive cry of the toucan; the screech of the hyacinthine macaw in flight; the mournful and mocking laugh of the urataui, or phantom bird, which the natives call *mae da lua,* or "mother of the moon"; the "hypocritical whining notes" of the black eagle, or caracaraí; the harsh, grating hiss of the *cigana*, or hoatzin, that sometimes seems more lizard than bird; the bellowing of big tree frogs; and, among insects, the locomotivelike whistle of the jakiranamboia. Fortunately, all these are not heard in unison, but each adds its part to the tensions of the novice in the jungle. Even those who live in the shadow of the great forest never quite accept these sounds with equanimity, though they may try to explain them out of the rich folklore of the Tupi race.

Other companions of man in the wilderness are the boa constrictor and the anaconda, or *sucurujú*. The former does not live up to its bad reputation and is sometimes kept in the native huts as a ratter. The anaconda, which shares the rivers with the alligators and the savage *piranha* fish, grows to great lengths and is much feared by the jungle dwellers. More dangerous are the venomous *jararaca* and other smaller snakes, which lurk in the low bush of the *varzea*. The much maligned vampire bat, which may have a wing spread of over two feet, and whose hideous appearance led Bates to call it a "mocking imp of fable," he considered "the most harmless of all bats." [33] It is the little gray *Phyllostoma* which is a true bloodsucking monster.

The real curse of the Amazonia is the insects. They successfully occupied it long ago and are the masters of its solitudes. Mosquitoes, both *culex* and *anopheles,* range far and voraciously, though the plague of *carapanás* is much worse in some localities than in others. Certain sections of the valley are relatively free of them, but there are places like Carapanátuba, or "Many Mosquitoes" on the Solimões, where they add a special pungency to living. Working on the day shift are the pium, a terrible scourge, whose bites leave persistent itching welts on the skin, the large and aggressive motuca fly, which favors the eyelids in its attacks, and the tiny mocuim, whose effects are similar to those of the American chigger.

The ants rule the land. The *saubas* devastate the plantings of the river people, and have forced the abandonment of whole areas. The tiny red fire ants cling to the vegetation of the *varzea*, and if one should lean against a tree or brush against a limb, his body is covered immediately by these flaming torments, from whom the only escape is to leap into the nearest river. The foraging *Eciton rapax* and *drepanophera* move over the ground in vast and ferocious hordes, and, in the words of Bates, 'Whenever they move, the whole animal world is set in commotion, and every living thing tries to get out of their way.' [34] Of other ants, the giant and vicious *tucandeira*, which is an inch long, inflicts an exceedingly painful bite.

Not all the animal life of the jungle is hostile to man, or repellent in appearance, like the antedeluvian sloth or the owl-faced "night ape." In the river are frolicsome pink dolphins, or *botos*, and in the far country there are pigmy deer that belong in Hudson's *Green Mansions*. There are fantastic big fireflies that shoot white, red, or green lights at will from their eyes, and marmosets seven inches long, and nosy coatis and comical *barrigudo* monkeys that make one laugh. In the forest is the blazing orange cock-of-the-rock, the *realejo*, or "organ-bird," whose flutelike song seems to be produced by a human voice, and the little virá-purú, whose notes have the sweet and silvery tunes of an old music box. And in the forest glades one sees the shimmering blue wings of the *morpho* butterfly, that are sometimes eight inches across. Tomlinson saw one in a flash of light in a forest trail—"a superb butterfly, too bright and quick to be anything but an escape from paradise." [35]

So those who live in the Amazonia are likely to be melancholy and taciturn and restless. The gloom of the forest oppresses their spirits and its silence represses their natural urge to talk. They are wanderers by instinct and the eternal lure of the rivers encourages their vagabondage. Nomads at heart, and by long habit, they do not make a dependable labor force for a large plantation enterprise which demands continuity of employment for the success of its long-term plans. Also, since man here is so little in so much, he has a sense of his own insignificance. His greatest efforts seem so puny and there is so little to build up his ego that he is generally humble.

When far removed from the settlements that are outposts of civilization on the edge of the great wilderness, the inhabitant of the Amazonia sometimes becomes a moral anarchist. He is released from the normal bonds of society that are represented by local custom, the church, and the power of the state. He may become rapacious and sadistic and prey on his fellow men as cruelly as do the animals of the jungle. This explains the famous Putumayo "outrages" in the forests of Peru, and similar incidents on the Javarý, the Purús, and the distant no man's land of the Abuná during the rubber boom of the early nineteen hundreds. It also explains the capricous tyranny of the barons of the rivers who long held sway over some of the principal industries of the Amazon or large areas of their basins. The island of Marapatá in the Rio Negro at Manoas used to be known as a "lazaretto of souls," where men bound for the rubber forests left their conscience behind as useless baggage. Two islands at the mouth of the Juruá and the Purús had lost their original names and became known as the "Isles of Conscience," or *"Ilhas da Consciencia."* "It is truly a fixed idea," says Le Cointe; "he who is on the point of crossing the threshold that leads to the diabolical paradise of the 'seringaes' abandons his noblest instincts and, laughing, himself gives expression to this terrible irony." [36]

The largest desert area in Latin America is that which extends the length of Peru and thence southward to the latitude of Coquimbo in Chile. This arid zone includes a coastal strip of varying width and the lower contiguous mountains on the Pacific side of the Cordillera. Much of it is an absolute desert; that is, it is practically rainless, an utter waste of sand and rock in which no plants grow.[37] Some eighty streams flow down from the Andes across this strip of desert, about half of which run dry for part of the year. Practically all of these streams are in Peru. Two of the best known are the Santa, which comes down out of the spectacular "box canyon" of the Callejón de Huaylas in the high Peruvian Sierra, and the Rimac, near whose mouth Lima is situated. Ages before the Spaniards came, the native peoples of the coastal shelf spread the waters of these rivers over the land to feed a large population and to support great cities like the long-dead Chan-Chan of the Chimu. On the same lands today there are plantations of cotton and sugar cane and vineyards and fields of alfalfa, as in the fine oasis of Arequipa. The Spaniard, who had lived among irrigated fields in the vegas of Granada and Valencia, and elsewhere in the peninsula, was perfectly at home here, as he was in Mendoza and Tucumán on the other side of the Andes. Unlike the Arab, with whom his blood was mingled, he nowhere chose the life of the desert nomad, though in Lower California and other parts of northwestern Mexico, he and the Mexican after him came to habituate himself to desert conditions where the water was as scarce as in the Peruvian Sechura.

In the sertão of northeastern Brazil, centering in the state of Ceará, there is a large region which has pronounced desert characteristics. This is the area of the great *seccas*, or prolonged droughts, where famine has occasionally scourged the population and given rise to mass exoduses to other parts of the republic, particularly to the Amazon Valley and, in 1952, to the south of Brazil. In this land of the Caatinga, or scrub and xerophytic vegetation, the annual coming of the rains is always uncertain. Sometimes they do not come at all, and then there is desperate suffering, as the inexorable sun burns up the countryside and the hungry population drags itself down to the coast in search of food and water.

The precarious living conditions in the hinterland of the "bulge" of Brazil have developed special characteristics in the Cearenses and their neighbors which set them off from their countrymen who live in a more favored habitat. They are the people whom Euclydes da Cunha describes in *Os Sertões*, the story of the rebellion of the mystic, Antonio Conselheiro, and his fanatical followers against the authority of the Brazilian government.[38] They are a leathery people, hardy and tenacious, spare of words and given to intense religious fervor, and probably the nearest to a typical desert folk of any in Latin America.

EARTHQUAKE AND HURRICANE

The plains and mountains and jungles were fixed quantities in the physical environment of Latin America. Their influence on the civilization of the continent persisted with little variation from one century to another. On the other hand, the violent manifestations of nature—earthquakes, volcanic eruptions, and hurricanes —were unpredictable in their incidence and ephemeral in their duration. Yet, though their occurrence has been only occasional and spasmodic, their effects on the life of the countries might be long-lived.

Of these cataclysmic factors, earthquakes have been the most important in their consequences, material and psychological. Job Hortop, one of Hawkins's men, who was left at Veracruz in 1568 and spent several years in Mexico, said that "In the Andies ordinarily three times a yeare bee wonderful earthquakes, which put the people in great feare and danger." [39] The region of the Cordillera from Mexico to Chile is subject to violent seismic disturbances. Geologically a relatively young region, the combination of narrowness and great height for much of its length accounts for potential subterranean stresses and strains that constitute an ever-present menace of earthquakes. The presence of active or quiescent volcanoes in certain localities, as in Central America and Ecuador, is further and constant evidence of the threat.

Seven of the Latin American capitals have suffered severe earthquakes. Juan and Ulloa, the Spanish naval officers, who were in Peru in the middle of the eighteenth century, list sixteen in the history of Lima.[40] There were particularly destructive quakes in 1630, 1687, and 1746. In 1687, the first shocks came at four o'clock in the morning, when the city was still asleep, and heavier shocks followed two hours later, after most of the terrified survivors had fled to the plazas and the streets. At the same time, Callao, the port city of Lima, was wiped out by a tidal wave, and far to the north in the highlands of Colombia, "the Great Noise" struck terror into the people.[41] At ten-thirty in the night of October 28, 1746, most of the city of Lima was destroyed in about three minutes. Over two hundred shocks were counted in twenty-four hours, and they continued for several months. Again Callao was overwhelmed by a tidal wave and only 200 of its population of 4,000 survived, while nineteen ships were sunk in the harbor. Of Arequipa, the second city of Peru, Juan and Ulloa wrote: "These pleasures and advantages are allayed by the dreadful shocks of earthquakes to which it is so subject, that it has been four times by these convulsions of nature laid in ruins." [42] The city was first wrecked in 1582 at which time thousands were killed. In 1600, the volcano of El Misti erupted violently and the newly rebuilt city suffered the dual calamity of volcanic eruption and earthquake. Four years later there was another earthquake, and again in 1725.

Following the destruction of Cumaná, on the Venezuelan coast, in 1797, Caracas was virtually wiped out on March 26, 1812.[43] Out of a total population of 50,000, about 12,000 persons were killed, nearly 4,000 of whom had taken refuge in the churches. Another 8,000 died in other parts of the country. After the disaster, a quarter of La Trinidad looked as if a mine had exploded underneath it. The shocks continued for weeks, and on April 5 they were almost as violent as the first tremors, with the ground in undulating motion for several hours.

No country has suffered more from earthquakes than has Ecuador. In 1698, Ambato was destroyed by an eruption of Cotopaxi, accompanied by an outbreak of the volcano of Carhuairaso. At the same time, Latacunga was completely ruined by earthquakes, only four houses out of seven hundred being left standing in the city. In 1743 and again in 1757 Latacunga was "entirely demolished." In 1797, the two cities and that of Riobamba were utterly destroyed. Humboldt called the earthquake which destroyed Riobamba the most terrible of all memory and tradition.[44] Virtually the whole population perished, in addition to many more in other parts of the province. "The face of the country," said Stevenson, "was entirely changed . . . mountains rose where cultivated valleys had existed, the rivers disappeared or changed their courses . . . The face of the country was so completely altered that no one knows the site of the largest farm in the province." [45] After a long respite, disaster from within the earth once more visited Ecuador in 1949, when Ambato was again destroyed.

The cities of Chile have also suffered repeatedly and severely from seismic disturbances. Santiago's most disastrous earthquake occurred in 1647, when the city was shaken to its foundations and thousands of persons were buried in the ruins.[46] Concepción was destroyed in 1570, only twenty years after its founding, and again in 1730 and 1751, after which the city was removed to its present site, only to be laid in ruins in 1835. There was a prolonged series of shocks in the central part of Chile in 1819, at which time Copiapó, farther to the north, was laid waste, after having been destroyed at twenty-three-year intervals beginning in 1773. Disaster has struck Arica at least three times in a combination of earthquake and tidal wave. Father Vásquez de Espinosa witnessed the first one in 1618. The worst calamity in the history of the city occurred in 1868, largely as a result of a tidal wave or "sea-quake" of unusual violence that destroyed shipping in the harbor and deposited an American gunboat a long distance inland in the desert, where its skeleton may still be seen. The latest earthquake of major intensity in Chile was in 1939, when the southern city of Chillán was reduced to a heap of rubbish and some 30,000 of its inhabitants perished.[47]

Of other countries, Mendoza in Argentina was completely wiped out in 1861 by an earthquake and a fire which accompanied it, causing the death of between 10,000 and 12,000 persons. The city of San Juan, in the adjoining province, after being wrecked by an earthquake in 1894, was rebuilt, only to be destroyed again in this century. Central American cities which have been the victims of disastrous earthquakes in the present century are Cartago, in Costa Rica, Guatemala City, Managua, and San Salvador.

The material damage wrought by earthquakes has been tremendous. The cost includes not only the loss in wrecked buildings, sometimes mounting to the virtual ruin of an entire city. At times, these catastrophes have been accompanied by the dislocation of the very landscape, the diversion of rivers from their customary courses, and the disruption of irrigation systems. In one earthquake in Peru the earth was so violently churned up that the cultivated lands along the coast were sterilized over large areas and food had to be brought in from Chile, until the irrigation canals could be reconstructed and the fertility of the ground restored. An example of the disastrous chain of consequences that may follow an earthquake occurred in the Peruvian Andes in 1941, when a quake weakened the alluvial wall that retained the waters of a glacial lake in the Callejón de Huaylas. At the same time, the body of the glacier itself was loosened and slid into the lake forcing its contents into the valley below. A high wall of water overwhelmed the city of Huaraz, drowning about 12,000 people and spreading devastation over a wide expanse of fertile lands that were stripped of their top soil and strewn with boulders.

The psychological effects of these calamities on the stricken population are often very deep and disturbing. This is particularly true when the shocks continue over a period of weeks or months before the earth subsides and men can again walk on it with confidence. Mass hysteria and paroxysms of terror are often followed by a state of fatalism and resignation. The hypertensions of panic may result in outbursts of fanatical religious fervor or end in downright madness, as the mind breaks from the memory of horrors and the suspense of waiting for the repetition of disaster.

We have much first-hand evidence of the mental and social consequences of earthquakes. Captain Basil Hall, the British naval officer who was in Chile during the Wars of Independence, has much to say about them. Of the earthquake which destroyed the provincial city of Copiapó in 1819, he writes: "After the first great shock, which levelled the town, the ground continued in motion for seven minutes, sometimes rising and falling, but more frequently vibrating with great rapidity; it then became still for some minutes, then vibrated again, and so on, without an intermission longer than a quarter of an hour for several days. The earthquake now abated a little; the intervals became longer, and the shocks not quite so violent; but it was not till six months afterwards that it could be said to be entirely over for the ground during that period was never long steady, and the frightful noises in the earth constantly portended fresh calamities." [48] A Chilean remarked to him: "These earthquakes are very awful. . . . Before we hear the sound, or, at least, are fully conscious of hearing it, we are made sensible, I do not well know how, that something uncommon is going to happen: everything seems to change colour; our thoughts are chained irrevocably down; the whole world appears to be in disorder; all nature looks different from what it was wont to do; we feel quite subdued and overwhelmed by some invisible power, beyond human control or comprehension. Then comes the horrible sound, distinctly heard; and, immediately, the solid earth is all in motion, waving to and fro, like the surface of the sea. Depend upon it, Sir, a severe earthquake is enough to shake the firmest mind."

Captain Hall tells a story that illustrates the nervous tensions to which people were exposed in places subject to earthquakes. He was attending a party in a home in the suburbs of Valparaiso when a slight tremor was felt. The women of the family were singing, one was playing a harp and another a guitar, when everyone suddenly jumped to their feet, shouted *"Misericordia!"* and dashed out into the street.

His countrywoman, Mrs. Graham, who was in Chile during the same period and witnessed many similar experiences, wrote: "I can quite understand, now, the effect of great general calamities in demoralizing and loosening the ties of society." [49] She tells of the outburst of religious fervor which followed a long series of shocks: "Since the 19th the young women of Santiago, dressed in white, bare-footed, and bare-headed, with their hair unbraided, and bearing black crucifixes, have been going about the streets singing hymns and litanies, in procession, with all the religious orders at their head. At first, the churches were crowded, and the bells tolled the distress incessantly, till the government, aware that many of the belfries and some of the churches were cracked, shut them up, lest they should fall on the heads of the people; so that now they perform their acts of devotion in the streets, and each family devotes its daughters to the holy office."

It was customary for people to consider these disasters as divine punishment for their sins, so they were generally followed by acts of penance and expiation. After the destruction of Santiago in 1647, the survivors indulged in a mass propitiation of an angry God. The bishop stationed forty or fifty confessors in the plazas of the city, and altars and pulpits were set up in the open, from which priests called the inhabitants to repentance. Processions moved through the streets to the sound of wailing and of flagellation on the bare backs of the penitents. Similar scenes took place in Lima after the quake of 1655. After a priest had exhorted the people, they gave themselves up to a prolonged agony of hysterical devotion and self-abasement that left many of them mentally sick and bordering on insanity. The earthquake of 1687 is said to have led to a great revival of religious zeal among the terrorized population of Bogotá.

Boyle relates his impressions of the earthquakes which occurred in Granada, Nicaragua in 1865. "The air was one hideous scream of terror," he says; "even the sounds of the earthquake were drowned in that frantic yell . . . the wail of a whole people maddened with fear." [50] Of the tremors which followed several weeks later, he wrote: "Eighty distinct shocks took place between 9 o'clock at night and 4 o'clock of the following afternoon. . . . Brave men were wild with fear and helplessness, (and) hundreds were already raving mad. A frantic crowd besieged the confession boxes night and day, and mass never ceased at the altars." [51] "But who could wonder," he added, "if the whole city had gone mad?"

The Antilles are the only part of Latin America which is subject to tropical hurricanes, though destructive windstorms may occur on the east coast of Mexico and in Central America, where they laid waste a large area of banana plantations in Guatemala in 1951. Hurricanes generally originate in a limited area of low barometric pressures lying to the south of Cuba and move thence in a northerly arc through the line of the larger islands, sometimes reaching the United States before their force is spent. Columbus experienced the fury of one of these storms on his second voyage and ever since they have been responsible for much damage to property and loss of life in the West Indies. Particularly destructive hurricanes have been those which struck Havana in 1926 and the one which virtually demolished the old city of Santo Domingo in 1930. Though they may still lay waste crops and groves and raze the flimsier constructions in their path, the improved meteorological services of the island republics enable the cities to prepare better for their coming and enable shipping to move out of the danger zone in time. Moreover, since they are liable to occur only during a few weeks of the year, their influence on life in the hurricane belt is limited in time.

So men learned to live with the land as they found it. Sometimes the learning came very easily, as it did in the vale of Chile and in Paraguay and the basins of the Mexican highlands and the Colombian valley of the Cauca, where nature was friendly and benignant. Sometimes, as on the Pampa and in the high Andes and the Amazonia, where nature was on too large a scale for man's finite comprehension and the setting was too grandiose for his proud ego, the learning was harder and the period of adjustment was longer. As a rule, the more supple Portuguese learned more easily than did the too inflexible Spaniard. Where nature was too inhospitable, man sometimes changed it within the limits of his strength and his ingenuity, as the Aztecs and the Incas had done before him.

In a process that has been greatly accelerated by modern engineering and science, men conquered many of the waste places by irrigation and the eradication of diseases. To make life more bountiful and satisfying or more decorative, they brought from the Old World to the New the crops and animals, and the fruits and flowers that were an integral part of the substance of living in the peninsula. The sight of an orange or fig tree by the door, of grapes ripening in the sun, of a fine Arab horse tethered nearby, of roses in the patio, a cat by the hearth, and onions strung from the kitchen rafters gave them a sense of belonging to this New World. And if their descendants are unlike them in certain respects, the change is due not only to the circumstances of four centuries of history and to the ethnic dilutions of their Hispanic blood, but to the silent and subtle influence of nature.

NOTES

1. See the illustrations in José Ortíz Echagüe, ed., *España: Pueblos y Paisajes* (Bilbao, 1947).

2. Father Acosta, who was the first to write at length and intelligently regarding the "natural history" of the New World, said: "When we goe out of Europe to the Indies, wee wonder to see the land so pleasant, greene, and fresh." José de Acosta, *The Natural and Moral History of the Indies* (tr. from the Spanish, 2 vols., London, 1880), I, 163.

3. Peter Martyr d'Anghiera, *De Orbe Novo* (tr. from the Latin, 2 vols., New York, 1912), I, 365.

4. Peter Martyr said of Santa María Antigua de Darién, Balboa's port on the Isthmus: "To say the frank truth, the town is nothing but a swamp." *Ibid.*, I, 354.

5. Hernando Cortés, *Letters—to the Emperor* (tr. from the Spanish, 2 vols., New York, 1908), I, 322.

6. "The Anonymous Conqueror," *Narrative of Some Things of New Spain and of the Great City of Temestitán, Mexico* (tr. from the Spanish, New York, 1917), p. 15.

7. Pedro de Cieza de León, *Travels* (tr. from the Spanish, London, 1864), p. 141.

8. *Ibid.*, p. 155.

9. Pedro de Valdivia, *La Conquista de Chile: Cartas al Emperador Carlos V* (reprinted, Santiago, 1940), *passim*.

10. José de Acosta, *op. cit.*, I, 170.

11. Pero de Magalhaes, *The Histories of Brazil* (tr. from the Portuguese, New York, 1922), p. 26.

12. Quoted by Samuel Putnam, *Marvelous Journey: A Survey of Four Centuries of Brazilian Writing* (New York, 1948), p. 3.

13. *Ibid.*, p. 75.

14. Hans Staden, *The True Story of his Captivity* (tr. from the German, New York, 1929), p. 129.

15. Alexander von Humboldt, *Voyage aux Regions Equinoxiales du Nouveau Continent* (Paris, 1817), IV, 64. Quoted by Walter Prescott Webb in "Ended: 400 Year Boom," *Harper's Magazine,* October, 1951, p. 32.

16. Cieza de León, *Civil Wars in Peru: The War of Las Salinas* (tr. from the Spanish, London, 1923), p. 179.

17. Carlos Monge, *Acclimatization in the Andes: Historical Confirmations of "Climatic Aggression" in the development of Andean man* (Baltimore, 1948). Dr. Monge, a distinguished Peruvian medical scholar, has made extensive research in the biological effects of altitude in the Andes. Of Cerro de Pasco, in the Peruvian Andes, Lieutenants Herndon and Gibbon observed: "The temperature is so rigorous here that the hens do not hatch, nor the Llamas procreate; and women, at the period of their confinement, are obliged to seek a more genial climate, or their off-spring will not live." *Exploration of the Valley of the Amazon* (2 vols., Washington, D.C., 1854), II, 108.

18. "Man in Mexico, for all his works, is but a puny creature hidden in some inaccessible gully, scratching at the earth with his wooden stick or iron hoe. The mountain mass overshadows all his efforts. . . . As a human habitat . . . this scenery merely provides a splendid setting for a difficult world and a hard life. . . . It is only with the greatest difficulty that even a sparse living may be won from its smiling but recalcitrant earth. Mexico is a beautiful place in which to live, and a hard place in which to make a living." Frank Tannenbaum, *Mexico: The Struggle for Peace and Bread* (New York, 1950), p. 8.

19. "The Pampas are so vast that even the men who know their lands best sometimes are lost in them." Lucio V. Mansilla, *Una Excursión a los Indios Ranqueles* (Buenos Aires, 1942), p. 26. Col. Mansilla was an officer of the Argentine Army and his book is a classic of Indian lore in Latin America.

20. Juan de Garay was the second, and definitive, founder of Buenos Aires; "Martín Fierro" was a poetic creation of José Hernández and the exemplar of the Gaucho.

21. Robert Bontine Cunninghame Graham, *The Conquest of the River Plate* (London, 1924), p. 57. "A flat emptiness of sun, grass, and wind." Christopher Isherwood, *The Condor and the Cows: A South-American Travel Diary* (New York, 1949), p. 198.

22. Ezequiel Martínez Estrada, *Radiografía de la Pampa* (2 vols., Buenos Aires, 1942), I, 12.

23. W. H. Hudson, *Far Away and Long Ago: A History of my Early Life* (New York, 1918), p. 65. See also Cunninghame Graham, *op. cit.*, p. 255.

24. Domingo Faustino Sarmiento, *Facundo: Civilización y Barbarie* (1st ed.; Buenos Aires. 1845).

THE ENVIRONMENT 35

25. See Martínez Estrada, *op. cit.*, p. 23.

26. On the history of the Gaucho, see Madaline Wallis Nichols, *The Gaucho, Cattle Hunter, Countryman, Ideal of Romance* (Durham, N.C., 1942).

27. On the llanos, see Miguel Triana, *Bulletin of the Pan-American Union,* November, 1922, quoted in A. C. Wilgus, ed., *Readings in Latin-American Civilization* (New York, 1946), p. 248.

28. See W. L. Schurz, "The Amazon, Father of Waters," *The National Geographic Magazine,* April, 1926.

29. Henry Major Tomlinson, *The Sea and the Jungle* (London, 1912), p. 131.

30. *Ibid.*, p. 117.

31. Paul Le Cointe, *L'Amazonie Brésilienne* (2 vols., Paris, 1922), II, 5. This is the most extensive scientific work ever written on the Amazon Valley.

32. H. M. Tomlinson, *op. cit.*, p. 142.

33. Henry Walter Bates, *The Naturalist on the Amazons* (1st ed.; London, 1863, New York, 1910), p. 355. Bates spent eleven years in the Amazon Valley, from 1848 until 1859.

34. *Ibid.*, pp. 368-72.

35. H. M. Tomlinson, *op. cit.*, p. 187.

36 Paul Le Cointe, *op cit.*, I, 328.

37. "Sahara is a 'thing of beauty,' and Arizona a 'joy forever,' compared with the coast of Peru." Ephraim George Squier, *Peru: Incidents of Travel and Exploration in the Land of the Incas* (New York, 1877), p. 25.

38. Translated into English by Samuel Putnam under the title, *Rebellion in the Backlands,* and published by the University of Chicago Press, 1944.

39. In Hakluyt, *Voyages* (Everyman Edition), VI, 347.

40. Jorge Juan y Santacilla and Antonio de Ulloa, *A Voyage to South America* (tr. from the Spanish, 2 vols., London, 1806), II, 81.

41. Bernard Moses, *The Spanish Dependencies in South America* (2 vols., New York, 1914), II, 104.

42. Juan and Ulloa, *op. cit.*, II, 138. See also Antonio Vázquez de Espinosa, *Compendium and Description of the West Indies* (tr. from the Spanish, Washington, D.C., 1942), p. 505.

43. Alexander von Humboldt, *Viage á las Regiones Equinocciales del Nuevo Continente*, II, 213.

44. *Ibid.*, p. 272.

45. W. B. Stevenson, *A Historical and Descriptive Narrative of Twenty Years' Residence in South America* (3 vols., London, 1825), II, 267.

46. Bernard Moses, *op. cit.*, II, 172.

47. Benjamín Subercaseaux, *Chile: a Geographic Extravaganza* (tr. from the Spanish, New York, 1943), p. 160. See also an account of the effects of the earthquake by Norman Armour, *Bulletin of the Pan-American Union,* March, 1939.

48. Basil Hall, *Extracts from a Journal Written on the Coasts of Chili, Peru and Mexico, in the Years* 1820, 1821, 1822 (2 vols., Edinburgh, 1824), II, 42.

49. Maria Graham, *Journal of a Residence in Chile* (London, 1824), p. 315.

50. Frederick Boyle, *A Ride Across a Continent: a Personal Narrative of Wanderings through Nicaragua and Costa Rica* (2 vols., London, 1868), II, 18.

51. *Ibid.*, p. 118.

Chapter II
THE INDIAN

AS COLUMBUS gazed shoreward from the roadstead of Guanahani on that October morning of 1492 he saw a large number of naked people milling about on the beach.[1] Since, whatever their personal views, Spaniards have always had an official abhorrence of nakedness, the discoverer was careful to remind the queen that it would be good "to teach them to go clothed." When he mingled with the islanders that day his impressions of them quickly took form. He noted that they were "very well built, with very handsome bodies and very good faces," and that their eyes were "very lovely." As to their moral qualities, he found them, as he was to find the other inhabitants of the Antilles, a "simple" and "very gentle" folk, "artless and generous" and "most wondrously timorous." They showed "as much lovingness as though they would give their hearts." Later he wrote to the monarchs that "they love their neighbors as themselves, and they have the sweetest voices in the world, and soft and always they are smiling." These Arcadian savages were Tainos, of the far-flung Arawak race, of whose traditional enemies and oppressors, the fierce Caribs, Columbus heard, but did not meet, during his first excursion into the New World. To the admiral, who clung to the illusion that they dwelt on the outskirts of Cathay, they were Indians, inhabitants of the classical Indies, and ever since, they and all their kin for many thousands of miles about have been Indians. Thus, as the New World was named for a man who probably never saw it, so its inhabitants were named for a people who never dwelt there.

On his further progress among the paradisiacal isles of the Caribbees, Columbus took time from his promotional activities to dwell on the more prosaic demands of his mission, like the tourist brochure which, out of deference to the chamber of commerce, lists the investment opportunities of the community. He informs his royal and always hard-pressed employers that the Indians are "fitted to be ruled and to be set to work, to cultivate the land and to do all else that may be necessary." He adds significantly that they "have no arms" or "knowledge of war," and are so "cowardly, that a thousand of them would not face three." To temper the impact of so bold a statement of fact on the mind of the pious Isabella, he remarks that the Indians are "a people to be delivered and to be converted to our holy faith." As to the method prescribed for the salvation of their heathen souls, this was to be done "rather by love than by force." He poses here the irreconcilable dichotomy as to whether the Indian could be made both slave and Christian, which was long to plague the makers of Spain's imperial policies.

Wherever the Spaniards and Portuguese went there were Indians.[2] Sometimes they were members of small and inconsequential lingual groups that had been pushed into the less desirable corners of the continent by more powerful neighbors. Oftener they belonged to one of the great stocks which roamed over, or were firmly established in, vast territories as their own. The habitat of the Tupí-Guaraní race covered millions of square miles in what is now Brazil and the River Plate republics. The Inca Empire included most of the present area of Ecuador, Peru, and Bolivia, and reached far down on both sides of the Andes into Argentina and Chile, for a total north-south distance of over 3,000 miles.[3] On the Anahuac plateau of Mexico the restless Nahua peoples were still in motion, and the aggressive and dominant Aztecs had not yet consolidated their conquests or reached the natural limits of their expansion when the Spaniards interrupted the consummation of their destiny.[4] Beyond the forests of the isthmus the Maya and related tribes like the Quiché lived isolated and scattered in the lands from Yucatan southward into the highlands of Guatemala and Honduras.[5]

Wherever they may have come from—and it was probably from Asia by way of Bering Strait—they had been a very long time in the New World when the Europeans fround them. Human bones have been discovered in the same strata in Ecuador with those of the mammoth and of the primitive horse.[6] The Indians had lived on the continent long enough for radical differences to develop in their physical type. For there were small Indians, like the Maya, and big folk, like the Onas of Patagonia—though not the giants the Spaniards early reported them to be. In the high Andes they had evolved the barrel-like chests that enabled their lungs to take in enough oxygen from the rarefied atmosphere, and they had otherwise adjusted their organisms to the exigencies of life at those altitudes. While most of them were reddish-brown in color, some were quite dark and others were of a very light hue. The Spaniards found many individuals whose coloring was as light as their own, and selective breeding in the ruling dynasties of Peru and Mexico had produced a biological aristocracy, whose members were lighter complexioned, taller, and handsomer than the generality of these races. Though in the many millennia that the continent had been their home they had lost all identifiable memory of their Asiatic origins—ever in the shadowland of legend and folklore—time had not eradicated from their bodies certain Oriental stigmata, such as the occasional slant eyes and the tell-tale "Mongolian spot" at the base of the infant spine.[7]

The cultural differentiation which had occurred was even wider than the physical. In the degree of civilization which they had attained they ranged from the archaic culture of the miserable Yaghans of the Chilean archipelago to a level which in some respects compared with that of sixteenth-century Europe, as it did among the Indians of Mexico and Peru. Some civilizations had flourished, and then disappeared or retrograded or lost their identity by integration into the body of stronger but more backward peoples, like those who erected the cyclopean city of Tiahuanaco near Lake Titicaca, the Toltec builders of Teotihuacán, and the vanished folk who left beautiful artifacts strewn about the lower Amazon Valley. Like the ancient Egyptian empires, some of these races waxed and waned in long cycles, as did the great Maya, whose last period of glory had ended before the Spaniards arrived on the shores of Yucatan.[8] War and pestilence and the rising ratio of population as against the potential food supply took their toll of these precarious cultures, and often left them truncated in the process of their evolution.

INDIAN WAYS

The habits and techniques of living varied as greatly as the standards of culture or the natural wealth of the physical environment. As for diet, the more primitive tribes ate anything that lay about them, from ants and worms and earth to shellfish picked up at low tide along the beaches, or such few food plants as grew wild in the forest. From this low level the Indian's diet ranged up to the delicacies which Bernal Díaz pictured as the daily fare of Montezuma. In corn or maize, manioc, and potatoes the Indians developed the staple food plants that still provide the basic nourishment for most of the people of Latin America. The *tortilla* of Mexico and *farinha de mandioca,* the coarse brown manioc meal of Brazil, long antedated the coming of the European. Then, as now, it would be difficult to exaggerate the importance of corn in the life of pre-Columbian America, since it not only provided the foundation for a settled society for millions of people, but the processes of its cultivation were, to an extraordinary degree, an integral element of Indian folkways.[9] Corn was more than food; it was the mark of a way of life. These basic foods were supplemented in different localities by sweet potatoes, beans, squash, and other vegetables, many indigenous fruits such as the avocado and the pineapple, the nourishing quina grain of the Andes, and chocolate, and wherever possible, with fish and game. Among the game animals which were widely hunted were the guanaco of the pampas, deer and monkeys, wild turkeys and other birds like the mutúm, and the succulent agouti and paca of the Amazon jungle.

On occasion—and the occasion might be frequent—many of them ate their fellow men with great relish. The heart of the sacrificial victim might be eaten as a phase of the Aztec cult of Huitzilopochtli,[10] the war god, but the motive of anthropophagy was more often gastronomic than ritualistic. Though some of the Spanish chroniclers may have magnified the occurrence and horhors of Indian cannibalism, the evidence of the practice is too widespread to be ignored. The very word "cannibal" is derived from the name of the fierce Caribs of the Spanish Main, who were inordinately fond of human flesh and appear to have had a predilection for Spaniards.[11] The custom was particularly prevalent among the ferocious Pijaos and other tribes of the Colombian highlands, but was also a common feature of life among the Guaraní and Tupi peoples.[12] The Spaniards reported that some of the Colombian tribes were literally devouring one another.[13]

The Indians relished the stimulus of alcoholic drinks, as they still do.[14] They drank the pulque that was extracted from the maguey plant in Mexico, the chicha that was brewed from corn or other materials, the fiery juice of algarrobo berries, or the essence of most any nontoxic plant that was fermentable. Alcohol provided an interlude of hilarity or stupor as release from the monotony or troubles of daily existence. Sometimes, under alcoholic or narcotic stimulation, they staged orgiastic bacchanals in celebration of some tribal rite or just for the fun of it. In spite of the efforts of the priests to control their drinking habits, they later observed the religious festivals of the Catholic Church with the same pagan abandon, but with the added facilities for intoxication offered by the introduction of sugar cane and the vine.

The habitations of the Indians ranged from the earth under the open sky or "lean-tos" of palm fronds hastily thrown up in the jungle to vast thatched community houses, or *malocas,* in which the group lived in a smoky and odorous promiscuity, and even to substantial mansions of carved stone for the ruling classes of the civilized tribes. The Indians made good use of the building materials about them, and in spite of their lack of metal tools usually showed considerable skill in working up those materials into an abode that served their purpose very satisfactorily. As a rule, the dwelling of the average subsistence farmer of the Latin American tropics, such as the Arawak *bohio* of the Cuban *guajiro,* or countryman, is remarkably well suited to the exigencies of the environment, as was its Indian predecessor and model.

In the hot lands the Indians went naked, save for the small cotton apron or the aboriginal "codpiece" that served to cover what the Spaniards called their *verguenzas,* or "shames." During the colonial period they made few concessions to the expostulations of the Catholic priesthood on their nudity, except where an ample supply of cotton provided material for the wearing of garments such as the Mother Hubbard-like *tupoy* of the Guaraní women. In cooler climes, the Indian clothed himself with whatever materials were available for covering his body. In southern Patagonia and Tierra del Fuego he used raw furs as clothing. Over most of the continent the women wore garments of the indigenous tree cotton and, in the Andean highlands, of llama wool. The softer wool of the vicuña was reserved for the vestments of the Inca class. The introduction by the Europeans of the annual cotton plant and of sheep provided two useful fibers of which the Indians readily availed themselves for the manufacture of their clothing. The early Indian inhabitants of the coastal valleys of Peru attained an extraordinarily high level of skill in weaving and produced fabrics of great beauty and durability.[15]

Some of the aboriginal peoples had an extensive empirical knowledge of curative plants. The Spaniards were so impressed with the efficacy of the native pharmacopoeia of the Incas that they established a chair of Indian medicine in the University of Lima. The Catholic missionaries wrote treatises on the subject and the famous "Aztec Herbarium" has been reprinted in our own time. The materia medica of the Indians included remedies for digestive complaints, and for the treatment of surface infections of the body, powerful astringents for the control of hemorrhage, and the use of the coca drug as an anesthetic.[16] In addition to coca, their contributions to modern medicine include cinchona, ipecac, balsam of Peru, curare, and many other materials. In the field of surgery, there is evidence of much skill among the Incas in the trepanning of skulls in diseases of the brain. Along with the inevitable hocus-pocus of the medicine men of the forest tribes there was often considerable sound therapeutic knowledge, and the motivation of the magic that accompanied their ministrations was probably in large part psychological. In spite of their lack of formal education, their modern successor, the *curandero,* or "curer," like the native midwife, doubtless fulfills a useful function among the backward and scattered population of the interior of the continent, where the services of trained physicians are unobtainable.

Contrary to the common impression, the life expectancy of the Indian has never been great. Authenticated cases of unusual longevity are only exceptions to the general rule.[17] The infant mortality rate was always high, as it is today, and those who survived the trials of infancy often displayed great durability in the face of the normal hazards of Indian life. However, even among such relatively advanced and well-ordered societies as those of Peru and Mexico, the risks of exposure and accident were numerous and ever-present. Furthermore, the chances of fatality would have been much greater it if had not been for the traditional tenderness and solicitude of the Indian woman. The early chroniclers and later travelers often comment on the good physical appearance of the adult Indians whom they met and on the infrequency of crippled or deformed individuals.[18]

The Indian was weak in the realm of technology. He lacked inventiveness and a natural ingenuity in dealing with physical problems. The more civilized peoples, like the Maya and the Incas, carried out impressive engineering works with only a rudimentary system of mechanics. Architecturally, their cities—Cuzco, Copán, Mitla, Palenque, Chichen Itzá—rivaled those of ancient Asia and North Africa. They shaped and moved into place cyclopean masses of stone to form majestic edifices; they laid out in the Andes a system of paved roads which the Spaniards envied, but failed to maintain; [19] they threw wide causeways across the lake that encircled the Aztec capital and bold suspension bridges over the deep gorges of the Apurimac and other rivers, across which the conquerors moved their armies and their pack-trains; [20] they dug tunnels through spurs of the Andes to divert rivers from their course; they terraced the sides of the mountains to their crests; and they constructed irrigation canals on a scale then unknown in Europe.[21] All this they largely accomplished by main force, however daring the conception of their mighty enterprises may have been. The availability of a large and docile labor force compensated, as in ancient Egypt, for the inadequacy of tools and machines. Patience and the absence of a time sense were other factors in retarding mechanical development. Neither the wheel nor the true arch was known to the pre-Columbian world.

Their metallurgy was primitive and, though vast stores of iron ore lie on or near the surface of the ground in many parts of Latin America, the Indians never learned the secret of smelting it, as the African Negroes did. In much of the continent the hardest cutting tools were of obsidian, but where the metal was found in a pure state, as in parts of Bolivia, the Indians used tools of annealed copper.

If the Indians did not feel a compulsion for the invention of labor-saving devices in working with large bodies of stone and earth, some of them made remarkable advances in pure science. They applied their discoveries in astronomy and mathematics to their engineering operations, to the service of their agriculture, and to the regulation of the cycles of religious festivals that were so intimately identified with their collective life. The Maya calendar was more accurate than that used in Europe during the same period and through the deciphering of the chronological symbols on the early monuments it has been possible to fix many of the important dates of Maya history. The need of the Incas to establish the four pivotal points in the annual course of the earth around the Sun in connection with the observance of their solar cult had led to a calender that was only little short of the Maya in its accuracy. The alignment of the vast Toltec "citadel" of Teotihuacán, near the City of Mexico, and of other structures in Mexico and Peru gave evidence of a knowledge of geometry that would have done credit to the great architects of the Middle Ages. The Maya developed a vigesimal, or twenty-digit, system of numerals, in which they included the concept of the zero.

INDIAN POLITICS AND WAR

The aboriginal political systems of the New World varied from anarchism, or a complete absence of any recognized authority, to the highly developed state of the Incas. Sometimes the group was organized only in time of war, when an outstanding fighter was chosen to lead it to battle. Even the formidable Araucanians of

Chile had advanced little beyond this rudimentary stage of organization. At other times the old men of the tribe might exert a measure of control as repositories and guardians of custom and of the accumulated wisdom of the race. For these primitive societies were deeply conservative, and innovation was likely to be discouraged as an affront to the spirits who had watched over the tribe in good times and bad. The more civilized nations, like the Aztecs and the Incas, showed a remarkable aptitude for public administration. The Aztec Confederacy and the Inca Empire had an elaborate hierarchy of authority, with well-defined gradations of responsibility including the performance of specialized technical functions, for the government of their peoples. The Spaniards admired their political genius and preserved some of their machinery of rule at the lower levels of their colonial system.

War was a normal condition of pre-Columbian societies. Some peoples, like the Caribs, the Chichimecs,[22] and the indomitable Araucanians,[23] were as bellicose as the Sioux or the Iroquois. Others, like the Tainos of the Antilles, the Chimu of the Peruvian coast, and the Chibchas of the Colombian plateau, were essentially peaceful by instinct and were preyed upon by more aggressive neighbors. In their crudest form, these intertribal conflicts might be limited to the raiding of enemy villages for sacrificial victims—or a meat supply. This was a common practice of the Tupís and their kindred, the Guaranís. Sometimes the motive of war was the enslavement of individual enemies or of whole tribes, as it was among the Botocudos of Brazil. The Abipones, a South American tribe, after being dominated by their neighbors, learned to master the wild horses let loose on the plains by the Spaniards and turned the tables on their oppressors. In a society that prized personal valor above all other virtues, war offered the supreme test of manhood.[24]

With the Incas and the Aztecs, war took on many of the characteristics of military enterprises in Europe. Their imperialistic wars aimed at the permanent subjugation of other peoples and the acquisition of their lands. There existed a definite warrior class which, particularly in Mexico, enjoyed special privileges and prerogatives. Concepts of strategy were developed that were much superior to the primitive pattern of a nocturnal raid, followed by the seizure of prisoners and a quick withdrawal to their base. The rapidity with which the Araucanians learned and adopted the tactics of the Spaniards was one of the secrets of their long and successful resistance to the conquerors. To subdue their enemies without bloodshed the Incas sometimes resorted to psychological warfare, as they did with the Chimú nation along the coast.[25] Agents of the Incas penetrated into the Chimú capital, where they spread among the people the legend of their armies' invincibility and assurances of leniency if the Chimú should capitulate without resistance. The military process was then completed with the integration of the conquered people into the well-disciplined body of the all-embracing Incaic Empire, from which there was no escape by rebellion. If the conquered were a particularly warlike folk, like the Cañarís, they might be incorporated into the armies of the Incas as a combat force of Janissaries.

The Indian world had no money economy and its members no sense of gain or wealth. The individual accumulation of capital had no meaning to them. Among the more primitive peoples life was a feast-or-famine or hand-to-mouth affair, dependent on the often precarious fruits of fishing or hunting, or of an elemental agriculture or the spoils of war. Where gold or silver existed, they served no monetary purpose, but were used only in the arts. Probably the nearest approach to a currency was in the early use in Mexico of cacao beans as a measure of value. In some regions there was considerable intertribal barter of commodities that were necessary to the traditional life of the group, such as salt, obsidian, feathers for adornment, and curare for the poisoning of arrows. The Spaniards found in the Aztec capital public markets whose variety of goods and well-regulated operation amazed them, and whose cleanliness probably compared more than favorably with the present markets of Mexico City. The masses of the civilized nations were farmers and their economy was so intimately associated with the land that it often assumed a religious or cultural character, as it did among the Incaic peoples of the Andes. Here a paternalistic state took charge of the economic problems which concerned the larger community, such as the storage of foodstuffs against the chance of famines and the balancing of crops against the incidence of drought or other natural calamity as between the different regions of the empire. Agriculture was well rooted in the practical realities of the environment and, archaic as the Indian's tillage methods may appear to a mechanized farmer of today, they were generally well adapted by long trial-and-error to the natural conditions under which the Indian worked the ground. For example, the modern steel plow would be disastrous to the thin soils of Yucatan, where the Maya farmer has planted and cultivated his corn for a thousand years with no other implement than a sharp stick.[26]

THE INDIAN CULTURES

Both the Aztecs and the Maya had a hieroglyphic system of writing. Since the Aztec civilization was in full flower at the time of the Spanish conquest, it was possible to decipher the Mexican glyphs without difficulty. On the other hand, the Maya culture was then in such an advanced state of decay that the descendants of those who had long ago covered temples and stelae with carved inscriptions were unable to read them. Only a few of the manuscripts or codices which were extant at the arrival of the Spaniards have survived the destructive zeal of the conquerors, to whom they were only relics of paganism. It is only in the present century that scholars have made any headway in interpreting the Maya writing, and the majority of the characters still remain undeciphered. Most of the inscriptions so far revealed deal with astronomical and ritualistic matters and thus have the character of a religious almanac. Otherwise, beyond establishing certain key dates in their chronology, they shed very little light on the long and intriguing history of the remarkable race. The Incas never developed a true system of writing. However, by the early sixteenth century the ingenious device of the quipús, by which they recorded numerical data, had evolved to a point where it was possible to transmit other, though still limited, forms of information. The quipús were knotted cords, in which variations in the color, arrangement, and number of the knots were employed to record quantitative facts. The early Spanish chroniclers frequently expressed their surprise at the ability of the quipús to register other than purely numerical concepts.[27] None of the Indian peoples ever devised anything approaching a phonetic alphabet.

The artistic achievements of the pre-Columbian peoples were very great. Some of them showed a highly developed aesthetic sense combined with technical skill in working with a variety of media. Sometimes hieratic controls resulted in a conventionalized style of art, as it has among other peoples, like the Byzantine Greeks, whose cultural life was dominated by a priestly caste. Among the Maya, for example, such formalized symbols of their deities as the jaguar and the serpent are everywhere present in the various manifestations of their art. On the other hand, much of the pottery of the Peruvian coastal peoples, like the Chimú and the Ñazca, is entirely individualistic in its treatment of popular types and scenes.

The forms of Indian art included ceramics, painting, sculpture, lapidary work, gold and silver ware, textile design, wood carving, and arrangement of flowers and feathers.[28] Large collections of these treasures are preserved in the archaeological museums of Latin America and in museums in the United States and Europe. Until recently the Latin American republics were little interested in their Indian past and scorned its riches as relics of barbarism. However, with the growing appreciation of its intrinsic quality and of its part in the evolution of their national cultures, they now take great pride in these remains of pre-European art and generally forbid their removal from the country. The artistic production of the Indian has deteriorated greatly since the Conquest, and particularly since the period when he contributed his skill to the decoration of the churches throughout the colonies. This has been due largely to loss of the racial pride which inspired his earlier efforts, to the predilection of his Spanish and Portuguese masters for European art, and, in our time, to the competition of machine-made goods. The Revolution which began in 1911 has resulted in the recognition of Mexico's cultural debt to the Indian and the expression of the latent artistic sense of the Mexican people has been revived by her artists and anthropologists. As the admiration and interest of foreign scholars were largely responsible for the changed attitude of the Latin Americans toward the cultural wealth of their Indian background, so a few Americans like William Spratling in Mexico and Truman Bailey in Peru have done much to aid in restoring the original standards and techniques of native craftsmanship in those countries.

The Mexican peoples and the Maya excelled in the field of sculpture, though the Chavín area in the Andes was also a center of skilled stone carving. Much of the art served the purposes of architectural decoration, like the delicate geometrical tracery on the walls of Mitla, the rich ornamentation of Uxmal, the arabesques of Chan-Chan, a sculptured doorway at Copán, and the Assyrian-like bas-reliefs on the Gateway of the Sun at Tiahuanaco. Among other sculptured treasures are a carved stone disk from southeastern Mexico that has the cameolike quality of an ancient Syracusan coin, the riotously lush carvings on the stelae of Copán and Quiriguá, and a magnificent lintel stone of Piedras Negras with its thirteen figures.

In many areas of the New World the native races produced pottery of an infinite variety and often of great beauty and technical excellence. Working without the potter's wheel, their craftsmen fashioned with their sensitive hands vases, urns, jars, and figurines that tell us much of the living history of their race and of their quest for aesthetic satisfactions beyond the borders of daily realities. Indians of Mexico and the Maya and of the Peruvian coast were supreme in the ceramic arts, such as the fresco vases of the Maya, the individualized portrait pottery and the storytelling or genre figurines of the Chimú and the vivid polychrome vases of the Ñazca in southern Peru. Much of the Mochica and Chimú pottery was humorous in its realistic treatment of individual subjects, and caricature also reached a high level among some of the Mexican peoples, as in a statuette of a pompous and rotund man of importance from the Chiapas region and the figurines of the Tarascans in the western highlands.

Though much of the best gold work of the Incas was lost when the Sanish conquerors melted down the ransom of Atahualpa and the loot of Cuzco and Pachacamac or has subsequently been rifled from tombs by the "treasure hunters" of four centuries, enough has survived the greed and vandalism of later times to demonstrate the metallurgical skill and aesthetic sensibilities of some of the Indian peoples. The sensational discoveries in the tombs of Monte Albán in the Oaxaca region of Mexico have brought to light in our own time a fabulously beautiful collection of golden necklaces, plaques, and pendants that are a triumph of delicate and complex craftsmanship. In Cuzco the Spaniards found a great sun disk of gold set with emeralds in the façade of one of the Inca buildings and in the night of carousal that fol-fowed the sacking of the Inca capital a soldier had gambled it away on the throw of a die. Like the golden gardens strewn with effigies of animals and trees that Pizarro's emissary stared at with stupefied amazement in a palace of the Inca at Tumbes, the solar plaque of Cuzco disappeared into the furnace of a Spanish gold-smith. There remained, among other treasures, a golden ear of corn with silver leaves and tassels of silver threads. Among other skilled workers in gold were the Quimbaya people of Colombia and the tribes of the Cocle and Chiriquí districts of the isthmus, who produced such exquisite ornaments as the insect of gold and quartz crystal and the gold pendant with inset emerald in the form of a dragonlike animal, that are preserved in the University Museum at Philadelphia. The Indian artists worked in gold and silver, in copper, and in bronze and other alloys. The processes which they employed included casting by the *cire perdue*, or "lost wax," method, embossing, hammering, plating, gilding, engraving, inlaying, and sheathing.

The Maya were supreme among all the Indian peoples in the lapidary art, particularly in the carving of jade. Others who ex-celled in the cutting of gems were the Mixtecs and other Mexican tribes, who also did beautiful work in rock crystal, as in such pieces as the figure of the man-in-the-moon, that is now in the Musée de l'Homme in Paris. The lack of hard cutting tools makes the achievements of the Indians in this field all the more remark-able.

Peruvian weaving reflected the artistic instincts of those peo-ples. Fortunately, the dry climate of the coast lands has preserved many of the pre-Spanish fabrics to our time and they are now pre-served in the museums of Lima. These examples of Chimú and other textiles include tapestries, ceremonial robes and mantles, and ordinary garments such as ponchos, of amazing technical ex-cellence and great beauty of design and color. Among them are fine embroideries and brocades, as well as the tightly woven cloths that were typical products of the Indian looms. Though they may have equaled the work of the coastal folk of Peru, no examples of early weaving by the peoples of the Peruvian sierra or of those of Mexico and Central America have survived to this age.

Among other examples of Indian art are the painted murals in the inner chambers of the temples at Teotihuacán, Chichen Itzá, and Monte Albán, the decorated codices that were like illuminated manuscripts, and exquisite carving in wood or any other suitable material that was available on which to express their artistic urgings. Most of the Indian peoples had a natural gift for pictorial representation and probably the first example of "news photography" in modern times was the illustrated drawings of the Spaniards which the messengers of Montezuma carried back with them from their first meeting with the conquerors.

As a rule, Indian society was a remarkably smooth-working human organism. In its personal relationships there was much gentleness and mutual consideration. The Indians were low-voiced and soft-spoken in their conversation and there was little quarreling or violence between members of the tribe. Thus the superior politeness of the Mexican people is as much a heritage of the Indian as it is of the Spaniard.[29] Conduct was governed by certain rules that were learned early in life, and the tribal discipline was generally so strong that few dared to violate the fundamental custom of the group. This code of behavior was concerned with the observance of the traditional hierarchy of precedence or authority within the tribe, with its collective responsibility for the perpetuation of the community's existence against the menace of the dangers, real or imaginary, which imperiled it, and with the everyday give-and-take of group living. As a result, the frictions of tribal life were reduced to a minimum and the habit of cooperation in all the activities of the tribe was highly developed. Devoid as they were of a property sense or of instincts of covetousness, the Indians freely and unselfishly shared the product of their hunting or fishing with one another. They aided each other, as they still do, in tending their crops or in any enterprise that was beyond the strength of a single man.

In the great societies, like the Maya and the Inca, there was much high pomp and pageantry associated with the observance of their cults and the glorification of their rulers, and much popular festivity in connection with the harvest season and the other stages in the working cycle of an agricultural folk. With the Conquest the occasions for impressive drama and ceremony disappeared, and those of festive relaxation and merriment gradually declined in frequency and intensity as the burden of alien domination bore ever more heavily on the soul of the race. It was this spiritual hiatus which the Church attempted to fill, and with considerable success, with the festivals of the new faith, with music and processions and mystery plays and all the majestic ritual of Catholic Christendom.

THE CONQUEST

The impact of the Conquest on the Indian civilizations was catastrophic. Some lived on for a time, to wither gradually on the Spanish vine to which they were grafted. But the fruit they bore was no longer the same and sometimes they shriveled and died altogether for lack of the nourishment that had made them what they were. Sometimes it was very bitter fruit that the hybrid vine bore, as with the Incaic peoples. A few of them, like that of the Tainos in the Antilles, disappeared with the race itself in the first violent impetus of the conquerors. A few, like the Tupinambás in Brazil, salvaged their culture for a time by escaping into the far interior.[30] The Araucanians resisted so savagely and successfully that they were able to keep the traditional pattern of their tribal life. But the great Aztec civilization never recovered from the physical destruction of the Conquest and the various plagues which the Spaniards brought with them, and only a broken and spiritless remnant of a once proud people survived to serve as peasants of the victors.

The desperate courage which the Indians often displayed did not avail them against the military superiority of the Spaniards. For their undisciplined hosts were pitted against the invincible soldiery that rode rough-shod over the nations of Europe through the sixteenth century. It was not only a question of superior arms and the legend of the Spanish horsemen, or even of the magnificent fighting qualities of the Spanish foot soldier, but also of the leadership of supreme captains like Cortés. In all but numbers the odds were against the Indians, and disparity of numbers meant nothing to those paladins who marched so confidently into Tenochtitlán and Cajamarca.[31]

After the initial conquest the Indians seldom rebelled against the Spanish yoke. Some, like the Chichimecs in Mexico, held out longer than did their neighbors. Others, like the Caribs, had to be beaten into submission by a long and bloody process of attrition. When the Spaniards arrived in Yucatan the Mayan Itzás withdrew southward to an island in Lake Petén from which they were not flushed out until nearly two centuries later. Peoples who resisted the Spaniards too stubbornly, like some of the savage tribes of the Colombian highlands, were likely to be annihilated for their pains. The Chiriguanos, cousins of the Guaraní, who had kept the Inca's armies out of the low country to the east of the Bolivian *Collao,* drove an expedition headed by the great Viceroy Toledo back onto the plateau, only to be later subdued by the Jesuit missionaries. The Andean peoples rose twice in forlorn revolts against the Spanish power, the first time, in the sixteenth century, when the Conquest was not yet cold, and again in the late eighteenth century, when twilight was beginning to settle over the colonial empire of Spain. In both uprisings the leader was a descendant of the Inca dynasty—of the first, Manco Capac, and of the other, Tupac Amarú.[32] The wild Indians of the Argentine pampa were not disposed of until after the middle of the last century. Then, after a long period of raiding and killing and fighting in which no quarter was given on either side, the remnants of this recalcitrant people were pushed south of the Rio Negro by a military expedition under General Roca and left there for time and starvation to complete their extinction. It was only then that the peaceful development of the pampa's resources became possible.

Speculation on what might have been the ultimate possibilities of these truncated civilizations if they had not been cut off so violently in their evolution, is an idle, but intriguing, subject. The brilliance of the Maya world was already but a memory when the Spaniards came. Whether its glory could ever have been revived, as it was after the long sleep that followed the Old Empire, is problematical. Much depended on whether the Maya could have solved the problem of their food supply whose failure was probably responsible for the collapse of their corn-fed civilization. The Aztecs did not have time to round out and consolidate their conquests. It was as though Caius Marius had failed to defeat the Cimbri before the Romans had been able to break out of the peninsula on their imperial career. The Zapotecs and other peoples who ringed the domains of the confederacy in several directions remained to be reduced before the natural limits of expansion were reached. And embedded in the body of the Aztec state were such sore spots as the truculent little commonwealth of Tlaxcala. So far the Aztec dominion rested too much on a base of fear, and the sanguinary demands of their war god were not such as to conciliate the subject or tributary peoples and to permit the lasting peace that was needed. Superior as they were politically, perhaps the Aztec was not to be the last of the waves of conquest that had swept over Mexico during our Middle Ages. What the destiny of the Inca Empire might have been but for the Spaniards is an even more challenging question.[33] Like the Aztec state, it was still young as the lives of nations go. Until the death of Huayna Capac and the fateful partition of the empire it had generally been governed with extraordinary wisdom. The more thoughtful Spaniards had an immense respect for its memory.[34] Though it valued the virtues of security more than those of individual progress, it had already come far on the road toward a truly noble civilization. There was in it a great promise of capacity for advancement, and one cannot avoid the feeling that it may have been on the eve of a brilliant flowering. Its death was the supreme tragedy of the Spanish Conquest. As for most of the forest tribes of the New World, their cultures had long been static. Cut off by their isolation from the influence of the great civilizations and the pattern of their communal life set in a hard mould of custom, the prospect for their future was only an indefinite prolongation of their primitive past.

For all practical purposes, the Conquest was completed long before the end of the sixteenth century. Most of the native peoples quickly recognized the futility of further armed resistance. Their natural leaders, lead or seduced into the conquerors' camp by marriage or titles, and the shrines at which they had worshiped overturned in the iconoclastic fury of the Christians, they became a thoroughly subdued and broken people. Sunk in apathy and melancholy, they were resigned to their fate as a subject race. Large numbers committed suicide rather than live under the alien domination. The Indians gradually drew within themselves and assumed the attitude of passive resistance that was to preserve important vestiges of their culture and their very racial identity to our times, particularly in the Peruvian Andes.

Meanwhile, the aboriginal population had declined very radically over wide areas.[35] Large numbers had died in the holocaust of the Aztec capital and in the Indian beleaguerment of Cuzco, for native losses in battle were always disproportionately heavy. The oppression of the first colonists like Roldán virtually wiped out the Tainos in the Antilles. Wherever the Indians continued to resist, as did the Caribs in Venezuela and the wild tribes of the Cauca Valley in Colombia, the Spaniards showed them no mercy and some groups that refused to yield were all but exterminated. Yet many more doubtless died of smallpox and other diseases introduced from Europe than in battle. Starvation also took its toll in regions where the Indians' agricultural economy was disturbed by the violence of the Conquest, and sometimes the Indians deliberately refused to plant their crops in order that the Spaniards might not be able to harvest them.

THE SPANIARD AND THE INDIAN

The Spaniards early established a pattern for the exploitation of lands and mines with the Indians as an involuntary working force. There was a variety of institutional devices for the utilization of the Indians' labor. At first, under the simple arrangement known as the *repartimiento* a number of natives would be assigned to work for a particular Spaniard, or the colonist might waive further formality and round up as many Indians in the vicinity as he required for his service. At its worst, which was common enough, this amounted to legalized slavery. Large numbers of Indians were enslaved along the Spanish Main and carried to Santo Domingo to replenish the exhausted labor supply in Hispaniola. In southern Brazil, the slave raids of the famous "Mamelucos" were a normal source of Indian labor for a long time. It was the arbitrary abuses attendant on this loose form of impressment that led to innovation of the *encomienda*, which remained the basic design for the regulation of agricultural labor throughout the colonial period. The encomienda took the form of a specific grant of land together with the right to the labor of the Indians who dwelt on the property. At the instance of the Church, an elaborate set of regulations was early issued to safeguard the interests of the natives. The encomienda was granted only for the lifetime of the original recipient. However, after the rebellion of Ganzalo Pizarro in protest against the application of the so-called

New Laws for the protection of the Indians, the life of the encomienda was progressively extended until the descendants of the
original grantee eventually came to have a virtually permanent
tenure. The system of the *mita* was especially designed to provide
a steady flow of laborers for the operating of the mines. It was a
kind of *corvée*, whereby the communities within reach of a particular mining center, like Potosí, were required to supply a quota
of Indians for the workings. The law specified the distance which
they might be sent from their homes, the period of their inden-
ture, and other conditions of their service.

In the time of the famous Viceroy Francisco de Toledo
(1569–81), who set the definitive pattern for the government of
the vice-kingdom, the status of the Indian in the social and economic life of Peru was fixed for the duration of Spanish rule.
Toledo, an able, but harsh, administrator, broke up large numbers
of old Indian communities in order to concentrate their populations in centers where they could be more effectively controlled.
The machinery of control was largely in the hands of the *corregidor,* the royal agent in the colonial city, who was directly responsible to the viceroy.

In the "Laws of the Indies" there is embodied the elaborate
and humane legislation which was designed to protect the Indian
against oppression by his Spanish masters.[36] No other colonial
power of the time showed such solicitude for the welfare of its
subject peoples as is expressed in that remarkable code. Some
of the laws are general in their application; others are aimed at
specific abuses to which the Indians had evidently been subject.
For example, Indians were not to be forced to dig for treasure
in the tombs of their ancestors, to have their hair cut short when
they were baptized, to carry a Spaniard in a hammock or litter,
except in case of "obvious sickness," or to bring ice from the
sierra into Lima. The ecclesiastical and secular courts were commanded to "favor and support" the Indians in their jurisdiction,
and one law provided that "crimes against Indians are to be punished with greater severity than those against Spaniards." [37] A
law repeated six times between 1526 and 1548 said that "the Indians are to be free, and not subject to servitude."

The regulation of native labor was the principal concern of
the Spanish government. Here official opinion was torn between

a desire to protect the Indian against exploitation and downright cruelty on the one hand and a realization that if the Indians did not work for the Spaniards, the whole Spanish empire would become an economic liability, and might as well be turned back to its original occupants. In their efforts to strike a balance between these extremes, even the Spanish partisans of the Indian were plagued by his apparent reluctance to exert himself for the monetary advantage of his new masters—what one law called "the repugnance of the Indian to work." According to another law, "the Indians are to be employed at their trades, field work, and other occupations, and they are to wear clothes." The decree goes on to say that "if it is necessary, they are to be forced not to be lazy, since (work) is so important to their life, health, and conservation." Another decree provided that "the good treatment of the Indians is to be of such a nature that they do not stop serving and working." In other words, the Indians were to be treated well, but not pampered. The same law comments that "the Indians receive great damage, harm, and oppression in their persons and property from some Spaniards, corregidors, friars, and priests, for whose profit they perform all kinds of labor, but being miserable persons they make no resistance or defense and do whatever they are told to do." Safeguards were thrown about all kinds of labor which the Indian might be expected to perform, whether in the mines, the fields, or personal service for Spaniards. Indians were not to work in the textile *obrajes*, which were the "sweatshops" of the times, or in cane fields, which was considered work for Negroes. To those who had to come to work from a distance up to ten leagues, they were to be paid on a "portal-to-portal" basis. The custom of overloading Indian bearers is decried as an "obstacle to their conversion, multiplication, and health"— and is ordered to be stopped. But the Indian was a beast of burden before the Spaniard came and, in some parts of Latin America, he still is, even though he is his own master.

These benevolent and humanitarian laws were inspired by the Church, but particularly by the Dominican Order, which early assumed the special role of protector of the Indians. The Franciscans and other missionary orders also labored valiantly in the interest of the Indians, as the Jesuits did later. They not only aimed to rescue the Indian's spiritual nature from the abject depression which followed the Conquest, by offering him the comforting alternatives of Christianity. In the early period of the Mexican viceroyalty they established excellent schools for his education. They boldly defended him against the cruelty of conquerors like Nuño de Guzmán, as Bishop Zumárraga did, and against the cupidity and callousness of all the lay element among the Spaniards. They went alone among barbarous tribes who were yet unconquered. They learned the languages of the Indians and wrote learned treatises on their history and customs, as did Father Motolinia of the Franciscans, Father Torquemada, and Father Sahagún. Vasco de Quiroga, Bishop of Michoacán and follower of Sir Thomas More, attempted to apply his utopian philosophy to the creation of an ideal Indian state in the lands of his episcopate, in western Mexico. The famous Dominican friar, Bartolomé de las Casas, was given an opportunity to put his religious and social ideas into practice in the Province of Vera Paz in Guatemala, where the Indians were governed without the intercession of the lay authority. It was Las Casas whose sensational book, translated into most of the languages of western Europe, was responsible by its exaggerations for the "Black Legend" of Spanish cruelty toward the Indians that has ever since blackened the name of Spain. In the Dominicans at the royal court the Indians always had advocates who would plead their cause in high places. The first half of the sixteenth century was one of the most glorious periods in the history of the Church.

With the Jesuits, who came into the missionary field later than the older orders, the mission system for the social and religious governance of the Indians was perfected. This great international brotherhood established a chain of missions whose links constituted a theocratic empire within the heart of South America. The series of the Society's missions extended transversally across the continent from the Mainas region of the upper Amazon basin, that was the scene of the labors of Father Samuel Fritz, by the Beni plains about Trinidad and the remote Chiquitos country of eastern Bolivia, to Paraguay and the Argentine Misiones and Charrua lands by the River Plate. A similar group of missions reached northeastward up the coastal zone of Brazil. Though the pattern followed was everywhere much the same, whether in Lower California or on the banks of the Uruguay, the best-known of these establishments were the so-called Paraguayan "reductions." The Indian population of a particular locality was gathered into the premises of the mission, where it became subject to the peculiar civilizing regime of the Jesuit Fathers. What the members of these paternalistic theocracies lost in their former freedom of movement and action they gained in security and certain new embellishments of living. Under the direction of the two priests who governed the mission, they built the large churches that were the centers of community life. In addition to the regular religious instruction, the Indians were taught the elements of music and painting, and also of certain handicrafts, for all of which they displayed a considerable and enthusiastic aptitude. The men spent much of their time at work in the fields or in tending the mission's herds of livestock, and since the Jesuits were the best farmers in Latin America, their Indian charges were always assured of a plentiful supply of food. Any surplus beyond the needs of the mission population was sold in Asunción or Buenos Aires and the proceeds used for the purchase of articles which could not be produced locally. In these Arcadian oases the Indians were kept scrupulously isolated from the corrupting influence of the lay Spaniards and the temptations of the outside world in general. However, when the Society of Jesus was expelled from the Spanish and Portuguese colonies in 1767 and the missions secularized, the mission Indians had lost their power of initiative and were unable to adjust themselves to either the ways of their ancestors or to those of the worldly Spaniards who dwelt in the towns and cities. Much of the work of the Jesuits was undone in these years of confusion and disintegration that followed the departure of the Fathers, but the docility of the mission population was later to make the members of the Guaraní race apt subjects for the dictators of the Paraguayan Republic. The great Jesuit experiment in transforming a race was thus cut short before it was possible to observe what might have been its ultimate chances of success. The famous chain of Franciscan missions which was established in Upper California in the latter part of the eighteenth century contributed nothing to the original pattern of the mission system as developed by their exiled predecessors in the field.

The worst abuses in the treatment of the Indians were associated with the forced labor system of the *mita*. Though a similar practice had prevailed in the Inca Empire, especially in the construction of public works, the taskmasters were men of their own race and the hardships incident to labor of that kind were tempered by the Incas' humanitarian concern for the welfare of their subjects. Under the Spaniards, the predominance of mine work naturally lent itself to great abuses, due to the basic motive of the industry and to the hard conditions that were then inseparable from labor in mines. Frequently assembled from a long distance, the Indians were generally kept in the mine beyond the term of service prescribed by the law, and were often released broken in health and after the season had passed for planting their crops in the fields from which they had been taken. They were forced to carry heavy loads of ore up steep ladders from the bottom of the mine and to work all day in cramped and airless galleries that frequently caved in on them for lack of proper shoring with timbers. Sometimes they were locked inside the mine all the week and only let out on Sunday to attend the mass at a neighboring chapel.[38] At the mercury mines of Huancavelica in Peru, a church had been created inside the mine, so that it was not necessary to go outside for the consolations of the divine service. Conditions in the *obrajes,* or textile mills, were usually as bad, and it was customary in this industry to confine the *mitayos* indefinitely, while their wives brought their food each day to the place of their confinement.[39]

The *encomienda* system lacked the extreme abuses that were identified with the *mita.* The Indian worked on the land and at tasks with which he had always been familiar. At night he could return to his family and normal associations with his fellow men were possible in his hours of leisure. Beyond that his lot largely depended on the character of the individual *encomendero* whose man he was, and on whether he lived on the encomienda or left its administration to a major-domo. For the evils of absentee ownership appeared very early in the New World, where the lords of the land yielded increasingly to the lure of life in the cities as urban existence became more attractive. In such cases the Indians were likely to suffer most from the brutality of mestizo overseers, who too often spent the force of their social frustrations on the members of their mothers' race. As a rule, the Spanish encomendero was a humane and considerate master.[40] At worst, his solicitude for the well-being of his Indian tenants as valuable capital assets was dictated by a selfish concern. The system which he represented had great possibilities for good and might have perpetuated some of the principal values of the Inca civilization that were to be irretrievably lost after Toledo's time. At least, it would have tended to preserve much of the former stability of Indian society against the disruptive influences of the colonial regime. But the government of the Spanish Empire never permitted the encomienda to develop its natural potentialities as a conservative force in colonial life until it was too late. The encomendero was never allowed to feel secure enough in his position to identify himself completely with his lands and his dependents, as a great many of his class would doubtless have done. He never felt sure that the Crown, out of fear that the *encomenderos* might develop a strong and concerted vested interest in the colonies or out of misdirected considerations of humanity, would not some day revoke the title to his lands.

Many of the evils of the Spanish colonial system as it bore on the Indians were due to the avarice of the *corregidor,* who was the agent of the Crown in the cities. In addition to their police powers, which made them responsible for the maintenance of order in these often turbulent centers, they had the duty of enforcing the special laws which applied to the native population. This prerogative invoked the regulation of the *mita* and of Indian labor in general. In collusion with the mine owners and other elements of the ruling minority, the corregidor frequently condoned violations of the Indian code to his own financial advantage. Under one guise or another he might exact money from those to whom he supplied Indian laborers or from the Indians themselves. Sometimes he carried on a trading business of his own and forced the Indians to buy from him goods which they did not need and which they could not afford from the pittance of their wages. The *curacas* or Indian magistrates, freed from the discipline of their former rulers, and eager to curry favor with the royal officials, were also often guilty of petty tyrannies toward their own people.

The "Black Legend" to the contrary, the record of the Spaniards and the Portuguese in their treatment of the Indian compares favorably with that of the English and the Americans.

Quantitatively, the problem was different, for the Indian population in what is now Latin America was far larger than in the present territory of the United States. Therefore, the Indian represented a relatively much more difficult problem to the Hispanic conquerors and colonizers than he did to the English colonists in North America. When Indians died from mistreatment at the hands of the Spaniards, *more* of them died, so that, statistically, the record of Spanish cruelty was darker, just as the death of a thousand persons draws larger headlines and better position in a newspaper than does the death of a hundred. Moreover, there was no imaginative English Las Casas to report the "destruction of the Indians" in the thirteen American colonies.

The Indians whom the English encountered were "barbarians," as the Spaniards called those of a similar level of culture whom they found in South America. Unlike the civilized natives of Mexico and Peru, they were of no interest to the English colonists in their plans for the settlement and development of the lands between the Atlantic seaboard and the Appalachians. The northern colonist, ready to work with his own hands, looked for no help from the Indian. And the more aristocratic colonists to the south of the Potomac quickly found in the Negro slave the labor force which they required for their plantations. Like the Pampas of the Argentine plains and the Pijaos of Colombia, the Iroquois and the Delawares were only obstacles to the advance of the white man and to be dealt with accordingly. In such cases, the methods used were quite similar: the destruction with fire and sword of the last refuge of King Philip's people in the Connecticut Valley and the virtual extermination of the Six Nations in the Mohawk Valley. Except for a few individuals, like the Rev. John Eliot, Roger Williams, and William Penn, the Indians found no friends or protectors among the English colonists. There exists no such benevolent body of legislation in English colonial jurisprudence as is found in the Laws of the Indies.

After independence the lot of the Indian did not improve. Once beyond the Alleghenies, the scope of action was only enlarged and the tempo of the Indian's discomfiture speeded; the formula and the results remained the same. General "Mad Anthony" Wayne harried the Indians out of the Ohio country. Thence, south to the Gulf and west to the Rockies the process

went on unceasingly until it was finished and the survivors of the
race confined in those glorified concentration camps called reservations. Mingled with bursts of humanitarianism, too much of the
story is one of raids and warfare and broken treaties, of violence
and perfidy and greed. The Indian stood in the way of the pioneer and of those who came after him. Therefore he had to go.
And the sentimental myth of "the noble Red Man," cultivated
by Cooper and others, as it was also by José de Alencar in Brazil,
came too late to save the Indian from the inevitable. The Spaniard could not have done the job more thoroughly than we had
done it. And today members of the ruling classes in the Latin
American republics that are still predominantly Indian sometimes
express their envy of the finality with which we settled *our*
Indian problem.

THE MIXING OF THE PEOPLES

Some of the difference was due to the greater prevalence of miscegenation in the Spanish and Portuguese colonies. Interbreeding
on a vast scale produced a new race of mestizos in whom was
mingled the blood of the Indian and of conquerors. The Hispanic
peoples had no prejudice of race and few of the early arrivals
brought their womenfolk with them. The easy compliance of the
Indian women, proud of even a temporary alliance with their new
masters, or resigned to their fate, as part of the booty of conquest,
provided the other condition necessary for the process of hybridization. The mixing went on with greater speed and completeness
in some areas than in others, particularly in Brazil and Paraguay. Throughout the Brazils the Lusitanian libido was on the
loose, and the resultant of this carnal fury was the creation of
the vast class of mixed breeds that are known today as *caboclos*.
In the São Paulo region they were the enterprising Mamelucos,
who enslaved their Indian half-cousins of the interior as far as
the Jesuit missions of the Guayrá on the borders of Paraguay.
In Paraguay itself, the Spaniards who came up the river from
the abandoned site of Buenos Aires indulged in the carnival of
lechery with the Guaraní women that early fixed the permanent
mold of the Paraguayan nation. For Paraguay is today a mestizo
state in which the Indian's cultural elements, including the language, are as important as those inherited from the Spaniard, and

in some respects are more dominant. Miscegenation was on a wholesale scale, since each Spanish soldier maintained a harem of concubines about the growing settlement. And Asunción grew apace with the vast brood of mestizo children that were born to these multiple unions. As they reached manhood, the young half-breeds greatly outnumbered their aging fathers. Vital and restless, they set the tone of the colony and dominated its burgeoning life. For a time their loyalties gravitated between Spain and the land of their Guaraní mothers, only to strike a balance in their attachments that preserved the province of Paraguay for the Spanish Empire, but at the cost of a civilization that was as thoroughly mesticized as their blood. Under strong Spanish leaders like Martínez de Irala, their energies found fruitful outlet in bold enterprises to the south. It was the young mestizos from Asunción who founded Santa Fé on the lower Paraná, and, pushing on down the river, resettled Buenos Aires in 1580 under Juan de Garay. As the fecund colony became a secondary center of expansion, its sons spread over into the Corrientes country on one side of the great river and westward across northern Argentina to meet the current of settlement that came down from Peru. Under Ñuflo de Chaves they crossed from the upper Paraguay into the plains of eastern Bolivia to found Santa Cruz de la Sierra. Later venturesome Spaniards and mestizos from Paraguay and Peru, from the River Plate country to the south and from Chile and the province of Cuyo on the west, moved out onto the open wastes of the pampa. There, with a casual brutality, they took the women of the Indian tribes who fought their encroachments so bitterly and left behind them the famous Gaucho breed of horsemen who eventually drove the Indians from the Argentine plains. Over the Andes in the valley of Chile and along the fighting frontier of Arauco the same wild biological ferment created the sturdy *roto* class that was to be the plebeian basis of a strong Chilean race.

Alliances between the Spanish conquerors and women of the native aristocracies set an example at a higher level to the less discriminating, but no less concupiscent, rank and file of the soldiery. For one Pocahontas, there were dozens of Aztec and Inca "princesses" who became the mistresses or the legitimate wives of the captains of the Conquest. Many of these mates of the conquerors were women of gentle breeding and refined manners, as well as of superior physical attractions, fit candidates for any nobility. On the Isthmus, it was the attachment of Balboa to the devoted daughter of a local Indian ruler that caused him to hesitate at the *mariage de convenance* with a daughter of his enemy, Pedrarias Dávila, and was one of the factors that lead to his doom at the hands of his presumptive father-in-law. In the same locality, Diego de Almagro, the partner of Pizarro, sired the gallant son who later headed his father's party in the civil wars of Peru. Francisco Pizarro himself, who never married, either in Peru or in the Indies, had several daughters by noblewomen of the imperial dynasty of the Incas, who were for a time his mistresses. One of them married his half (and only legitimate) brother, Hernando, and became a great lady in Spain.

The most famous of the mestizos of the period of the Conquest was Garcilaso Inca de la Vega. His father, who came of one of the most illustrious families of Spain, was one of the conquerors of Peru. His mother was an Inca princess, who became the mistress of his father, Garcilaso de la Vega, but was abandoned when he retired to Spain and married a woman of the Spanish nobility. Young Garcilaso grew up in his father's house in Cuzco, where he associated with other mestizos and Spanish youths of good families. He resented the disparagement of his class that had already begun as a form of racial snobbery, and considered himself a Peruvian rather than a Spaniard, though he spent much of his manhood in Spain and died there. In the Royal Commentaries of the Incas he wrote the story of his mother's people, and he also wrote a history of the Spanish conquest of her country, that is probably more accurate than his better-known work.

As in Peru, the conquerors of Mexico mated freely with women of the native aristocracy. When the little army of Cortés entered the country of their allies, the Tlascalans, the alliance was sealed by the bestowal of high-born Indian maidens as concubines of the Spanish captains. Later, princesses of the Aztec ruling house became the wives or mistresses of several of the conquerors. The famous Doña Marina, a scion of the local gentry of the Isthmus, who served Cortés so well as interpreter and adviser, gave her illustrious lord and lover a son, Martín.

Concubinage was not a phenomenon that ceased with the Conquest. In spite of all the efforts of the Church and the Crown to moralize the habits of the Spanish population, its popularity continued throughout the colonial period, to the greater increase of the mestizo population and the added demoralization of customs. In fact, it has remained an accepted feature of Latin American society, though surrounded by a certain protocol that mitigates its effects on family life.

The Indians Under the Republics

The Independence movement in the Spanish and Portuguese colonies had little effect on the conditions of the Indians.[41] Except in the ill-fated uprising of Father Hidalgo in Mexico, the natives generally remained as bystanders in the wars of liberation that raged over the continent. As the republics supplanted the colonial system, with its ill-balanced mechanisms of repression and protection, the Indians stolidly awaited their fate under the new dispensation. Under the "Enlightened Despotism" of Charles III in Spain and of the Marquis of Pombal in Portugal, a beginning had already been made in integrating the aboriginal population into the civil community. The *pueblo* was substituted for the mission, especially wherever the Jesuits had been forced to abandon their theocratic dominion, though new life was momentarily given to the mission system by the advance of the Franciscans into California. For the Indian, the transition was seldom a source of satisfaction. He had only lost his accustomed guardian and found himself orphaned in a strange world that offered him few real compensations for what he had given up, and in which there were many new and unfamiliar problems of adjustment to be met. He was not ready for citizenship in the European sense.

It is true that for many years after the *Independencia*, the Indians were left on their own. In places they profited from the confusion of the period to restore fragments of their ancestral culture, but their gains proved to be insignificant and ephemeral. It was too late to recover the momentum which had been lost by their conquest in the sixteenth century, though, through inertia and long habit, they managed to keep what they had retained throughout the colonial period. Too much had happened for them to replace the broken threads in the fabric of their cultural pattern.

In reality, the Indians were to find that they had only exchanged one set of masters for another. For their labor was to
prove too valuable to the new landowners, mine operators, indus-
trialists, and lords of the rubber forests for them to be permitted
to work out their economic and social salvation outside the modern structure of the republics. Abuses accumulated wherever the
Indian was brought into the new economic order. The local aris-
tocrats and capitalists were generally callous where the Indians
were concerned. The clergy, their traditional protectors, had lost
their old missionary and humanitarian zeal. They often became
petty exploiters of the Indians, as many had been in the latter
part of the colonial period, and lost the opportunity for moral
leadership which might have saved the better elements of Indian
culture, such as the solidarity of the native family. Later the
priesthood was to reappear in its original guise, as new missionaries began to minister to the special needs of the forest tribes
and to champion them against their exploiters.

The lot of the Indian under the republics varied greatly,
though for long the prospect for its improvement was nowhere
favorable. In Argentina, the "barbarians" were driven from the
pampa and left to die on the barren fringes of Patagonia.[42] Sometimes the death of the survivors was hurried by diabolical methods. In the north, others were exploited in the sugar cane fields
of Tucumán and in the new lands of the Argentine Chaco.

It was in the Amazon Valley that the Indians were ushered
into the industrial age with the greatest harshness. Previously
inexperienced in a wage economy, they were lured or forced into
the service of the lords of the rivers who controlled the production
of rubber. The high price of the product, the frequent lack of
an alternative labor supply, the isolation of the region, and the
lack of supervision by government formed a combination of circumstances that favored the exploitation of the Indian. Conditions were probably worst among the Huitotos of the Putumayo,
among the Campas between the Javarý and the Huallaga, along
the Purús and the Abuná, and in the Beni area of Bolivia, that
is, in the more remote parts of the Amazonia where the native
population was predominantly Indian rather than mestizo.

After the beginning of the present century some of the governments became interested in the condition of their aboriginal

populations. Sometimes the motive was genuinely humanitarian, the belated recognition of a responsibility for the welfare of all citizens of the state. At times, their action was prompted by a desire to incorporate the Indians more fully into the economic life of the nation and so better to avail themselves of their potential value as a labor force and as consumers of goods. The new liberal constitutions contain pious statements about the Indian that usually bear little relation to reality. "Days of the Aborigines," that pay lip service to the original inhabitants of the republics, are received with the skepticism which they deserve. The Aprista party in Peru has made much of its sincere concern for the Indian, but its political ineptness has prevented it from translating its idealism into action.

One of the basic tenets of the Mexican Revolution was the restoration of the Indian to a place in the national life consistent with his numbers and his great historical heritage. Some of the philosophers of the Revolution, like Soto y Gama and the archaeologists, Manuel Gamio and Dr. Atl, worked and wrote on behalf of the Indian. However, of all the generals and *políticos* who have passed across the Mexican scene since 1911, the only one who displayed more than a perfunctory interest in the future of the Indian was Lázaro Cárdenas. Though much has been done for the Indian by the restoration of community lands and in education, the Revolution has given him much less than was promised to him. In both a physical and spiritual sense, he still remains apart from the main currents of Mexican life and distrustful of the glib mestizo opportunists who rule the republic.[43]

The Mexican idealists were largely responsible for the wider *Indianista* movement that embraces all the "Indian countries" of the hemisphere. *Indianismo* also has a considerable following among intellectuals in the Andean countries, such as Luís Valcarcel in Peru. This cult of the aborigine has proved a central motif for the activities of the Inter-American Indian Institute.

This organization, which has its headquarters in Mexico City, is a part of the official machinery of Pan-Americanism. It has an elaborate program, some of it very practical, for the improvement of the Indian's lot and for the general dignification of his position in the life of the Americas. A few years ago, a charter of the Indian was drafted by a Congress of *Indianistas*, held, very

appropriately on the shores of Lake Pátzcuaro within the epis-
copal jurisdiction of the famous Bishop Vasco de Quiroga, who
had anticipated the essentials of their program four centuries
before.

Probably the most intelligent and humane Indian policy of
any of the national governments is that of Brazil. The Brazilian
Indian Service reflects not only the deep humanity of that people,
but even more the personality of General Candido Mariano da
Silva Rondón, the great man who founded it. General Rondón,
himself almost a full-blooded Indian, explored the vast jungle
areas of Matto Grosso and the lands to the north of the Amazon,
where he won the confidence of the scattered forest tribes. His
program involved the protection of the aborigines against exploitation and provocation by rubber gatherers, the improvement
of health conditions among them, and their integration, only if
they so desired, into the life of the republic. Rondón and those
who succeeded him in the Indian Service have worked with great
patience and understanding and often under severe provocation
from the more belligerent and suspicious tribes. The Chavantes,
the last of the tribes to accept the overtures of the Indian Service,
have lately made their peace with the Brazilian government.

Whatever the measures to protect him and his archaic society,
the days and the years of the Indian are numbered. All the forces
and processes of the modern world operate against the continuance of his separate existence. His passing as a unique social
entity will be delayed longest where he is still inaccessible to the
direct action of modern influences, as among the forest tribes of
the Amazon basin, or where his numbers are relatively great, as
in the Andean countries. But the arm of government reaches deep
into the jungle and offers him the alternative, however benignly,
of accepting the pattern of the dominant civilization or of ultimate extinction. The last stronghold of the Indian, the distinctive
shadow world of the Incas among the Andes, will gradually dis-
integrate, as is happening in Mexico.[44] The forces that make inevitable its eventual doom, in spite of its millenial inertia, are the
inexorable progress of miscegenation; changes in the local economy, whether voluntarily adopted by the natives from immediate
self-interest or imposed by their overlords; the subtle infiltration
of ideas through education or personal contacts or the radio loud-

speaker in the village plaza, or through the creeping seduction of customs that emanate from the cities and travel out to more isolated communities by all the new means of communication; and the play of time and hopelessness on peoples from whom the heart has long since gone out.

There is much idealism among those who would guide the process so that it would not destroy or impair those values of the Indian which should be conserved for the enrichment of the larger society. But they are seldom in places of power and more "practical" men may dictate the terms of the transformation as the tempo of evolution gains in momentum. For a world that would accept him as equal the Indian has much to give of latent skill and industry, of devotion, and of deep attachment to the earth that surely needs his loving care.

NOTES

1. On the relations of Columbus with the Indians, see Samuel Eliot Morison, *Admiral of the Ocean Sea: A Life of Christopher Columbus* (2 vols., Boston, 1942), *passim*. Quotations are from *The Spanish Letter of Columbus to Luis de Sant' Angel Escribano de Racion of the Kingdom of Aragon Dated 15 February 1493* (Eng. tr. published by Bernard Quaritch, London, 1893), and *The Voyages of Christopher Columbus: being the Journals of his First and Third, and the Letters concerning his First and Last Voyages, to which is Added the Account of his Second Voyage Written by Andreas Bernaldes* (tr. and ed. by Cecil Jane, London, 1930).

2. The most important compilation on the Indians of South America is the monumental and scholarly *Handbook of South American Indians* (edited by Julian H. Steward and published by the Smithsonian Institution, Washington, D.C., in 6 volumes, 1946–1950).

3. On the Incaic or Peruvian civilizations, see Philip Ainsworth Means, *Ancient Civilizations of the Andes* (New York, 1931). Though later archaeological studies have changed some of his conclusions, the first chapters of Prescott's *Conquest of Peru* and the companion work on Mexico still have much of interest on the culture of the Aztecs and the Incas.

4. On the Aztecs, see George C. Vaillant, *Aztecs of Mexico* (Garden City, N. Y., 1941). Vaillant wrote of the paradoxical dualism in what Alfonso Reyes, the Mexican scholar, has called "that charming and cruel people" *The Position of America and Other Essays* (tr. from the Spanish, New York, 1950), p. 5: "Freedom of thought, individual liberty, personal fortunes. were nonexistent, but people lived according to a code that had worked well and continuously for centuries. An Aztec would have been horrified at the naked isolation of an individual's life in our western world." P. 122; "The Aztecs were no pitiable craven savages. They lived upon variegated and delicious foods and dwelt in houses that were comfort-

able and airy. Their dress stimulated the exercise of marital self-satisfactions, not to be confused with the compensations of vanity. Their manner of life enabled them to take advantage of their personal aptitudes and exchange the products of their own creation for whatever they lacked. Articles for daily and ceremonial use were made with the loving care of master artisans, and rare indeed was the object that did not have the impress of some little decorative touch that makes a pleasant possession of a drab utensil." P. 138.

5. On the Maya civilization, see Sylvanus G. Morley, *The Ancient Maya* (Stanford University, California, 1946). According to Morley, of the five basic steps in human advancement—(1) the control of fire; (2) the invention of agriculture; (3) the domestication of animals; (4) tools of metal; (5) discovery of the principle of the wheel—the Maya "were acquainted with and enjoyed the use of only the first two." P. 448. "When their whole cultural attainment is judged by the light of their *known cultural limitations,* which were on a par with those of early Neolithic Man in the Old World, we may safely acclaim the ancient Maya, without fear of successful contradiction, as the most brilliant aboriginal people on this planet." *Ibid.,* p. 455. The Incas had made all but the fifth step. Of the Incas, Jorge Basadre, the Peruvian scholar, says: "No civilization in antiquity had at its disposal such limited means." *Peru: Problemas y Posibilidad* (Lima, 1931), p. 16.

6. See *Handbook of South American Indians, op. cit.,* II, 782.

7. Morley, *op. cit.,* p. 23.

8. "Near the village of Copán there are some grand buildings, from an immemorial past. . . . Among these ruins are things extraordinary and admirable. . . . These ruins give proof . . . that there was once in these parts a people of great intelligence, energy, and efficiency, and great cities, which long lapse of time has obliterated" Antonio Vázquez de Espinosa, *Compendium and Description of the West Indies* (tr. from the Spanish, Washington, D.C., 1942), p. 242. Father Vázquez was in Central America in the early 17th century.

9. See Lesley Byrd Simpson, *Many Mexicos* (New York, 1941), chapter II, "The Tyrant." Humboldt had much to say about corn in Mexico. *Political Essay on the Kingdom of New Spain* (tr. from the German, 4 vols., London, 1811), II, 307 ff. Of the importance of corn among the Maya: "From 75 to 85 per cent of everything a Maya eats is Indian corn in one form or another." Morley, *op. cit.,* p. 142; "I am convinced that fully 75 per cent of all their thoughts still center around the same important cereal." P. 441. Of corn in Peru: "The maize has ever been the delight of the Indians." Jorge Juan y Santacilla and Antonio de Ulloa, *A Voyage to South America* (tr. from the Spanish, 2 vols., London, 1806), I, 465.

10. Concerning the human sacrifices to the Aztec war god and the attendant cannibalism, see Bernardino de Sahagún, *Historia General de las Cosas de Nueva España* (reprint, 5 vols., Mexico, D. F., 1938), I, 136 ff. Father Sahagún also tells of slaves who were sold in the market at Azcapotzalco for eating. He said they were cooked with corn, but without chile peppers. *Ibid.,* p. 141. On the sacrifice to Huitzilopochtli, see James George Frazer, *The Golden Bough* (abridged edition, New York, 1925), pp. 587-92. ("Killing the God in Mexico.") Of the motives of Aztec cannibalism: "The advancement of Mexico rested for support on a system of perpetual extortion from defenseless tributaries, and a system of perpetual war, remorselessly maintained against neighboring peoples, ostensibly to procure victims

for sacrifice, but really to provide animal food for the privileged class engaged in it; and the religious ritual had been so expanded as to ensure for them, by a sacred and permanent sanction, an almost continuous cannibalistic carnival." E. J. Payne, *History of the New World Called America* (2 vols., Oxford, 1892), II, 250. See Blanco Villalta, *Antrofagia Ritual Americana* (Buenos Aires, 1948).

11. "Most ferocious are those new anthropophagi, who live on human flesh, Caribs or cannibals as they are called." Peter Martyr d'Anghiera, *De Orbe* (tr. from the Latin), I, 315. "They were bloodsuckers both of Spaniards, Indians, and all that light in their laps, not sparing their own countrymen, if they can conveniently come by them." John Hawkins, in Hakluyt, *Voyages* (Everyman Edition), VII, 24. In 1578 and 1580, an "anthropophagous horde" of Caribs crossed the llanos and invaded the Valencia region in the Venezuelan highlands, from which they were finally driven by a famous Spanish captain named Garcí-González. Humboldt, *Viaje a las Regiones Equinocciales del Nuevo Continente*, II, 353.

12. Hans Staden, who, as a captive of one of the Tupí tribes in Brazil, was part of the reserve meat supply of the community, naturally has much to say about the cannibalistic practices which he saw going on all about him. He was surprised by the nonchalance with which the victims accepted their fate as though they were losers in a game. Of the preparations for strangling a prisoner with a rope, he wrote: "The man agreed that all was in order, only the rope was too short, for it wanted some six fathoms in length, and he added that with his people the matter would have been better arranged. And he spoke and acted as if he were going to a merrymaking." *The True Story of the Captivity of Hans Staden 1557* (tr. from the German, New York, 1929), p. 92. He tells of how one night two "Mamelucos" were roasted in the camp where he was held prisoner. He called one of the victims "Hieronymus" and wrote: "and this man spent the whole night roasting Hieronymus, scarcely a step from the spot where I lay." *Ibid.*, p. 108.

13. Herrera tells of a tribe in New Granada, which returned from a raid with the quarters of 200 of their neighbors. "Because of their appetite," he wrote, "there was no peace between father and son, or brother and brother." *Historia General* (5 vols., Madrid, 1726-30), *decada* VI, *libro* 8, p. 172. If captives were too thin, it was customary to put them in cages, where they were fattened, as Oviedo says, "like capons in Aranda del Duero." Of the gruesome lore of New World anthropophagy, probably no chapter is more forbidding than Oviedo's story of the Spaniards in Iñigo de Vascuña's expedition in Venezuela, who took to cannibalism after the fashion of the Indians whom they were fighting. *Historia General y Natural* (4 vols., Madrid, 1851-55), II, 289, 291.

14. "The vice of drinking was general in the Indies." Herrera, *op. cit.*, p. 172. Of the Peruvian Indians, Lieuts. Herndon and Gibbon said: "The drinking of chicha was a portion of the primitive worship of the aborigines. They no doubt honestly believed that the more happy they made themselves while paying respect to the Creator of all things, the better he was satisfied." *Exploration of the Valley of the Amazon* (2 vols., Washington, D.C., 1854), I, 166. Ulrich Schmidel wrote of the Guaranís: "They know no other pleasures than those of making war and getting drunk, of drinking night and day, and dancing." *Viaje al Rio de la Plata* (tr. from the German, Buenos Aires, 1942), p. 97. "Towards evening, descending the spur of the volcano, we met several hundred Indians returning from the cere-

monies of the Holy Week (at Quetzaltenango, Guatemala), and exceeding in drunkenness all the specimens we had yet encountered." John L. Stephens, *Incidents of Travel in Central America, Chiapas, and Yucatan* (2 vols., New York, 1849), II, 219. "The Indians maintain that there are not under the sun enjoyments more pure and exalted than intoxication and idleness." F. Depons, *A Voyage to the Eastern Part of Terra Firma, or the Spanish Main, in South America, during the Years 1801, 1802, 1803, and 1804* (tr. from the French, 3 vols., New York, 1806), I, 202. Mme. Calderón de la Barca said of the Mexican Indians: "If they did not so often end in deadly quarrel, there would be nothing so amusing as to watch the Indians becoming a little intoxicated." *Life in Mexico During a Residence of Two Years in that Country* (Everyman Edition) p. 261. Colonel Mansilla has drawn a vivid picture of the gargantuan drinking bouts of the Ranqueles, in which he was forced to participate. "As long as there is anything to drink, they will drink, for an hour, a day, two days, or two months." *Excursión a los Indios Ranqueles* (Buenos Aires, 1942), pp. 120, 134.

15. There is a large display of ancient Peruvian textiles in the Magdalena Museum at Lima.

16. On the widespread chewing of the coca leaf by the Andean Indians, see Herndon and Gibbon, *op. cit.*, I, 182.

17. Observations on the longevity of the Indians vary greatly. Of the Maya, Father Vázquez wrote: "The Indians in this country (Yucatan)... live to a hale old age; in fact, when the Spaniards discovered it, they found many old men there and among them one 300 years old, as was attested in the Indians' annals, and another of 140, who was very active." *Op. cit.*, p. 121. According to Sylvanus Morley, about 70 per cent of all Maya children die before the age of five years, and 90 per cent of all Maya die before 40. However, "the adult Maya is strong and robust and not given to sickness." *The Ancient Maya, op. cit.*, pp. 23-24. Of conditions in Peru, William Stevenson wrote: "Longevity is common among the Peruvian Indians. I witnessed the burial of two in a small village, one of whom had attained the age of 127, and the other of 109; yet both had enjoyed unimpaired health to a few days within their decease. On examining the parish books at Barranca, I found that in seven years, 11 Indians had been buried, whose joint ages amounted to 1207." *A Historical and Descriptive Narrative of Twenty Years' Residence in South America* (3 vols., London, 1825), I, 405. Ulrich Schmidel, the German soldier, said that among the Surucusís in Paraguay he had seen no Indian over 40 or 50 years old. *Op. cit.*, p. 66. Of the Andean Indians, Juan and Ulloa wrote: "They who escape, or recover from these distempers (smallpox, etc.) reach to an advanced age; and both sexes afford many instances of remarkable longevity. I have myself known several, who, at the age of a hundred, were still robust and active." *Op. cit.*, I, 421.

18. Humboldt says that he never saw an Indian with a natural deformity. *Viaje, op. cit.*, II, 134. Of the Indian men on the isthmus, Lionel Wafer, the buccaneer, wrote: "They are streight and clean-limb'd, big bon'd, full breasted, and handsomly shap'd. They are very nimble and active, running very well. I never saw among then a crooked or deformed Person." *A New Voyage and Description of the Isthmus of Darien*, p. 344. (Reference is to the 3d edition, London, 1729).

19. Father Vázquez de Espinosa said that the famous highways of the Inca,

Huayna Capac, who died in 1523, were in ruins a century later. "These were achievements worthy of such a wise and magnanimous king; it would have been very sensible to have taken more care of the roads, for that would have been to the advantage of the Spaniards; but, as no one looks beyond his own private interest to the general good, it is all going to ruin." *Op. cit.*, p. 586. Victor W. Von Hagen is now (1953) making an on-the-ground survey of the "Inca highways."

20. See Pedro de Cieza de León, *The Travels of Cieza de León, A.D. 1532–50* (tr. from the Spanish, London, 1864), pp. 314, 319.

21. "I do not believe that there is any people or nation in the world who could lead irrigation ditches over such rugged and difficult places as do these Indians." *Ibid.*, p. 405.

22. According to Giovanni Gemelli Careri, the globe-encircling Italian druggist, who saw four naked and painted Chichimec warriors in the viceregal palace in Mexico City, "They desire above all things to kill Spaniards." In Churchill, *A Collection of Voyages and Travels* (4 vols., London, 1704), IV, 545. See Philip Wayne Powell, *Soldiers, Indians, and Silver: the Northward Advance of New Spain, 1550–1600* (Berkeley and Los Angeles, 1951).

23. Father Acosta called the Araucanians "a rough people and friends to libertie." *The Natural and Moral History of the Indies* (tr. from the Spanish, 2 vols., London, 1880), I, 170. Lopes Vaz, Francis Drake's Portuguese pilot, told Richard Hakluyt that the Araucanians were "the most valiant and furious people in all America." *Voyages*, VIII, 193 (Everyman Edition). Francis Pretty, who was one of Cavendish's men on his voyage around the world, said: "These Indians are marveilous desperate and carelesse of their lives to live at their own libertie and freedome." *Ibid.*, p. 217. "War is no impediment or loss to them; indeed, they rather consider it as a desirable occupation." Juan and Ulloa, *op. cit.*, II, 278. Capt. F. B. Head, a British mining engineer, who was in Argentina and Chile in the 1820's, wrote of the Pampas Indians, who were cousins of the Araucanians: "The occupation of their lives is war, which they consider as their noble and most natural employment. . . . As a military nation, they are much to be admired, and their system of warfare is more noble, unincumbered, and perfect in its nature than that of any nation in the world." *Rough Notes Taken During Some Rapid Journeys Across the Pampas and Among the Andes* (London, 1826), pp. 121-33.

24. Of the Aztecs, The Anonymous Conqueror said: "They are very warlike and face death with the greatest resolution." *Narrative of Some Things of New Spain and of the Great City of Temestitan, Mexico* (tr. from the Spanish, New York, 1917), p. 19.

25. According to Garcilaso de la Vega, tribes against which the Inca Capac Yupanqui waged war "saw that many times he could have destroyed them, but did not wish to, and when he had them hard pressed and in straits, then he offered them peace with greater mildness and clemency." *Comentarios Reales de los Incas,* II, 29.

26. "The modern Maya method of raising maize is the same as it has been for the past 3,000 years or more." Morley, *op. cit.*, p. 141.

27. See Garcilaso on the mystification of the Spaniards at the results which the Indians obtained with the quipus. *Historia General*, I, 199. In the early 19th century, William Stevenson found an old Indian at Riobamba in Ecuador "who could

knot and interprete the meaning of the quipus." *Op. cit.,* II, 269. See description of the quipus by Antonio de la Calancha, *Crónica Moralizada del Orden de San Agustin,* in Harriet de Onis, ed., *The Golden Land: An Anthology of Latin American Folklore in Literature* (New York, 1948), pp. 67-70.

28. Morley rates the artistic and technological attainments of the Indian peoples in the following order: architecture, Maya; pottery, Maya or Inca; painting, Maya; weaving, Peruvian (Nazca); lapidary work, Aztec; metal working, Aztec and other Central Mexican; highway building, Inca. *Op. cit., passim.*

29. "In the service and manners of its people, their fashion of living was almost the same as in Spain, with just as much harmony and order: and considering that these people were barbarians, so cut off from the knowledge of God and other civilized peoples, it is admirable to see what they attained in every respect." *Letters of Cortés,* I, 263. See the advice of an Aztec father to his son, in Sahagún, *op. cit.,* I, 529. Miles Philips, one of John Hawkins' men, wrote of the Aztecs, "amongst which Indians I learned their language or Mexican tongue very perfectly, and had great familiarity with many of them, whom I found to be a courteous and loving kind of people, ingenious and of great understanding." Hakluyt, *op. cit.,* VI, 323. Of the consideration shown by the Brazilian Indians toward those of the same tribe, Pero de Magalhaes wrote in the 16th century: "In every house all live together in harmony, without any dissension among them; on the contrary, they are so friendly with one another that what belongs to one belongs to all, and when one of them has something to eat, no matter how small, all his neighbors share in it." *The Histories of Brazil* (tr. from the Portuguese, New York, 1922), p. 87. "The Indians are extremely polite to each other." Herbert Cerwin, *These are the Mexicans* (New York, 1947), p. 37.

30. Father Cristóbal de Acuña, who came down from the Quito country into the Amazonia in 1639, encountered the Tupinambás on the large island in the lower Madeira that was their final refuge. *Descubrimiento del Amazonas* (reprint, Buenos Aires, 1942), p. 95.

31. Father Acosta believed that the conquest of Mexico and Peru would have been impossible if the Indians had been unified in those countries. Of the Indian resistance, he writes: "Chile standes yet . . . where our Spaniards could not yet winne one foote of ground, although thay have made warre there above five-and-twenty yeares, without sparing any cost. For this barbarous nation, having once lost the apprehention of horse and shotte, and knowing that the Spaniards fall as well as other men, with the blow of a stone or a dart, they hazard themselves desperately. . . . How many yeares have they levied men in New Spaine, to send against the Chichimecos, which are a small number of naked Indians, armed onely with bowes and arrowes; yet, to this day, they could not be vanquished . . . but contrariwise, from day to day they grow more desperate and resolute. But what shall we say of the Chunchos, of the Chirihuanos, of the Pilcoçones, and all the other people of the Andes? Hath not all the flower of Peru beene there, bringing with them so great provision of armes and men, as we have seene? (Father Acosta accompanied the Viceroy Toledo on his disastrous campaign against the Chiriguanos.) . . . What did they? . . . They returned very happily in saving of their lives, having lost their baggage. Let no man think that they are men of nothing. If Montezuma in Mexico, and the Inca in Peru, had been resolute to resist the Span-

iards and to stop their entrie, Cortés and Pizarro had prevailed little in their landing, although they were excellent captaines." *Op. cit.,* II, 529.

32. On the rebellion of Tupac Amarú, see Vázquez de Espinosa, *op. cit.,* p. 596.

33. See Arnold J. Toynbee, *The Study of History* (abridged edition), pp. 33, 271.

34. Of the Incas, Cieza de León wrote: "They performed such great deeds, and ruled with such wisdom, that few in the world ever excelled them. They were very intelligent and learned without having letters, which had not been invented in those Indies. They introduced good customs into all the conquered provinces. . . . They thought much of the immortality of the soul, and of other secrets of nature. They believed that there was a Creator of all things. . . . They were very astute and artful in turning enemies into friends without having resort to war." *Travels, op. cit.,* p. 136. "It appears to me that few nations in the world had a better government than the Incas." *Ibid.,* p. 220. Father Vázquez de Espinosa said of the Incas: "They governed with great consideration and were obeyed, respected, and worshipped by all their vassals." *Op. cit.,* pp. 557. According to Roger Merriman, "Probably never in the world has a communistic experiment, on a large scale, attained a greater measure of success, and it is reasonably certain that it never will again." He ascribes its success to the following circumstances: (1) the government was an absolute despotism; (2) with the exception of the *amauta,* or men of learning, who were in the service of the Inca, i.e., the state, there was a very uniform level of knowledge and culture; and (3) there were no foreign relations. *The Rise of the Spanish Empire in the Old World and in the New* (4 vols., New York, 1918–34), III, 551. Of the Indians' nostalgia, Herndon and Gibbon wrote: "The grateful recollection of the present race of Indians for the kindness, gentleness, and humanity of the Inca rulers towards their ancestors, are often compared disadvantageously with the sufferings and privations they think they experienced from subsequent governments." *Op. cit.,* I, 77.

35. Like Father Las Casas in his *Destruction of the Indies,* Spaniards generally took liberties with their statistics. According to Oviedo, over 2,000,000 Indians disappeared in the Castilla de Oro country of the isthmus between 1514 and 1542. *Op. cit.,* III, p. 125. He said that, whereas there were probably a million Indians in the islands at the time of the discovery, not more than fifty of the original inhabitants were left in Santo Domingo. *Ibid.,* I, 71. Note the comments of Cieza de León on the depopulation of regions in South America: "There are few Indians in the neighborhood of Panamá, for nearly all have been destroyed by the evil treatment they received from the Spaniards and by sickness." *Travels, op. cit.,* p. 17; "All these meadows and plains (the Popayán country) were once very populous. . . . Now there are few Indians, owing to the war with the Spaniards, and to their custom of eating each other, and also to the great famine which was caused by their not sowing the crops; with the hope that, there being no food, the Spaniards would leave their country." *Ibid.,* p. 109; Of the province of Chincha in Peru: "The valley was so populous, that many Spaniards say, when the Marquis conquered it, it contained more than 25,000 men. At present, I believe, that there are barely 5,000." *Ibid.,* p. 261; "Formerly the Indians in this province of Andahuaylas were very numerous, but the wars have reduced them, as they have the other Indians of this kingdom." *Ibid.,* p. 317. Also, see Cieza, *The War of Chupas,* p.

339: "I know from my experience gathered during a long residence in the Indies that there were great cruelties and much injury done to the natives." See the study of Sherburne F. Cook and Lesley Byrd Simpson, *The Population of Central Mexico in the Sixteenth Century* (Berkeley and Los Angeles, 1948). "In less than two centuries the Indian population (of the Andean country) was more than halved." George Kubler, *Handbook of the South American Indian, op. cit.*, II, 337.

36. *Leyes de Indias, libro* 6. The headings of some of the sections in this part of the *Recopilación* are significant: "Of the liberty of the Indians"; "Of Indian reductions and villages"; "Of personal service"; "Of service on farms, in vineyards, olive orchards, weaving mills, sugar mills, pearl fisheries, roadside inns (*tambos*), mule or wagon trains, houses, cattle ranches, and canoes"; "Of service on coca and indigo plantations"; "Of service in mines"; and "Of the Indians of Chile," a very special problem.

37. According to Henry Hawks, who was one of John Hawkins' men abandoned at Veracruz, "The Indians are very much favoured by the Justices of the country, and they call them their orphanes. And if any Spaniard should happen to do any of them harme, or to wrong him in taking any thing from him . . . or to strike any of them . . . they are as well punished for the same, as if they had done it one Spaniard to another." Hakluyt, *op. cit.*, VI, 293.

38. See Vázquez de Espinosa, *op. cit.*, p. 624. According to Father Vázquez, the mines of Potosí had a right to the labor of 13,300 Indians, who were rounded up by the local corregidor from all over the Collao. "After each has eaten his ration, they climb up the hill, each to his mine, and go in, staying there from that hour until Saturday evening without coming out of the mine; their wives bring them food."

39. Father Vázquez describes the abuses in the *obrajes* in Puebla, Mexico. *Ibid.*, p. 133. See Bernard Moses, *The Spanish Dependencies in South America* (2 vols., New York, 1914), II, 140.

40. Acknowledging that those in authority had "committed many cruelties and outrages on the Indians" during the conquest. Cieza de León said: "Nor do I affirm that all the Christians ill-treated the Indians; for I have seen many temperate and God-fearing men treat them well, curing and bleeding them when they were ill, and performing other charitable acts." *Travels, op. cit.*, p. 12. Cieza observed much improvement after the violent passions of the civil wars among the conquerors had subsided and the effects of the "New Laws" had become apparent. "I remember that, when I was in the province of Xauxa a few years ago, the Indians said to me with much satisfaction: 'This is a happy time, like the days of Tupac Inca Yupanqui;' a king of ancient times whose memory they hold in great veneration." *Ibid.*, p. 13. And, "The government of this kingdom is so good, in these times, that the Indians are complete masters of their goods and persons. By the will of God the former tyranny and ill-treatment of Indians have ceased." *Ibid.*, p. 425. On conditions in the lifetime of Francisco Pizarro, see Cieza, *The War of Las Salinas*, p. 230. "Few foreign writers have rendered to the Spanish government the justice which is due to it, with respect to its treatment of the Indians." Depons, *op. cit.*, I, 226.

41. John Stephens wrote of the action of the Constituent Assembly in Guatemala: "The Assembly decided that the law should be applied (against the Indians)

by Las leyes antiguas de los Espagnolas, the old laws of the Spaniards, the severities of which had been one of the great causes of revolution in all Spanish countries. There was something horrible in this retrograde legislation." *Op. cit.*, I, 302. According to Mme. Calderón de la Barca, who was the wife of the first Spanish Minister to Mexico, and who was in that country in the 1850's, "Certainly no visible improvement has taken place in their condition since the independence. They are quite as poor and quite as ignorant, and quite as degraded as they were in 1808, and if they raise a little grain of their own, they are so hardly taxed that the privilege is as naught." *Op. cit.*, p. 368. Juan Bautista Alberdi, the political philosopher of the early republican period, said: "We accuse them (the Spaniards) of having been cruel with the Indian savages. Are we any more humane than the Spaniards with our fellow countrymen, the Indians who are left." In William Rex Crawford, *A Century of Latin American Thought* (Cambridge, Mass., 1944), p. 24.

42. "The warfare is too bloody to last; the Christians killing every Indian, and the Indians doing the same by the Christians." Charles Darwin, *The Voyage of the Beagle* (reprint, New York, 1906), p. 98. Darwin was in South America between 1832 and 1835. He said that the favorite occupation of General López of the Province of Santa Fé was hunting Indians. A short time before, he had killed 48 of them and sold their children into slavery at the rate of three or four pounds apiece. *Ibid.*, p. 111.

43. See Herbert Cerwin, *op. cit.*, p. 33.

44. The Department of Anthropology of Cornell University is carrying on a large-scale study of the Quechua Indians in the Callejón de Huaylas, in Peru, with a view to determining their capacity for improvement. Lieuts. Herndon and Gibbon, who spent considerable time among the Indians of the Andean countries in the middle of the last century, made many acute observations concerning the Indians in the various parts of Ecuador, Peru, and Bolivia, which they visited. In some places, they commented on the apparent happiness of the Indians and their capacity for enjoying themselves, but usually in localities where they were freest of dependence on the will of the "creoles." However, they concluded that the Indian civilization was completely static and offered little prospect of advancement. Yet, they had great admiration for the native virtues of the Indian: "They are truthful, honest, and respectful, one toward the other; they have no affectation. Disinterested kindness and politeness are found there in their purity." *Op. cit.*, I, 83. Bates, who also made many interesting reflections on the Indians and mixed breeds of the Amazon Valley, said: "Before the Indians can be reclaimed in large numbers, it is most likely that they will become extinct as a race; but there is less difficulty with regard to the Mamelucos (mestizos), who, even when the proportion of white blood is small, sometimes become enterprising and versatile people." *The Naturalist on the Amazons* (Everyman Edition), p. 278. See particularly p. 260 on the Indian character.

Chapter III

THE SPANIARD

EIGHTEEN OF the twenty Latin republics of the New World are Spanish American. Together they account for nearly fifty-seven per cent of the area of Latin America, or about 4,400,-000 square miles of land. About sixty-four per cent of their total population—about 100,000,000 people—are heir to more or less of Spanish civilization, more rather than less, if one excepts the predominantly Indian countries. In the three centuries of her imperial adventure, Spain left her mark on the map of the New World from Cordova and Valdez in Alaska to Tierra del Fuego. She left her mark very deep in the minds and souls of men and on their tongues wherever she made the land her own for long.

In spite of complex origins—a compound of the original "Iberian," Greek, Phoenician-Punic, Roman, Arab, Germanic, North African, and a few ethnic odds-and-ends like the Basque [1] —the Spaniards are a singularly uncomplicated folk. It is probable that the character of the basic Peninsular race was so firmly fixed in very early times that successive waves of conquerors and colonists could not materially alter it. For, as writers of classical antiquity, like Strabo, described the Spaniards, so in large part are they today.[2] The latecomers only added minor details to a general pattern that had long since been set for good and all. Once the fighting was over and Spaniards had accepted the rule of Rome, the integration of Hispanic and Roman elements presented no serious problems and in time Spain became more Roman than Italy. For the two had much in common and as equals lived together congenially and with mutual respect. Later, the heavy infusion of North African blood found a suspiciously receptive medium in the native Spanish stock, which seemed to invoke some deep biological atavism.[3]

There is a great permanence and durability about Spain. In Madrid and Barcelona, cosmopolitan pressures have worn the flinty edges of old custom a little and some superficial concessions have been grudgingly made to alien ways. But in the ancient towns that are the essence of Spain—the Arévalos and Cuencas and Rondas—life has gone on from century to century with little change in the essentials. When Borrow adventured about Spain in the 1830's, he observed that people and things must have been much the same as they were six hundred years before.[4]

The Spaniards are much easier to understand than, for example, the Germans, or, for that matter, we Americans. That is, for one who is willing to accept the Spaniard's idiosyncrasies on faith or who does not try to apply his own standards of behavior to a people who have another system of psychology and a different set of values. The Spaniards are obviously so unorthodox and distinctive a folk that foreigners are discouraged at the outset from any effort to analyze the Spanish psyche in terms familiar to themselves, and just accept them "in principle" as being an irrational and unusual people. There are no irreconcilable or undigested ingredients in the Spanish temper. One quality—individualism—dominates the whole, so that the Spaniard does not act at cross purposes with himself, as we are likely to do. In a given set of circumstances, his line of conduct is generally predictable and very Spanish in its essence. One can be certain that out of the process will come *cosas de España*—those things that can happen only in Spain—things as identifiable in terms of race as a *chinoiserie* or an Hibernicism, and often as incomprehensible to a foreigner.

Yet, there is much that is conflicting and paradoxical about him.[5] There is the eternal dichotomy of Don Quixote and Sancho Panza, the seemingly incongruous coexistence in the same personality of the practical and the impractical, the earthy and the visionary, realism and idealism. When the quixotic mood is on him, any attempt to "make sense" of a Spaniard's actions and reactions is facilitated at the outset by the assumption that to a stranger they do not make sense anyway. That basic premise once accepted, the motivation of his conduct becomes as clear as the irrational is ever intelligible. Thus, after Gonzalo Jiménez de Quesada, the conqueror of Colombia, had apparently obtained all his heart's desire and was of an age to settle down and enjoy it, he risked everything he had won by going off on a wild-goose chase into the wilderness in search of El Dorado.[6] In the conquest of Chile, some of Valdivia's men planned to send gold to Peru in violation of his orders. When he learned of their plans and seized the gold as it was being loaded into a ship, one of the soldiers, who was musician as well as man-at-arms, in a gesture of outraged pride, dashed his precious guitar to pieces against the side of the ship. When the French armies invaded Spain during the Peninsular Wars, the *alcalde* or mayor of Móstoles, a village in Castile, sent Napoleon Bonaparte a solemn declaration of war on his own account. During the revolutions in Mexico, when a young soldier of a defeated force took refuge in a tree and his enemies were about to shoot him from his perch, he called down to them, "I am a poet," the officer in charge of the company below ordered his men to lower their rifles. These are a few of the immortal breed of Spain who have been possessed by the *locura* of the beloved visionary of Cervantes. One comes to the conclusion that a Spaniard knows his illusions to be illusions, but cherishes them none the less for the unattainable vision of perfection which they give to him. So he dreams with open eyes, while his feet firmly grip the earth.

The Spaniards have, to a superlative degree, the quality of *character*. They are a very strong and immensely vital people. They are possessed of a deep wisdom about life that was not gained from books, for they are not a reading people, but from having lived so long and so intensely and so close to the elemental facts of existence.

Their worldly and pragmatic philosophy of living is well expressed in their lush store of proverbs.[7] As King Solomon "spoke three thousand proverbs," so Spaniards are accustomed to talking in proverbs, the homely sayings, often improvised in a language that lends itself to rhyming, and which reflect their everyday experience with things and people, the empirical balance of their defeats and victories.

Certain primitive or savage traits survive in the Spaniard.[8] These are largely related to his fatalism and contempt for death, and to his sense of the tragedy and uncertainty of life. He is a congenital pessimist and, always expecting the worst, is likely not to be disappointed. He also has the outward simplicity and directness and candor of the savage. Life has always been hard for him, so that he has never been softened—or overcultivated—by ease or opulence. He has never known what "security" is, except for the assurance of unremitting struggle against the loaded dice of fate. What he has gotten has been by his own exertions, his wits, the turn of chance, or the favor of his friends. Save for the few, that has never been much, for there is little abundance in Spain. But it has been enough to provide for the survival of this gaunt and steely race, and with a surplus sufficient for the endowment of its national genius. Yet the circumstances of history have left too little opportunity for the cultivation of the external refinements and urbanity of the French and Italians. In fact, the Spaniard could move back into the caves of Altamira and feel "at home" without too violent a shock of readjustment.

His fundamental conservatism and his distrust of foreigners and outsiders in general are also a mark of the primitive man. The Spaniard does not easily change his ways for those of others or accept the living devices or mechanics of other peoples without a most critical examination and instinctive misgivings as to their usefulness. It is difficult to convert him to anything. Of Spanish xenophobia, the Duke of Wellington wrote in 1820: "There is no country in Europe in the affairs of which foreigners can interfere with so little advantage as in those of Spain. There is no country in which foreigners are so much disliked, and even despised, and whose manners and habits are so little congenial with those of the other nations in Europe." [9]

The Spaniard is a man of passion.[10] He is not necessarily demonstrative or vocal or violent about it, for the fire in him may burn inwardly, so that it is not apparent to another, but it burns none the less ardently. So he may not do things according to reason or logic or cold calculation, for his mind is not orderly or systematic, but according to the light of intuition and the urge of strong feeling.[11] He may even do something for no good reason at all, but only by the prompting of caprice. Then he will act under the blind impulse of *gana*, or the moving of the spirit. Angel Ganivet suggested ironically that to fulfill the "juridical ideal" of the nation, "every Spaniard should carry in his pocket a charter of privileges (*fuero*) with the single provision—that this Spaniard is authorized to do what he wants to do." [12] If one wishes to influence such a man, he must appeal to sentiment or conviction, not to intellect, or even to interest. A Spaniard is not given to reflection and is not likely to lose himself in "the pale cast of thought"—the aimless brooding that never ends in action —or in a cautious weighing of alternatives.

It has been the ideal of the Spaniard to rise above the influence of external circumstances. He has desired that his spirit should be proof against "the slings and arrows" of life, all the things that can crush or dispirit lesser men. In this connection, it is significant that the Spanish-born Stoic, Lucius Seneca, has been the favorite philosopher of Spain, almost ranking with its favorite saints of the Church. The Cordovan's essay, *De Constantia Sapientis* ("On the Constancy of the Wise Man") is a preachment on the virtues of impassivity in the presence of adversity, which has appealed strongly to his ancestral people as a peculiarly Spanish doctrine of behavior. The manner in which Seneca carried out Nero's order of suicide also served to enhance his moral prestige among Spaniards. Only one of themselves, they believed, could, after falling from such a high estate and meeting so tragic an end, have died with quite so much dignity and equanimity. But they were to find that the natives of the New World could be stoical in the face of violent death, as Cuauhtemoc and Tupac Amaru and thousands of others were to demonstrate to them *in extremis*.

Though death was the ultimate test of character, it was for any practical purpose the most futile, except as an example to others of how to die with propriety. But Spaniards were little concerned about the practical aspects of death. They were impressed with its imminence and convinced of its inevitability and very much interested in perpetuating their personal identity and name beyond the tomb. They were prepossessed with the fact of death and sometimes were likely to dwell on it with morbid insistence, as they did in their religious art.[13] But they were prone to accept its coming with calmness and without heroics or hysterics, because a Spaniard should die that way. They are a very courageous people in the presence of death. Some have considered them more brave than discreet, as did Braccio da Montone, the *condottiere* of Perugia, who was in the service of the Aragonese king in the Italian wars. "You think it more honorable," he said to the impetuous Spanish soldiers, "to allow yourselves to be cut to pieces by the enemy than to escape with your lives and reserve yourselves for the day of revenge." And French troops who refused to fight the forces of the Great Captain, Gonsalvo de Córdova, said: "These mad Spaniards value a little honor more than a thousand lives and are incapable of enjoying this life." [14] As the *fiesta de la muerte*, the bullfight has had a special fascination for Spaniards, because death rides the bull's horns, and the matador can trick him out of his prey with courage and grace and skill.[15]

SPANISH STOICISM

For a people who were proverbially so little concerned with the material conditions of life, stoicism fortified them against the incidence of poverty and pain and the inhumanity of other men, things that were generally prosaic and undramatic, but with which one might have to live all his days. So Spaniards have generally lived austerely and temperately.[16] Self-denial has always come easy to them and they bear privations much better than most peoples, for they have been accustomed to doing with so little. It is remarkable how little the wealth of the Indies in the sixteenth and seventeenth centuries contributed to the comfort and pleni- tude of life in Spain. Unlike the merchant and capitalist class of north European cities during the same period, there was little in the way of material well-being to show for all the treasure that poured into Spain from the New World. There are very few new private palaces, and the houses of even the well-to-do remained as barren as ever. Practically all the great churches had been built before Columbus discovered America, but much money was spent on their internal adornment for the greater glory of the Virgin. Certainly Spaniards did not eat more bountifully, and there was probably less food to go around in the seventeenth cen- tury than there had been in the fifteenth. But tightened belts have never brought food riots among this sober and abstemious people, who in all their history have known so little of indulgence and luxury. In the conversation of Spaniards, one seldom hears talk of such things as "prosperity" and "profit," for they are un- familiar to them. If the "little man" in Spain often seems avari- cious and "penny-pinching" it is only because the barest living usually comes so hard to him and he can therefore ill afford to waste anything. But even with his pittance, he will make a princely gesture of liberality to another. And there is no such generosity or hospitality in the whole western world as there is among this meager race. For no others place so little value on things and so much on the riches of the spirit.

The indifferentism of Spaniards about their material fate is largely responsible for the serenity or tranquillity of spirit with which they make the most of life. In a harried world of furrowed brows and chewed fingernails, this philosophic calm is likely to be very refreshing and comforting. On the other side, it may lead to resignation toward conditions which could perhaps be easily changed by a little exercise of the dormant wills. But to the Spaniard, the improvement might not seem worth the bother. The charge that his unconcern is bad for business and may mean death to progress would, of course, not move him in the least. In this mood, he closes the discussion with a *"No importa"* (it doesn't matter) and appropriate gestures of finality.

With a stoical attitude toward life, there has gone control of the outward expression of feeling.[17] A *caballero* should be *contenido*, that is, restrained, imperturbable if possible, always master of self. He should *contain* or hold back any revelation of deep inner emotion, as Philip II did on receiving the news of the debacle of the Armada. It is this quality of restraint which makes the faces of the Spaniards in portraits of the classical age appear so immobile and stony. Except for a certain haughtiness, they seldom tell anything of what goes on behind the mask. For example, there may have been nothing at all behind the vacuous and saturnine façades of Velásquez' kings, but as much could scarcely be said of his portraits of the Count-Duke or of the Admiral Pulido-Pareja.

THE SPAINS

There were, and are, several Spains: the Castiles, Aragón, Galicia, Asturias, Andalusia, Catalonia, Vizcaya, and so on. A few of them, like Andalusia, have never been political entities; most of them were formerly independent (and mutually hostile) kingdoms. Separately, they represented the centrifugal tendencies and local loyalties which are the territorial counterpart of Spanish individualism. When the long process of unification came to an end late in the fifteenth century, one of the old provinces remained outside the new state as the Kingdom of Portugal. Others, like Catalonia and the Basque Provinces, have always remained restless within the central structure of Spain.

Men of all the Spains participated, though in varying degrees, in the conquest and colonization of the New World and in its subsequent development, as the later comers from the Peninsula still do. Some have favored certain regions, usually for a real or fancied resemblance to their home province. In the settlement of Peru, for example, the Andalusians and Gallegos generally remained on the coast; the Basques and Estremadurans preferred the sierra country.[18] After remarking on the prominence of Andalusians and Canary islanders in Venezuela, Asturians and Basques in Mexico, and Catalans in Buenos Aires, Alexander von Humboldt made these observations early in the last century on the persistence of Spanish regional traits in the New World: "They vary essentially in their aptitudes for agriculture, the mechanical arts, trade, and the other spheres of activity which depend on the progress of the intelligence. Each of these peoples has conserved the peculiar physiognomy, the mildness or roughness of its character, its greater or less interest in gain, its warm hospitality or its urge for solitude." [19]

The regional variations are more striking than significant, even with the Basque and the Catalan, who, with the Andaluz, differ most from the national norm.[20] Beneath the trappings of regionalism—the distinctive costumes and customs and peculiarities of speech, or the other externals as they appear in Sorolla's murals in New York's Hispanic Museum—there is always a Spaniard of sorts. Above all things, he is his own man, whatever his local origin.

Castile was the catalytic nucleus around which the other regions gradually coalesced to form Spain.[21] She had a habit of command and an imperial touch that early predestined her to leadership. Prototype of the race, the Castilians were the embodiment of *españolismo*, the combination of qualities which, either in kind or degree, distinguish Spaniards from other peoples. Their principal rivals for the headship of Spain were the Aragonese, a hard and rugged folk, who had gathered to themselves dominion over peoples so different from themselves as the matter-of-fact Catalans and the violent Valencians, and who had made an empire of their own in Italy before ever Columbus found the Indies for Castile. The Catalans are kin to the French of Languedoc and, of all Spaniards, probably are temperamentally at the farthest pole from the Andalusians in the opposite corner of the Peninsula. A thalassic people, with their faces to the sea and their backs to the rest of Spain, their interests had long been Mediterranean rather than continental, and, as the subjects of Aragón, they were largely responsible for the impulse behind that kingdom's empire building in Italy. Though enterprising and commercial-minded, they had very little to do with the conquest of the New World or the early exploitation of its resources.

All the mystery of the Basques is in their ethnic origin. For this frank and forthright folk is little given to deceit and deviousness. Virile and sturdy, and a very solid and reliable people, they are the proudest of the proud, but their pride is rather an expression of their aggressive and stubborn sense of racial superiority and individual equality than of any pose or pretense of position. They were latecomers in the New World, but, with their Asturian neighbors, they were to lead in developing the principal mining areas of Mexico and Peru, and later they came to play a very important role in the life of Chile. In the far northwestern corner of the Peninsula is Spanish Galicia. The Gallegos are much like the Portuguese in their habits, and in the tone of their speech. They are a steady and dependable people, though a little unimaginative, and their industry has made a valuable contribution to Cuba and Argentina, and to the other countries in which numbers of them have settled.

THE ANDALUSIAN

One of the most interesting tribes of Spain is the Andalusian. Like the Sicilian, the Andalusian has been conditioned by long and intimate—including the biological—contacts with many peoples, particularly with his Moorish cousins from across the strait. Several millennia of residence in an alluring habitat have imprinted its features indelibly on his ancient and impressionable soul. As in the look and ways of him, so in the monuments strewn about his sunny land—the Bronze Age copper mines of Rio Tinto, the ruins of Italica, the Alhambra and the Alcázar, Cadiz itself—one is conscious of his heterogeneous ancestry. Heroes of legend or history have frequented his shores—Odysseus and the nameless masters of the ships that came to biblical Tarshish, Hannibal and Caesar, St. James and Tarik the Moor, Columbus and Magellan and del Cano, and the conquistadores of the New World. Infinitely old, like the Chinese, as Ortega y Gasset has observed,[22] the Andalusians have weathered many empires and dominions and other tribulations, so that what the day offers them is enough, without worrying about what the future may bring. For their eyes have seen too much for them to harbor any delusions. There are no enchantments or mysteries to baffle them, and with a shrug of the shoulders they have looked the Sphinx in the face and answered all its riddles. A supple people, they have learned to bend to the human siroccos that have blown over them.

They are alternately irreverent and fanatical, as though they did not believe anything very deeply. Good actors that they are, the Sevillanos can turn from the oppressive solemnity of the *Semana Santa* to the *carnavalesque* frivolity of the *feria* with only a change of facial expression to mark the transition of mood. The stranger suspects that deep in their hearts they keep a pagan pantheon of their own, with altars for all the divinities they have worshipped through the ages—for Astarte and Aphrodite and Isis, and Dionysus and Helios and the goat-god Pan, so congenial to their own caprine instincts, and perhaps a shrine for Baal and Mithra and some gay Romany god of the road. And under the spell of the crescent moon, they may turn toward Córdova of the caliphs and make a discreet salaam to Mohammed.

They take life as it comes and jest nonchalantly at the whole human show about them. Though they generally own little but a stake in time and the sun and the resources of their own spirit, they have an epicurean capacity for enjoyment and pleasure. Theirs is the classic land of the supreme dances of the world and of the lithe Gaditanas and Sevillanas who dance them,[23] of fighting bulls and the pantherlike men who fight them, and of the wailing of flamenco songs to the music of guitars. Alone in all Christendom, there is dancing once a year in the great cathedral of Sevilla, and though it is measured and ritualistic, it is, after all, a dance and so a concession to the underlying paganism of Andalusia.

Sensual and unashamed, mercurial and volatile, indolent and unheroic, the Andalusians are a devil-may-care people, who bear within them the gift of vivid life, stripped of much of the baggage with which less assured men cushion themselves against the shocks of fate. The least primitive of Spaniards, they have the instinctive sophistication of alley cats, and, too, a feline grace about their movements.

While Sevilla is the mecca of every Spaniard bent on escape from his local or internal frustrations and inadequacies, and the most beloved city of all the Spains, the grimmer and more purposeful Spaniards outside Andalusia do not take its lively denizens very seriously; nor, after all, do the Andalusians themselves. Others ridicule their outlandish speech and their mannerisms, their garrulousness, their apparent insouciance on all occasions, the rodomontade into which their exaggerations seem to slip so naturally, and their aversion to sacrificing themselves for whatever convictions they may have.

In the conquest of the New World, a large part of the common soldiery were Andalusians,[24] who distinguished themselves by their quick wit and resourcefulness and a certain swaggering gallantry, as well as by their irresponsible ways and their refusal to accept the official version of anything as the gospel truth. They have always shown a remarkable talent for survival against odds, and a lightness of touch that has pleasantly diluted the impressive heaviness of their fellow Spaniards wherever the two were mingled, as they have done in the New World, in Guadalajara and Havana and Lima.

THE SPANIARD IN THE NEW WORLD

Spanish influence in the Americas was exercised directly for over three centuries, first, in the guise of conqueror and colonizer; later, as governor, priest, and teacher of subject peoples; always as the progenitor of mixed races; finally, after the Independencias, as immigrants into countries that were no longer theirs to rule. In Argentina and Cuba, this infusion of new Spanish blood has been heavier than it was during colonial times and has given a special cast to the character of those peoples. In its transfer across the Atlantic, the Spanish character underwent certain changes. Its vigor did not diminish during the course of the *conquista,* but it was diffused over a vast area and a numerous population of alien customs. The agents of the Hispanicizing process were always too few and something was inevitably lost in the transplanting. Generally, what was lost was a degree of intensity, rather than that some pristine and inherent quality of Spain was displaced altogether by the passive power of the new *genius loci.* Perhaps the leaven was not heavy enough to give the full flavor of Spain to the hybrid civilization which resulted. It was diluted by other influences—the physical habitat, the strange and varied racial ingredients that went into the mixture, the impact of extraneous cultures like those of France and the United States, and historical experience.

The grist that went into the mills was so different that no uniform type of Spanish American came out of the grinding.

There were Cubans and Mexicans and Chileans and so on, each with his distinguishing features. But, in spite of the divergences, there was a strong "family resemblance" among them—a sort of spiritual solidarity that had its roots in Spain. There was a certain common pattern of thinking and behavior behind all the variables that developed in the New World. Above all, the deep imprint of Spanish individualism remained with its ramifications in the field of conduct. Somehow, *the man* contrived to survive all the forces working for his extinction as a separate unit in the national society, though he is never and nowhere so independent as he is in Spain, where he still defies the state or any conglomeration of people to absorb his personality, or to make him like anybody else.

A Castilian in the lonely emptiness of the Argentine pampa or the steaming jungle of the Colombian Chocó was never quite the same person again. He was less a Spaniard and more a man of the New World. For his rock-bound character was no more proof against the erosive power of nature than a hillside was against the beating of the tropical rain. Also, it was hardly to be expected that Spanish civilization could preserve all its original purity in the presence of the aboriginal cultures of the Indies. Some of the cultures, like the Incaic, were of so high an order that their local practitioners saw no good reason for exchanging them for the ways of the Spaniard. Of these offerings they took what suited their fancy and their convenience and all in their own good time, as the Spaniard borrowed some of the Indian's pharmacopoeia and cuisine, and an occasional apt word from the native tongues. Sometimes, as happened with particular force in Mexico, Spaniard and Indian saw eye to eye on many things, so that the implanting of Spanish civilization was made easier. So much for the Creole, or colonial of unadulterated Spanish blood, whose leanings were naturally toward the Peninsular mores and values.

However, as a result of the genetic catholicity of the Spaniard, there were—and are—in most parts of the Indies more mestizos and mulattos than pure-bloods of Spanish ancestry. And the mixed breeds were torn between the parent cultures. It was not altogether a matter of voluntary choice as to which would prevail, for the mestizo could never escape from the "call of the blood." After the initial meeting of Spaniard and Indian, the fifty-fifty ratio of the resultant chromosomes shifts with each subsequent generation, but the biological balance is liable to become progressively weighted on the Indian side, especially if the line of heredity persists in the lower levels of society. There is, of course, no precise formula to demonstrate how Spanish a particular people or person might turn out to be, given a certain set of antecedent conditions. The possible degrees of *Spanishness* are of infinite variety. Many of the factors which enter into the problem are subjective and incommensurable, or entirely fortuitous in their incidence. However, in time one can observe in a particular population, where the miscegenative process has long been operative and has finally leveled off, a general similarity of physical type and cultural attitudes. For example, this stage of evolution has clearly been reached in old mestizo countries like Chile, Paraguay, Colombia, and El Salvador, or in certain socially "settled" localities of other republics, like the Venezuelan Andes and *llanos* and northern Argentina. On the other hand, the Indians have either been long since absorbed by the more numerous whites, as in Uruguay, or otherwise removed as a separate cultural factor, as happened in the Argentine pampa. In regions where the racial composition is predominantly Indian, as in Mexico, Guatemala, Peru, and Bolivia, it is still too early for a definite balance to have been struck between the major ethnic elements in the amalgam. In these countries, the tendency is for the deliberate withdrawal of the aboriginal population within itself, though mixing continues along the lower fringes of the national society, so that the ultimate creation of a single race is thereby prorogued still further into the distant future. In the meantime, these yet formative cultures have been subjected to alien influences, emanating particularly from the United States and France, and—by way of large-scale immigration—from Italy. Out of the interplay of all these complex forces there comes eventually something that is not all Spanish, but has much of Spain about it.[25] Whenever men of these lands come together, they do not meet as total strangers, but are instinctively drawn together by the pull of common heritage.

As a prolific mother of nations, Spain held nothing back from her children overseas.[26] If she did not give them political liberties, it was because she did not have them to give. If she restricted their economic development where it might compete with her own, so did all the other colonial powers of the age. Otherwise, she gave them all she had, and ungrudgingly; her strong and sonorous language, the Hispanicized jurisprudence of Rome, Christianity as it was molded by a millennium of Spain, the concept of the family as the center oî national society, the tradition and pattern of the city as the ultimate vehicle of civilization, and all the rest of the institutional framework and paraphernalia of Spanish life. She gave them Don Quixote and Las Casas and Calderón and Santa Teresa, and received from them in return Sor Juana Inés and Alarcón and the Inca Garcilasso and Heredia.

SPANISH INDIVIDUALISM

Individualism or personalism is the key to the genius of Spain. Man is the center of the Spaniard's universe, not a philosophical concept of man or mankind as an abstraction, but a man of flesh and blood, and of loves and hates.[27] First of all, it is himself who matters, whether Juan Gómez or Fernando Alvarez de Toledo, Duke of Alba. From this homocentric ego, his regard may move outward to take in other individuals, those bound to him by ties of love or blood or friendship. Into the impersonal and collective gloom which lies outside that restricted circle of sentimental attachments, his myopic gaze does not penetrate. For it is peopled by neighbors, fellow citizens, and foreigners—anonymous abstractions all, except as their members happen to impinge, perhaps momentarily or involuntarily, on his own personality. All through life his guard is up against the intrusion of the nameless ones from beyond the intimate circle.

Such a person is loath or unable to merge his identity with others, just because they live near him or in the same country, much less on the same planet.[28] A man is what he makes of himself, with at most a little lift from family and friends. He has no debt to pay to society. It is very difficult for him to sacrifice the interests of his own personality to the demands of group action or enterprise. He is devoid of the civic or neighborly virtues. He does not want to be a pillar of society, and if he indulged in pillars, it would be the kind atop which St. Simeon Stylites sat in the Syrian desert. In the intellectual field, he prefers the humanities—the study of man—to the social studies. He is not

"social-minded." He is little concerned with reconciling the conflicts and confusions of society. He does not wish to "integrate"
or "co-ordinate" anything or anybody. Associations and assem-
blies, clubs and committees, congregations and congresses, whatever form the free coming together of men for a serious purpose
may take, are not to his liking.[29] The two strongest organizations in the life of Spain, the Army and the Church, owe their
strength to the fact that they embody principles—honor and religion—which have an unusually strong hold on the Spanish people. But above all organizations is the family, in default of whose
bonds Spain would fall into social anarchy. Sharing in an organization subtracts too much from a Spaniard's ego, and, lone wolf
that he is at heart, in the final reckoning he himself is all that he
can be certain of.[30] If the organization is, by chance, efficient, the
spontaneous spirit which prompted it is likely to go out of it and
leave it wooden and uninspired; if it is inefficient, then confusion
and disorder will prevail for want of organization and what was
to be done does not get done or is done badly. So many a fine
and promising enterprise that began with high hopes and enthusiasm has died a-borning.

There has been much violent controversy over the part which
communism is alleged to have played in the Spanish Civil War
of the 1930's. With the usual immoderation of debate in Spain,
little attention has been given to the basic plausibility of the
charges. For, after the initial enthusiasm and excitement have run
thin and the novelty has worn off, the Spaniard makes a very indifferent and undependable Communist. No dogma less congenial
to their true nature was ever offered to Spaniards, for no real
Spaniard would endure indefinitely or even for long the discipline
that communism imposes on its followers.[31] This deep-seated incompatibility was well illustrated by the disillusionment and de-
fection of Valentín González, the Communist partisan leader who
was made much of in Moscow for his exploits in the Spanish Civil
War.[32] On the other hand, the Spaniard is a natural anarchist,[33]
and it is no accident that doctrinaire anarchism has flourished
volubly and ineffectually in Spain, particularly in Valencia and
other parts of the Spanish Levant.

The Spaniards' collective incapacity and aversion to group
action are evident in every field of endeavor. Spanish history is

largely a chronicle of individual performance, which explains the important role of the adventurer in the life and literature of Spain—of the Cid and Amadis, Hernán Cortés and Alonso de Contreras, *conquistador* and *pícaro*. Organization and co-operation, those mainsprings of modern "progress," mean little to the Spaniard, and are, in fact, antipathetic to his nature.

In the political sphere, at least beyond the limits of the city, democracy has so far proven unworkable in Spain. In spite of a universal social equality which unconsciously sets the tone of Spanish life, experiments with popular government in Spain have failed. An atmosphere suitable to the practice of political democracy has not existed so far. To start with, the Spaniard has a cynical and profound distrust of government and politicians.[34] Except for very brief periods, he has always been better than those who ruled him, for only one political regime, that of Ferdinand and Isabella, has ever been worthy of the people it governed. The worst aberrations of his own qualities are likely to be present in the bureaucracy which he considers to be composed of time-servers or scoundrels who bode him and the country no good. Save by compulsion or coercion, he hopes to have as little truck as possible with the government. "All the efforts of political propagandists," says Madariaga, "to make the Spaniard feel like a citizen have failed. He feels like a man—and quoting Unamuno— 'nothing less than a whole man.' "[35]

Every Spaniard tends to be his own private political party, and compromise and concession are not his idea of how to run a government, but are considered signs of weakness. "Discussion" is only an opportunity for him to air his views to those who will listen until their own turn comes. Sooner or later, political issues are reduced to personalities and thereby become comprehensible to the generality of Spaniards. Personalism is the rule, and government is rather an affair of men than of laws or principles. Thus, *caciquismo*—or *caudillismo* in the larger theater—is the natural form of Spanish political association. Under such a system, the *caudillo* or *cacique* (*jefe político* in Spanish America) is the political chieftain or boss of the community, as the *patrón* is in other relationships. The tie between him and the local citizenry is a personal one, with well-understood responsibilities on both sides. It is not democracy, but it does help to give some order to the normally inchoate structure of Spanish politics. When the formal or hierarchical relationships established by law stand in the way of this personal relationship so congenial to the national character, it cuts across them or by-passes them. Then things may get done "on a personal basis" that could never be done by following the impersonal rules. For, in the final resort, men are more important than laws—which also explains the frequency with which Spanish courts resort to equity in order to temper the rigor of statutory justice.

In the same way, the individualism of the race militates against the conduct of large-scale economic enterprise. Though the Spaniard prefers the partnership device in management to the impersonal corporation, or *sociedad anónima*, a business may be too large to permit the play—and the possible caprices—of personality. The organization then becomes more important than any individual in it. At this stage of industrial evolution, the Spaniard may find himself out of sympathy with the realities of the situation, that is, out of step with what he considers an economic treadmill. The business is no longer a game or an arena for the exercise of his personal prowess. He finds it impossible to feel any loyalty to an inanimate corporation. Its actual operations may be divorced from its management, so that he is left dealing with papers and figures rather than dominating other men and mastering machines. In fact, the machine itself may become his master—for a Spaniard the ultimate indignity.

As he dislikes the enforced impersonality of big business, neither does he take kindly to much of the new occupational machinery of a modern business civilization. He is the despair of advertising and public relations men and efficiency experts. In another field—he no more wants a psychiatrist prying into the labyrinths of his mind than he would have a gossip columnist reporting his private goings-on to the rabble.

If free from the compulsions of economics, the force of habit, or the bonds of discipline, it is the instinct of the Spaniard to work only when it pleases him. He is likely to be impatient of results and to leave a job unfinished. He is bored, or the engine of his will has run down for the time being. If the original impulse does not have enough momentum to complete the task that is begun, it may never be completed. He may expect an inspiration which does not arrive, or count on improvising a way out of his dilemma. He refuses to glorify such virtues of an industrial society as diligence or steadiness.[36] He is not a plodder, but prefers to work by spurts, according to a rhythm and when the mood is on him—*cuando se le de la gana*. So his rhythm of effort is probably very irregular and unpredictable—and very unbusinesslike.[37] Peaks of volcanic activity may alternate with deep—and wide—valleys of apathy. But sometimes the apathy is likely to be more apparent than real, for even when the individual is physically passive and inert, the brain can be busy preparing for another burst of action.

Spain herself lives according to a similar rhythm, that swings in great arcs, sometimes centuries long, between alternating periods of intense movement and of national lethargy and indifference.[38] Thus, the *Decadencia* of the seventeenth century followed the splendor of the sixteenth though the vitality of the sixteenth century did not bear its full fruit in art and literature until the first half of the 1600's. The brief beginnings of a renaissance occurred again in the later eighteenth century; but it was too artificial and the fire burned out quickly. Since then she has vegetated, as though she were waiting for the spark of some new enthusiasm to revive all the latent power which is stored up in the smoldering recesses of her spirit.[39] Meanwhile the world passes her closed doors, and she is little concerned about what goes on in the street outside. In her periods of depression and inertia, the individual citizen's mood is affected and he is less creative and sanguine than when his country is riding the crest of the wave of her greatness. During the present century, there has been much national soul-searching by probably the most brilliant group of analytical thinkers in Europe that includes Unamuno and Ganivet, Francisco Giner de los Rios and his nephew, Fernando de los Rios, Ortega y Gasset and Menéndez Pidal and Madariaga.

The Spaniard is not lazy, except by the standards of more orderly peoples, and the sum total of his accomplishment may be as great as is that of a more even tenor of exertion. He is capable of the most prodigious productivity. Thus, Lope de Vega, the dramatist of the Golden Age, composed over 1,800 comedies and 400 *actos sacramentales,* or mystery plays.[40] He once completed five comedies in fifteen days, and there are said to have been times when his plays were on the stage within twenty-four hours after he had begun their composition. In the same tradition, though with a different tempo of creation, José Toribio Medina, the Chilean historian and first of Latin Americanists, wrote more than three hundred books during his extraordinarily originative career.

A people so contemptuous of all conventional routine of effort could scarcely be slaves of hours and minutes. No modern people are so lacking in a time sense. None are so disinterested in knowing the time of day or in doing at its appointed time whatever has to be done.[41] With them, punctuality is no virtue and dilatoriness no vice. Of the dual sense of the word, they are more concerned with *tiempo* as weather than as time. *Mañana* is a convenient dumping ground for today's obligations and promptness is only for those who cannot afford, or do not dare, to be tardy. The result is that the conduct of business and of social life in the Spanish world is bedeviled by a general disregard of time. However, in parts of Latin America, if it is seriously intended that an appointment be kept as made, the time agreed upon may be specified as *hora inglesa,* or "hour of an Englishman."

In war, every Spanish soldier is at heart a guerrilla, and it is significant that the word "guerrilla" itself is of Spanish origin. The military annals of Spain are a saga of the exploits of the individual soldier. Even her greatest captains commanded bodies of men so small that they were manageable by Spanish standards and in which the soldier did not lose his individual identity. Bernal Díaz' listing by name of his comrades, who shared with him the conquest of Aztec Mexico, is a classic example of the Spaniard's horror of anonymity and of his insistence on the right of immortality. The mass armies of today, in which the soldier may be little more than a number on a "dog tag," are no place for this independent battler, who has always felt crowded and out-of-place in any army larger than a regiment.[42] Spain is as out of step with modern warfare as she is with modern economics.

In other spheres of activity, unless there are ties of friendship, harmonious and satisfying association with other men on terms of equality is difficult to attain. For example, Spain and the Spanish lands in the New World have produced highly gifted painters, but very few have founded schools that would carry on the tradition of their genius or their characteristic style. Neither have her most profound philosophers or other scholars of Spain left behind them a body of disciples to perpetuate a system of thought. The only Spaniard ever to succeed in organizing a large and enduring body of followers was Ignacio de Loyola, the Basque founder of the Society of Jesus. In music, the Spanish world excels in soloists, both vocal and instrumental, but is weak in choral and orchestral work. And in sports and athletics, it is not easy for men of Spanish blood to accept the restraints of "teamwork" on their rampageous egos.

The gregariousness of Spaniards is not inconsistent with their individualistic temper, as it might appear to be.[48] Though no one can be more self-sufficient, the Spaniard is naturally "sociable" and enjoys the company of others. He likes to talk and to match his wits in conversation. No people are more vocal or express themselves with greater fluency or force. In a roomful of talking Spaniards one sometimes has the impression of being in the presence of verbal lightning, as ideas or opinions are bandied back and forth until they become incandescent and explosive. It is difficult to imagine a Spaniard as tongue-tied or at a loss for words for any occasion. This gift of tongues was transmitted to the New World in full force, though in some places it was to take on a tropic floridness. But wherever the Spanish strain was heavy in the population the same lingual facility and volubility survived and flourished to the dismay and confusion of the taciturn and soft-spoken aborigines.

The very language is a fit medium of expression for so virile a people.[44] It has no soft edges and is full of strong hard consonants separated by rolling melodious vowels. The sounds seem to come from anvils and deep-toned bronze bells and kettledrums and cymbals, but seldom in a cacophony, regardless of how many persons are talking at once. Even where it has been barbarized, as in Andalusia and Argentina, it has kept its original power and dignity and majesty. It is a male and imperial tongue, and the King-Emperor Charles, who had been raised to the guttural sound of Flemish, said that it was the only language in which to address monarchs and God.

One of the by-products of Spanish individualism is true social democracy. Regardless of class distinctions or other category,

Spaniards are accustomed to treat one another as individuals.[45] There is a natural and unself-conscious manner in this relationship, without an "I-am-as-good-as-you" attitude or servility on the one side, or condescension or snobbery on the other. Strangely enough, it has no bearing whatever on *political* democracy. It probably springs from the Spaniard's deep consciousness of the brotherhood of man, which has its basis in Christian doctrine. As such, it has made a man very important in his own right and given a natural dignity to the individual. The tacit acceptance of this egalitarian arrangement by both parties eases potential interclass frictions, which in most countries bedog society. In this connection, it is worth noting that injustices in Spanish society are economic rather than social. The jurisdiction of this man-to-man protocol extends from the ordinary servant-master tie at the bottom of the social scale to the former grandee-king relationship at the top.

SPANISH PRIDE

In the popular mind, Spain and pride have long been synonymous.[46] In Spanish, the very word *orgullo* has a haughty and imperious ring to it. Supremely self-assured and confident, the Spaniard is free from the inferiority complex that plagues Spanish Americans of mixed blood. Whatever inner doubts or fears he may have at times, he conceals behind this wall of pride. His fondness for honors and titles as seal and hallmark of his superiority are only confirmation of his self-esteem.

In its excesses, the pride of the Spaniard may degenerate into arrogance or vanity or envy, or become a cover for the individual's hollowness. The distance from a justifiably good opinion of oneself to vanity, as from modest pride to arrogance, may be very short.[47] Of course, there have been state occasions when arrogance or haughtiness or a gift for display have served the Spaniard or Spain well with impressionable peoples. But if a show of pomp is not called for by the circumstances of the moment, vanity may be only ostentation, calculated, like a gobbler's strutting, to impress one's own flock and to scare away other gobblers.

It is a failing of Spaniards, but more particularly of Spanish Americans, to be envious of those in the same field of endeavor, whether it be literature, art, or one of the professions. Rivalries are ruthless, and personal enmities easily grow out of professional rivalry. If one is outside the circle of favor, his achievements and triumphs are likely to be openings for scorn and tearing down of reputation; if one is within the circle, his partisans are inclined to be indiscriminate in their panegyrics. Writing of "envy, that distinctive element of the Spanish character," Menéndez Pidal says that "no one is willing to attach any value to the work of others, for it seems that to give any credit to another means to curtail one's own." [48] This tendency to disparage the work of others, Baltasar Gracian, Jesuit philosopher of the seventeenth century, called *malignidad hispana*. Contarini, Venetian Ambassador to the court of Philip III, said that "no nation suffers more from mutual jealousy." [49]

In such a battleground of strong feeling, objective criticism becomes impossible. The emotions that are invoked have no fine shadings. They are all in raw primary colors. One either admires or loves, or one hates, as the matador hates the bulls he stalks in the arena. There is nothing lukewarm, no middle way, about it.[50] You are on one side or on the other. Only Spain herself has the privilege of being neutral.

The Spaniard's extreme emphasis on the concept of honor was an expression of his pride and his independence. Calderón, in his play *El Alcalde de Zalamea,* says, "One's property and life belong to the king; but honor is patrimony of the soul, and the soul is of God alone." [51] It was a defensive armor that encased his personality and protected it from affront. It implied the existence of a reciprocal and subjective code of conduct—of things which others might not do to one, as well as of things which one might not do unto others. As such, it served as a "golden rule" of limited application. It was extended to cover members of the individual's family, particularly its female members who were within the range of his protective jurisdiction. Revenge for infringement of the code of honor accounts for the grim tragedy so frequent in the classic literature in Spain. When a question of *pundonor,* or "point of honor," was raised, vengeance could be swift and implacable. And where the personal honor of the individual was involved, punishment was not a business of the State. The offending person might be summarily removed from the population of Spain by killing him outright or by giving him a "fighting chance" in a duel.[52] On similar occasions, the "little man," who could not afford the luxury of a code of honor took such action as seemed appropriate and convenient at the moment, and did not trouble to rationalize what he did. Only the weak and helpless called in the impersonal justice of authority for succor in righting a wrong.

Ceremonious attentions and tributes to individuals by groups of their admirers or friends are a common feature of life. These *agasajos* or *homenajes* (homages) may be on the occasion of a person's departure for abroad or his return from a foreign country, or they may celebrate some personal success or honor. They can be very solemn affairs, with much speechmaking and exchange of compliments and drinking of toasts. A higher value may be placed on such an honorific recognition of superior effort or talent than on any momentary remuneration which might be forthcoming. Among a singularly unmercenary people,[53] it can compensate in good part for the lack of a more substantial reward. So does the seemingly inordinate emphasis placed on diplomas and titles, decorations and orders, citations and dignities, and other outward symbols of importance or warrants of prestige.[54]

Similarly associated with the Spaniard's addiction to pride is the weight which he attaches to personal appearance. He wishes always to show to best advantage—above all, to dress as a gentleman, even though it may require substantial sacrifices elsewhere. Even on a hot day in Madrid or in the tropics of Colombia, he would rather be uncomfortable than coatless. For a coat is a mark of caste. It used to be only a black coat, which ensured a corvine respectability for the wearer at all times and seasons. Also, it properly covered him during the long periods of mourning prescribed by Spanish etiquette, which in a numerous family could be virtually perpetual. It is only recently that men of Spanish race have begun to emancipate themselves from the tyranny of a style which was dictated by social tradition. The change is due partly to foreign influences, partly to a new awareness, particularly among the younger generation, that the body is more important than the clothes which cover it, or even than the observance of certain ancient prejudices. In some of Latin America there exists a cult of the necktie as a badge of freedom from the social stigma of manual labor. In fact, the social symbolism of apparel, as distinguished from its purely ornamental or concealing functions, is much more highly developed among Spanish peoples than in the United States.

To work with one's hands once demeaned a man to the level of a Moor or a serf.[55] The prejudice against manual labor is still strong in Spain. The wholesale granting of patents of nobility in the Middle Ages, exempting the beneficiaries from the disgrace of physical labor, has laid deep roots in the education and economics of a proud people. In technical education, it has caused an overemphasis on books as against the laboratory; in economics, it has separated the working population into salaried sheep and wage-earning goats. If one is in a position to give orders he no longer touches a tool or manipulates a machine, unless it is a robot or a very big and impressive piece of machinery. Similarly, a white-collar Spaniard or Spanish American does not like to carry even a small package in public. All of which tends to make Spain a land of the uniformed flunky, whose duty is to relieve more important men from tasks which might detract from their importance.

In this environment of the exaltation of the individual, any depreciation of personality becomes a major offense. The laws of libel and slander assume a severity unknown in most countries. Openly to defame the good name of any but the more humble members of society is to invite retribution, either judicial or personal. Unless the sins or crimes of a man are common and notorious knowledge—or he is without any social position whatever —no one goes on public record about them. Criticism may find an outlet in gossip, which can be quite as venomous and "character"-destroying as anywhere else in the world. To avoid the occasion of censure or ridicule, one is careful not to put himself in a compromising or embarrassing position before the public. He permits no disparaging news snapshot of himself to appear in the press. He tries always to be on his guard and never to expose a vulnerable side to the world at large. He insists on privacy for his private life, and strongly resents any invasion of its precincts. He thus reduces the area of his ego which is exposed to belittlement or scandal. The infringements on privacy and the other liberties taken with the person of the individual, which Americans accept with indifference or helpless resignation, would be intolerable to one of Spanish race.

An example of a characteristic Spanish attitude is in the realm of autobiography. When a Spaniard writes his memoirs they are an *apologia,* a studied justification of his actions. There is little revelation of his human weaknesses. These can only be documented long after his death in his correspondence with his intimates, as Philip II concealed even his better side from the world until centuries later, when his letters to his daughters were found and published. Though the amatory practice is generally considered at most a peccadillo in the moral folklore of Latin America, the official guardians of the great Bolivar's reputation and artificers of his apotheosis have gone to the length of destroying his correspondence with his mistress, Manuela Saenz.[56] After all, very few men of Spanish blood have ever written autobiographies.

Last, but by no means least—courtesy is another manifestation of Spanish individualism. Good manners are an obligation of the caballero, a part of the code of a gentleman. They give him greater stature in his own eyes and in those of others, who it is assumed are duly impressed by the consideration shown to their own personalities. Courtesy tends to be formal and ceremonious, except among intimates, but none the less sincere than politeness anywhere. In Spain it is so universal that it has made a race of gentlemen. In relations with others, the potential irritants of Spanish pride are generally tempered by the demands of *caballerosidad.* Sensibilities are respected, as though a spirited people, who are at heart so honest and forthright with themselves and with the world, distrusted their own tongues. So the tensions of social intercourse are eased and explosions of passion are avoided. And since there is so little boorishness at any level of the population, there is less of needless hurt and much more of amenity in the ordinary give-and-take of human contacts.

NOTES

1. "So many racial currents have converged on the territory of Spain that it is almost impossible to define the ethnic composition of the Spanish people." Richard F. Pattee, *Introducción a la Civilización Hispano-Americana* (Boston, 1945), p. 32.

2. See Santiago Magariños, ed., *Alabanza de España* (3 vols., Madrid, 1940) I, *passim*.

3. Richard Ford, who spent much time in Spain in the 1830's, called the Spaniards, "these semi-Moors." *Gatherings from Spain*, p. 50.

4. *The Bible In Spain* (London, 1843), p. 299.

5. Salvador de Madariaga says of the Spanish character: "It is hard and human, it is resigned and rebellious, it is energetic and indolent." *English, Frenchmen, Spaniards: An Essay in Comparative Psychology* (London, 1928), p. 43.

6. The Venezuelan, Mariano Picón-Salas, comments thus on the restlessness of the conquerors, "the nostalgia of danger" which drove them to a tragic surfeit of adventures in the case of Cortés himself, Hernando de Soto, Pedro de Alvarado, Diego de Ordaz, Gonzalo Pizarro and many others: *"A lo sanchesco del disfrute, se mezcla el quijotismo de la aventura permanente."* *De la Conquista a la Independencia* (Mexico, 1944), p. 46.

7. See Gonzalo de Correas, *Vocabulario de Refranes y Frases Proverbiales y otras Formulas Comunes de la Lengua Castellana* (Madrid, 1924). This is a reprint of an old work. An example of Spanish proverbs is *"El amor y la fe, en las obras se re."* (Love and faith are known by their works.)

8. Richard Ford writes of "the inherent, inveterate ferocity of Iberian character." *Op. cit.*, p. 338. John Mackay calls the Spanish character "the most perfect expression in history of the humanly primitive and unsophisticated."

The Other Spanish Christ (New York, 1933), p. 3. "The Spaniard is, and remains today, in the best sense of the word, a savage." Havelock Ellis, *The Soul of Spain* (Boston, n.d.), p. 37.

9. Quoted by Winston Churchill, in *The Second World War*.

10. Madariaga calls the Englishman a "man of action" and the Frenchman a "man of reason." *Op. cit.*

As fruits of passion, Rafael Altamira, the famous Spanish historian, names, "violence, intolerance and exaggeration . . . among the characteristic tendencies" of his people. *A History of Spain, from the beginnings to the Present Day*, tr. from the Spanish by Muna Lee (New York, 1949), p. 358.

11. "[The Spanish people] . . . possess vision, divination, intuition, grace, and mother wit, power, grasp of reality, and a capacity for sudden discharges of almost unbounded energy." Madariaga, *The Genius of Spain*, p. 32.

"A people neither sad nor gay, but serious and stoic, Spain lived obsessed with the idea of personal dignity and an ambition for infinity." Fernando de los Rios, "Spain in the Epoch of American Colonization," in Griffin, ed., *Concerning Latin American Culture* (New York, 1940), p. 47.

12. *Idearium Español* (Madrid, 1905), p. 64. On the influence of *gana* in the Spanish world, but particularly in South America, see Count Hermann Alexander von Keyserling, *The Travel Diary of a Philosopher* (New York, 1925).

13. "The Spaniard broods over and emphasizes the naked majesty of death." Havelock Ellis, *op. cit.*, p. 26. "Spaniards are hardy people. Their tradition is one of extreme bravery and their nature includes a curious feeling vis-a-vis death—almost one of affection." C. L. Sulzberger, in *The New York Times*, February 7, 1951.

THE SPANIARD

14. See Ramón Menéndez Pidal, *The Spaniards in their History*, tr. by Walter Starkie (London, 1950), pp. 139-40.

15. See Rene de Visme Williamson, *Culture and Policy: the United States and the Hispanic World* (Knoxville, Tennessee, 1949), pp. 35-37.

16. Menéndez Pidal considers austerity "the basic quality of the Spanish character." *Op. cit.*, p. 119.

17. Borrow wrote of "the silent, reserved men of Spain." *Op. cit.*, p. 55. Captain Basil Hall, of the British Navy, who spent much time on the west coast of South America during the wars of independence, wrote of Spanish passivity of demeanor: "The Spaniards, in all things excepting politics, are a deliberate people, and, as their descendants partake of the same cautious spirit, it is not easy, at any time, to excite them to the expression of strong emotion." *Extracts from a Journal Written on the Coasts of Chili, Peru and Mexico, in the Years 1820, 1821, 1822* (2 vols., Edinburgh, 1824), II, 8.

18. Luís Alberto Sánchez, *Vida y Pasion de la Cultura en America* (Santiago, Chile, 1935) p. 21.

19. *Viage a las Regiones Equinocciales del Nuevo Continente, hecho en 1799 hasta 1804* (tr. from the German, Paris, 1826), II, p. 201.

20. Madariaga lists among the regional elements in the composite character of Spain: "the intensity, earnestness, and quaint lack of grace of the Basque; the intellectualism and imitative talent of the Catalan; the Mediterranean sense of eloquence and form of the Valencian; the graceful, and at times deeply significant, spontaneity of the Andalusian; the dry but warm inspiration of Castile; the primitive force of Aragon; the lyrical sweetness of Galicia; that classic charm which makes Asturias a kingdom apart among the kingdoms of Spain." *The Genius of Spain* (London, 1923), p. 71. Oliveira Martins, the Portuguese historian, thus characterizes the regional differences in the Spanish character: "the industrious Catalan; the melancholy and sedentary Valencian, wedded to his soil; the patient and laborious Gallego; the Aragonese, noble and haughty in his rags; the Basque, waspish and energetic, proud of his charters of rights; the grave and indolent Castilian; the blustering and lighthearted Andaluz." *Historia de la Civilizacion Iberica* (tr. from the Portuguese, Madrid, n.d.), p. 21. On the variations of provincial types, the Peruvian scholar, Francisco García Calderón, mentions "Asturian hardness . . . the rhythm of Andalusia . . . the impetuosity of Estremadura . . . the dryness of Catalonia . . . the tenacity of the Basques," . . . and "the proud idleness of the Castilian." *Latin America; its Rise and Progress* (London, 1915), p. 31.

21. See "How Castile made Spain" in José Ortega y Gasset, *Invertebrate Spain* (New York, 1937), p. 29.

22. *Op. cit.*, pp. 90-102.

23. Ford said of the Spanish dance that it was "matchless, unequalled, and inimitable, and only to be performed by Andalusians." *Op. cit.*, p. 349.

24. Since Andalusians outnumbered men from any other part of Spain in the *conquista*, "there developed a distinctly Andalusian tinge to Spanish civilization in the Americas." Charles E. Chapman, *Colonial Hispanic America: A History* (New York, 1933), p. 32.

25. "Her [Spain's] human spirit and social influence persist, with their strength

and weaknesses, as the controlling forces in the lives of some fifty million Spanish Americans today." Herbert Ingram Priestley, *The Coming of the White Man 1492–1848* (New York, 1929), p. 117.

26. "Spain came to America integrally. She gave America as much as she had; political institutions, social and economic organization, cultural foundations, arts, religion." Fernando de los Rios, "The Action of Spain in America" in Griffin, ed., *Concerning Latin American Culture* (New York, 1940), p. 52. "though . . . the American colonies declared and won their political independence, the language and culture which they had inherited from their mother country remain as their permanent possession. If empire be measured by standards other than the political and economic, the Latin American lands are still a part of the picture and the glory of having settled and civilized them belongs forever to Spain." Roger B. Merriman, *The Rise of the Spanish Empire in the Old World and in the New* (4 vols., New York, 1918–34), IV, 676.

"All [the Spanish American republics] remain in a sense Spanish. . . . They are nearer to one another than North Americans are to Englishmen. They have the broad features of Spanish character and temperament . . . the love of sonorous phrases, the sensitiveness to friendliness or affront, the sense of personal dignity, steady courage in war, and the power of patient endurance. And among men of education and thought the basis of intellectual character and the sense of moral values seems to be substantially the same." James Bryce, *South America: Observations and Impressions* (New York, 1916), p. 445.

27. Of the four greatest characters of European literature, Madariaga says that Hamlet is "too much of a dream" and Faust is "too much of an idea." But Don Quixote and Don Juan are *men,* and "they will live and grow as long as men are moved by love of justice or love of women." *The Genius of Spain,* p. 15. Of Don Quixote, Unamuno says: "And what has Don Quixote left, do you ask? . . . he has left himself, and a man, a living and eternal man, is worth all theories and all philosophies. Other people have left chiefly institutions, books; we have left souls; St. Teresa is worth any institution, any *Critique of Pure Reason.*" *The Tragic Sense of Life in Men and in Peoples* (London, 1931), p. 323. In another place, Unamuno says of Don Quixote: "Perhaps we must look for the hero of Spanish thought, not in any actual flesh-and-bone philosopher, but in a creation of fiction, a man of action, who is more real than all the philosophers." *Ibid.,* p. 313.

28. "In Spain, nobody agrees with anyone." Rufino Blanco-Fombona, *El Conquistador Espanol del Siglo XVI* (Madrid, 1922), p. 27. George Santayana, himself a Spaniard, said: "The Spaniard is an individualist; he can be devout mystically . . . but socially, externally, he distrusts everything and everybody, even his priests and his kings."

29. Madariaga calls it an "instinctive hostility to association." *Englishmen, Frenchmen, Spaniards,* p. 49. See *ibid.,* p. 136.

30. "In the great crises, he counts only on himself." Blanco Fombona, *op. cit.,* p. 35.

31. See John B. Trend, *The Civilization of Spain* (New York, 1944), p. 189.

32. Valentín González and Julian Gorkin, *El Campesino: Life and Death in Soviet Russia* (New York, 1952).

33. "Anarchy is the natural state of the Spaniard." Madariaga, *Cuadro Histórico de las Indias* (Buenos Aires, 1945), p. 371. "He is a born anarchist, and it is difficult to make him conform to systems and rules." Nicholson B. Adams, *The Heritage of Spain; an Introduction to Spanish Civilization* (New York, 1943), p. 3.

34. "All down through history every class in Spain displays its hatred for politicians." Ortega y Gasset, *op. cit.*, p. 51.

35. Madariaga, *Englishmen, Frenchmen, Spaniards*, p. 135. "The Spaniard is too much of a realist to attach much importance to his vote, and too much of an individualist to multiply its importance by co-operation with other voters." *Ibid.*, p. 166.

36. Unamuno condemns the so-called "regenerationist literature" which followed the Spanish American War, in these words: "[it] led us into the pedantry of extolling persevering and silent effort . . . prudence, exactitude, moderation . . . the social virtues. . . ." *Op. cit.*, p. 308.

37. Salvador de Madariaga, *Englishmen, Frenchmen, Spaniards*, p. 44.

38. See Menéndez Pidal, *op. cit.*, p. 136.

39. "The long coma of egotism and idiocy which has comprised our history for the last three hundred years." Ortega y Gasset, *op. cit.*, p. 39. Manuel Gálvez, the Argentine novelist, said: "In the modern world, Spain is sad, for she is at odds with its ideals, and knows her ways are not the ways of this new and powerful world." Quoted in William Rex Crawford, *A Century of Latin American Thought* (Cambridge, Mass., 1944), p. 154.

40. "Lope de Vega alone wrote as many plays as all the Elizabethan and Jacobean dramatists put together." Somerset Maugham, *Don Fernando*, p. 150.

41. Ford quotes the Spanish expression *Socorros de España, o tarde o nunca* ("Spanish help arrives late or never"). *Op. cit.*, p. 237. See Menéndez Pidal, *op. cit.*, p. 125, who quotes a writer of the 15th century: "The English remember before the event; they are prudent, the French never remember, until the event is upon them; they are proud and hasty. The Castilians never remember until the event has passed; they are lazy and contemplative."

42. "To organize an army that would at the same time serve for a war on the modern scale and for a war after the Spanish pattern, would appear to be a task for Romans." Ganivet, *op. cit.*, p. 59.

43. See Madariaga, *Englishmen, Frenchmen, Spaniards*, p. 246.

44. *"La lengua de Castilla es de una virilidad, de una sequedad, y de un enfatismo increíbles. Esta lengua apenas conoce medias tintas y suavidades, es lengua férrea para hombres de hierro. La lengua es campanuda, majestuosa, conceptuosa, heroica, elocuente, y es así porque el espíritu a que sirve de vehículo lo es."* Blanco Fombona, *op. cit.*, p. 86.

45. "Poverty is never insulted nor looked upon with contempt . . . in their social intercourse no people in the world exhibit a juster feeling of what is due to the dignity of human nature, or better understand the behaviour which it behooves a man to adopt towards his fellow-beings." Borrow, *op. cit.*, p. 139.

"With justice, Spaniards regard themselves as the most democratic of peoples." Ellery Sedgwick, "The Paradox of Spain," *The Atlantic*, September, 1952. "Spain is still the most democratic of countries." Havelock Ellis, *op. cit.*, p. 12.

"Distrustful of hierarchies, Spanish individualism created social and democratic forms. Traditions, doctrines, customs, and laws denoted an exact sense of human equality. . . . The King presided over a democracy of Knights, mystics, adventurers, and rogues." Francisco García Calderón, *op. cit.*, p. 37.

46. "Pride is our national passion, our greatest sin. The Spaniard is not avaricious like the French, nor drunk and stupid like the Englishman, nor sensual and histrionic like the Italian. He is proud, endlessly proud." Ortega y Gasset, *op. cit.*, p. 146.

47. *"L'Espagnol est souverainement ambitieux d'admiration; il ne fait rien que dans la vue d'etre admiré."* Jacques Casanova, *Mèmoires*, VII, 489.

48. Menéndez Pidal, *op. cit.*, p. 136. "Envy is the specific Spanish vice." Madariaga, *Englishmen, Frenchmen, Spaniards*, p. 224.

49. *Ibid.*, p. 163.

50. *"En España no hay términos medios."* Ganivet, *op. cit.*, p. 78.

51. *"Al rey la hacienda y la vida*
    Se ha de dar, pero el honor
    Es patrimonio del alma,
    Y el alma solo es de Dios."

For a view of the importance which a Spaniard of breeding in the early colonial period attached to the keeping of faith and other aspects of the code of honor, see Antonio de Herrera, *Historia General de los Hechos de los Castellanos en las Islas i Tierra Firma del Mar Oceano,* Decada VI, Libro III, 65.

52. "He says that it is so far from dishonor to a man to give private revenge for an affront, that the contrary is a disgrace; they holding he that receives an affront is not fit to appear in the sight of the world till he hath revenged himself." *The Diary of Samuel Pepys (for the year A.D. 1667)* (Wheatley edition, 10 vols., New York, 1942), VIII, 396.

53. "The Spaniard is constitutionally incapable of accepting the delusion that the best things in the world may be bought by money, or that a man's wealth consists in the abundance of his possessions." Havelock Ellis, *op. cit.*, p. 5.

54. Ludwig Pfandl, *Cultura y Costumbres del Pueblo Español de los Siglos XVI y XVII* (tr. from the German, Barcelona, 1942), p. 134.

55. Among comments of contemporary foreigners on Spanish habits in the second half of the seventeenth century, Altamira quotes: "They believe that it is contrary to the dignity of a Spaniard to work and provide for the future," and "Spaniards are poor because they are careless and lazy." *Historia de España y de la Civilización Española* (4 vols., Barcelona, 1913, 3d. ed.) III, 493.

56. See Victor Wolfgang Von Hagen, *The Four Seasons of Manuela: A Biography* (New York, 1952).

Chapter IV
THE CONQUEROR

"I AM A true conqueror," wrote Bernal Díaz del Castillo, "and the most ancient of all." [1] Like the old warrior of Cortés, many of the conquerors wrote of their deeds and of the things they saw. They wrote forthrightly, like the men they were, and as honestly as their passions would allow them.

If the conquerors were vain and boastful sometimes, as Bernal Díaz was, it was understandable. "I have . . . been present in 119 battles and engagements," the old Conquistador wrote, "and it is not extraordinary if I praise myself, as what I say is the mere truth." [2] They must have sensed that they were not ordinary men, and certainly the things they had witnessed were not ordinary things. "We then set forward on the road to Mexico," wrote Bernal Díaz, "which was crowded with multitudes of the natives, and arrived at the causeway of Iztapalapa, which leads to that capital. When we beheld the number of populous towns on the water and firm ground, and that broad causeway, running

straight and level to the city, we could compare it to nothing but
the enchanted scenes we had read of in *Amadis of Gaul,* from the
great towers and temples and other edifices of lime and stone
which seemed to rise out of the water. To many of us it appeared
doubtful whether we were asleep or awake, nor is the manner in
which I express myself to be wondered at, for . . . never yet did
man see, hear, or dream of anything equal to the spectacle which
appeared to our eyes on this day." ³ Of his recollection of the
Aztec populace on the day of the meeting with Montezuma, he
wrote: "The whole of what I saw on that occasion is so strongly
imprinted in my memory, that it appears to me as if it had happened only yesterday." ⁴ It was the first sight of the City of
Mexico from the pass in the hills that John Fiske called "the
most romantic moment in all history, this moment when European eyes first rested upon that city of wonders." ⁵ His mind set
on what might await him on the morrow, Cortés in his narrative
passed over that instant very casually. "The Spaniards," he wrote,
"followed the road until they reached the top of the Sierras, between which the road passes, and from there they behold the
plains of Culua, and the city of Temxtitán, and the lakes which
are in that province." ⁶

The wonders were as great in Peru as in Mexico. One of
Pizarro's soldiers, clad in armor, walked among the golden and
silver trees and flowers in the Inca's garden at Tumbes.⁷ After
probably the most audacious ride in history, Hernando de Soto
and Pedro del Barco gazed on the "incredible riches" of Cuzco
before the city had been stripped of its treasures by their companions. As the Inca's ransom, and gold and silver vessels brought
in by roving bands of Spaniards from Jauja and Pachacamac and
other places, accumulated in Cajamarca, the sight of it all must
have been a "thing of marvel," as Oviedo reported.⁸ But Oviedo
got the story from others, and there was no Bernal Díaz or
Cieza present among the open-mouthed conquerors to tell of these
wonders before they were melted into bars of bullion. Oviedo
says that among the pieces there was a golden seat, that must
have been of some great lord, with the water running into a
little lake, on which birds were swimming and around the river
men were dipping water.⁹ "It was all made of gold," he added,
"which was a thing much to be seen."

Sometimes, as did Bernal Díaz and Cieza de León and Oviedo, the chroniclers, they wrote a book—or books. Some of them, like the literate Cortés and Valdivia, wrote long dispatches to king or emperor which, when collected, had the substance and form of books. Still others wrote voluminous and labored accounts of their doings and their observations that ultimately found their way into the archives of the Indies at Seville. For those, like the Pizarros, who could not write or never found the occasion, the gaps in the story were filled by holy clerks, like Peter Martyr and Las Casas, and González Marmolejo and Father Simón, who either witnessed or heard from others those things of which they wrote, with official historians like Herrera, or front-seat spectators and first-hand reporters, like the Inca Garcilaso and the Venetian Pigafetta, who went along with Magellan for the ride. So we probably know more about the conquest and those who participated in it than we do about any other series of military enterprises up to that time, or, for the matter, until the wars of Napoleon.

Like Hakluyt in Elizabethan London, Peter Martyr, who chronicled the beginnings of the Conquista, received his stories fresh from the lips of the returning conquerors and explorers. "Not one of those who came to court," he says, "failed to offer me the pleasure, whether verbally or in writing, of reporting to me everything he had learned." [10] "I relate that of which I was an eyewitness," said Bernal Díaz, "and not idle reports and hearsay." [11]

"I have always given great attention to accuracy in my history," wrote Cieza, "and in what concerned the Spaniards I sought out wise men who were truthful, so as to gain information and obtain reports of the events of which I was not myself an eyewitness." [12] "I tell what I saw," said Oviedo.[13] He reflects on the public's enjoyment of his chronicle: "I hope the reader will be contented with what I have seen and experienced with many dangers, as he enjoys what I have written and learns without any danger for himself. He can read without enduring hunger and thirst, and heat or cold, and other innumerable privations, without leaving his native land, without venturing into storms at sea, or risking the misfortunes which befall men on land. For his entertainment and relaxation was I born and in my wanderings seen these things." [14] "I saw Columbus," wrote the old chronicler, "the first admiral and discoverer of these parts, and most of the first settlers; I knew the principal men who came here in those days and also those who have come since with high offices and responsibilities." The Inca Garcilaso wrote of his efforts to write objectively: "The obligations which a person who writes of the events of his time has to relate them to the whole world obliges and forces me to tell without passion or favor the truth of what happened."

What they wrote about was man's greatest adventure.[15] For the Conquest was a thing of superlatives and the men who took part in it were supermen. For never have sheer human will and force of personality accomplished so much through the efforts of so few and on so vast a stage. The conquerors not only "gave a new world to Castile and León"; their discoveries and conquests resulted in a world-wide economic and social revolution that radically changed the whole pattern of life in Europe and its overseas dependencies.[16]

DEATH AND THE CONQUERORS

The mortality rate of conquest was very high. Thousands died of starvation and disease or in battle with the Indians.[17] The losses appear all the greater in relation to the small numbers of the expeditionary forces. For it is probable that only three times during the conquest were more than a thousand Spaniards assembled on one occasion, under Mendoza on the River Plate, on Gonzalo Pizarro's entry into Lima in 1544, and on Cortés's final occupation of the city of Mexico. The death rate on Ojeda's early expedition to Darien was eighty per cent and on Nicuesa's it was even heavier. Many a small Spanish force was wiped out by the Indians. On the *Noche Triste* Cortés lost over 150 of his men, including one of his ablest lieutenants, Juan Velásquez de León. When Jiménez de Quesada reached the Colombian plateau, only 166 of the nearly 900 with which he had left the coast were alive. When the site of Mendoza's colony at Buenos Aires was abandoned, less than a fourth of the original number reached the new settlement at Asunción.[18] According to Girolami Benzoni, "Of those who went to Peru, there died eighty out of every hundred."

The same general ratio of survival probably held for the leaders of the Conquest.[19] Those who were killed by the Indians included Pedro de Valdivia, conqueror of Chile; and Francisco de Villagra, one of his lieutenants; Juan de Ayolas, Diego de Solís, and Juan de Garay, pioneers in the River Plate lands; Juan de la Cosa, the famous navigator; Juan Ponce de León, discoverer of Florida; "Adelantado of Bimini," and pacifier of Puerto Rico; Ñuflo de Chaves, who won the plains of eastern Bolivia for Spain; Francisco Hernández de Córdoba, discoverer of Yucatán and the Mayas; and Juan, youngest of the Pizarros. Among those who were executed by their fellow Spaniards were Vasco Núñez de Balboa; Cristobal de Olid, who deserted Cortés in Central America; Diego de Almagro and his son; Blasco Nuñez Vela, first Viceroy of Peru; and the rebels against the royal authority in Peru—Gonzalo Pizarro, Francisco Carbajal, Rodrigo Orgóñez, and Francisco Hernández Girón.

Francisco Pizarro and his half-brother, Pedro de Alcántara, Rodrigo de Bastidas, one of the first conquerors on the Spanish Main or *Tierra Firme*,[20] and Jorge Robledo, a conqueror of Colombia, were assassinated. Of the conquerors of Peru, Diego Centeno and Diego de Alvarado died under suspicion of poisoning by their enemies, as did Diego de Ordaz, one of the captains of Cortés, after his return from his disastrous foray into the backlands of the Orinoco. Like many another, Diego Nicuesa and the ill-starred Pánfilo de Narvaez were lost at sea in the waters of the New World. Hernán Pérez de Quesada, brother of the conqueror of Colombia, was struck by lightning, and Pedro de Alvarado, the perpetual conqueror, was crushed to death by a horse. Some, like Sebastian Benalcázar, conqueror of the Quito country, Hernando de Soto, and Gonzalo Sandoval, the favorite lieutenant of Cortés, died worn out by their exertions and privations.

Given the hazards to which they were exposed, it is remarkable that as many lived out their time as did. Among them was the great Cortés, though prematurely for one of his physical vigor. Jiménez de Quesada died of leprosy at eighty in the land he had conquered.[21] Very few survived the curse of Peru. Among them were Alonso de Alvarado, Lorenzo de Aldana, and Garcilaso de la Vega, father of the chronicler of the Incas. Hernando Pizarro, last of the five brothers, spent his retirement imprisoned in a castle in Spain, where his many enemies could not reach him, and lived to the ripe old age of 104! Father Vásquez de Espinoza tells of one of the conquerors of Venezuela, Diego de Henares Lozana, who died full of years and honors at 115.[22] One of the most durable of the conquistadores was the belligerent Francisco de Aguirre, who, after a long career as a virtual one-man conquering army, died somewhere between the age of seventy-three and eighty-one. Of 110 who went to Chile with Valdivia, one lived over a century, six between eighty and ninety years, nineteen between seventy and eighty years, and twenty-three between sixty and seventy years. In other words, almost half of them lived to at least the age of sixty, an extraordinary record of longevity, in view of the unusual hazards of war with the Tehuelches. Pedrarias Dávila, the evil genius of the Isthmus, already advanced in years, returned to Spain to outlive most of the 1,500 who had accompanied him to Darien, and to die at the age of 90. Domingo Martínez de Irala, founder of Paraguay and one of the ablest administrators among the conquerors, lived on for many years in his creole colony, a patriarch among his mixed people and in a very real sense one of the fathers of his country. Another who outlasted most of his companions and contemporaries was the peripatetic and quixotic Alvar Núñez Cabeza de Vaca, one of the anomalies of the Conquest and for a time rival of Martínez de Irala for authority over the Paraguayan colony.[23]

Oviedo tells of one of the conquerors of Venezuela, who found surcease from the endless wars with the Caribs in a comfortable marriage with a wealthy widow on Hispaniola.[24] "Recognizing the mockeries of the world," says Oviedo, "weary of struggling and laboring in vain, and wishing to put to better use what was left of his life, he decided to marry." So "the Lord provided the tired warrior with the company of a good woman suitable to his age." As an added consideration, she also had "the wherewithal for eating, a good house, six thousand head of cattle, and wide lands." Here he found "the safety and security which he had long lacked as a soldier searching for the fabled treasures of the Meta."

More fortunate than most of their leaders, many of the soldiery of the Conquest settled down with their memories on the *encomienda* that was the reward for their services or in some obscure town. Here they spun endless yarns of the wars for their grandchildren while the shadows lengthened in courtyard or plaza and their tales grew taller with the falling years. Of such was Bernal Díaz, who at eighty-four immortalized himself by writing *The True Relation of the Conquest of New Spain,* the greatest soldiers' story in the history of war. He was then a *regidor,* or councilman, of the city of Guatemala, with a large brood of descendants to care for from his modest properties. Like all old soldiers, he grumbled at his lot. "There only remain alive," he wrote, "five of the companions of Cortés, and we are very old and bowed down with infirmities, and very poor, and with a heavy charge of sons to provide for, and of daughters to marry off, and grandchildren to maintain and little incomes to do it withal; and thus we pass our lives, in pain, in labor, and in sorrow."

Bernal Díaz recites the fate of some of his companions-at-arms.[25] Only three of them apparently prospered beyond the ordinary. Juan del Espinar became "a very rich man," and both Juan Gómez and one Villalobos "returned rich to Castile." On the other hand, five of those who gained some wealth gave up their riches for a religious life. Two of them operated inns on the road between Veracruz and the city of Mexico, which must have been a very profitable business in those days. One veteran, Gaspar Díaz, gave away his wealth and became a famous and holy hermit in the pine forests of Guaxocingo. One Escalante, "a good soldier, of a gay disposition," joined the Franciscan order, turned soldier again, but ended his days a friar. In all, Bernal Díaz lists seven of his old company who became holy clerks.

In New Spain, the adjustment of the veterans of the Conquest to the demands of peacetime living was much easier than it was in Peru, where the long civil wars between conquerors tended to brutalize the soldiery and to make many of them unfit for civilian life. At best, they became ne'er-do-wells and "drifters"; at worst, they became hoodlums and chronic brawlers, who were perpetually disturbing the peace which the new viceregal government was trying to impose on the troubled land. These were the "badmen" of the new frontier, whom the harassed authorities sometimes rounded up and organized into bands, to be sent on wild-goose chases into the jungle beyond the mountains in search of some golden city, and so to be rid of for once and all. The best known of these desperadoes was the "rattlesnake-eyed" Lope de Aguirre, whose infamous career of crime in the interior of South America is one of the enduring legends of the continent.[26]

THE SPANISH SOLDIER

Only a minority of those who took part in the Conquest had had experience in the use of arms, though a few, like Valdivia and Carbajal, were veterans of the Italian wars of the House of Aragón. Among the mightiest of them, Francisco Pizarro was a swineherd and Jiménez de Quesada, conqueror of Colombia, was a man of laws and courts. Balboa was an attractive young rake in the household of a provincial nobleman. So with the rank and file. Among the comrades of Bernal Díaz was "a man of business," a fiddler and dancing teacher, and "a buffoon." Their individual backgrounds had little to do with their place in the ranks of the conquerors. Very few of them came, as did García de Paredes, the natural son of a famous captain in the Italian campaigns, from families with a military tradition. Few, except for Ponce de León and Pedro de Mendoza, had even remote connection with the families of the *Grandeza*. Most of them were nobodies, men without a past to record. At best, they were obscure country squires, unknown beyond the place where they were born. Some, like Valdivia and Pedro de Alvarado, did not even know their birthplace. Almagro and Benalcázar were nameless men, who were known by the name of their native town.[27] Bernal Díaz said that most of his companions were hidalgos, but hidalgos were a maravedi a dozen in Spain at the end of the Middle Ages.

The essential fact is that they were Spaniards of the sixteenth century and, therefore, superb fighting material. Aside from the qualities that characterized them as Spaniards, as Spaniards they were the end product of centuries of preparation for some supreme collective effort of the human will. For ages Castilian and Aragonese had fought one another or the Moslem, and the intervals of peace were never long enough to relax the tautness of nerves that were steeled to battle. Then a concurrence of circumstances at the end of the fifteenth century furnished the setting and occasion for the great adventure for which everything else had been a preparation. The forces of the kingdoms were united by the marriage of Ferdinand and Isabella, the Moors were expelled from their last stronghold in the peninsula, the Italian enterprises of Ferdinand sharpened the sword of Spain and mobilized its mind for the challenge that was to come, and a Genoese navigator in the service of Castile found a virgin world that was ready for the taking.

Though Cataluña was to play little part in the conquest of the New World, the fabulous exploits of the Catalan "free companies" in the Near East were bright threads in the martial tapestry of Spain, and the adventures of Roger de Flor and Berenguer de Rocafort gave an illusion of reality to the romances of chivalry which were the favored reading of the conquistadores. Much nearer in time, the Aragonese wars in Sicily and Naples and their sequels in Northern Italy under the Emperor Charles were closely linked with the course of conquest in the Americas. It was these campaigns, and particularly the victory at Ravenna over the French, which established the high military prestige of Spain in western Europe. Out of them came also the fame of Gonsalvo de Córdoba, "The Great Captain," who revolutionized the tactics and organization of the Spanish armies. From these wars there came the new army that was to be the instrument of the imperial designs of the Hapsburg kings on the continent. The core of this new military organization was the *tercio,* a compact combination of the various arms in a single combat unit which was to rank with the Macedonian phalanx and the Roman legion in the history of warfare. For a century the redoubtable soldiery of the *tercios* rolled roughshod over western Europe, until the French cavalry broke their close formation at Rocroi. These were the men who appear in the forest of lances in Velásquez' painting of the surrender of Breda. When the Sieur de Brantome watched the veterans of the Italian *tercios* as they marched to the north, they appeared to him to be all captains. "And one would have said that they were princes, they bore themselves so proudly and arrogantly and with such grace of movement."

The conquistadores were of the same haughty and swaggering breed as those who followed Leyva and Alva, and some of them had "broken a pike in Flanders"—or in Italy in that elite

company. But they fought in another world and against strange
and unorthodox foes. And their style of fighting was more that
of the truly Spanish *guerrilla* than the measured precision of the
tercios. As a result, their battles were likely to be the sum total
of the unco-ordinated blows and thrusts of a few hundred *individuals* bent on the destruction of their enemies.

To a superlative degree the conquerors epitomized the peculiar genius of Spain. In their rampant individualism, they could
be undisciplined to the point of anarchy, as they often were in
Peru, where the clash of uncontrollable iron wills led to civil
war.[28] Only a leader of the stature of Cortés could tame their
proud and savage spirits for long. It is a tribute to the generally
high level of leadership among the *adelantados* that the Conquest
produced so many able chieftains, like Balboa and Almagro, Valdivia and Martínez de Irala, Jiménez de Quesada, and Soto, who
could inspire the devotion of their followers and hold them together under the most trying conditions. When Jiménez de Quesada's men begged him to turn back to the coast, he told them
that "such weakness was not permitted to Spaniards." [29] In spite
of the independence of the conquerors, one of the paradoxical
sides of their character was their unquestioning loyalty to the
monarch—the quixotic fidelity of Spaniards in the New World to
even the most unworthy and ungrateful king, that persisted to
the bitter end of the colonial period.

The epic quality of the Conquest is not only due to the magnitude of the scene and the stakes, but to the legendary heroism
of the small companies of paladins who overthrew vast and warlike nations. They had an utter contempt for odds, as at Otumba
and Cajamarca and in the battles against the Araucanians. They
showed a reckless disregard for the dangers which they could not
see and, without calculating the risks, plunged headlong into
mountains and jungle where they might easily have been am-
bushed and annihilated. Whenever sheer weight of numbers
forced them to give ground, they never yielded to panic. Physically, they were well conditioned for the trials and exertions of
the Conquest by the sober style of living of their race, and the
fortitude and endurance of the Spanish soldier always amazed
their Indian foes, habituated to the environment.

They were also zealous in their faith and delighted in the destruction of heathen idols as the visible symbol of the Devil's domain over their foes. They naturally lacked a sense of future archaeological values and, in their crusade against the infidel, they no more respected the impressive temples of the official worship at Cholula and Mexico, and at Cuzco and Pachacamac than they did the humble roadside shrines of the common folk. In their campaigns, chaplains as hardy as they were, like Father Olmedo of Cortés's army, shared their hardships and ministered to their religious needs. And whenever one of the soldiers took an Indian woman as his concubine, the priest hurriedly inducted her into the Christian community and provided her with a familiar Spanish name.

In their writings, the soldier-chroniclers reveal the qualities of their own breed and the conditions under which they fought and lived. "As for the hardships and hunger they have faced, no other nation in the world could have endured it," wrote Cieza de León.[30] "The daring of the Spaniards is so great that nothing in the world can daunt them," he said without boasting. Again he added: "No other race can be found which can penetrate through such rugged lands, such dense forests, such great mountains and deserts, and over such broad rivers, as the Spaniards have done without help from others, solely by the valor of their persons and the forcefulness of their breed. In a period of seventy years they have overcome and opened up another world, without bringing with them wagons of provisions, or great store of baggage, or tents in which to rest, or anything but a sword and a shield, and a small bag in which they carried their food."[31] "God endowed Spain," wrote Oviedo, "with many valiant cavaliers and illustrious hidalgos, and He made its inhabitants of great boldness and determination and of a warlike nature."[32]

Sometimes the odds seemed too great for men to bear. The spokesman of one of the bands which penetrated into the back country of Venezuela, told their leader: "We do not want gold. We are dying here. Take us away from this evil land, and though later you wish to come back, take us just to Coro, so that we can get back our health and get new clothes and weapons. For we are naked and in need of everything. And, Sir, we will come back with you with new equipment and with better chance of success than if we keep on now. For, as we are now, we do not want gold or anything else, only our lives, and not to lose them to no purpose, fighting the sky and defying the impossible." [33]

THE "BLACK LEGEND"

Ever since the Conquest, the Spaniards have been charged with dire crimes against the aborigines of the New World. This "Black Legend" of Spanish cruelty originated very early in the propagandistic exaggerations of the famous Las Casas, who advocated the cause of the Indians against the excesses of their conquerors. Since his book, *La Destrucción de las Indias*, furnished a convenient text for the resentments of all the envious rivals of Spain, it was eagerly translated into other European languages. The result was that those nations who had no Indians of their own to oppress could moralize in their self-righteousness at the expense of the Spaniard. The damning tradition has been as persistent as the myth, inspired by Suetonius, that universal lechery was responsible for "the downfall of the Roman Empire," and in our own time it has been preserved for future generations in the canvases of Diego Rivera.

No people had a monopoly of cruelty or of mercy in the sixteenth century. In spite of the restraints of Christianity and the new dignity which the Renaissance gave to the personality of the individual man, it was a rough and ruthless age. Underneath the shiny new polish of western civilization, there was still much heartlessness and brutality, as was to be demonstrated in the religious wars of Europe. It happened that the Spaniards and the Portuguese were the first Europeans to be thrown into contact with "inferior" races and they probably dealt with them as humanely as any other European people would have done under the same conditions. And in their mutual hates, they could be as cruel to one another as they ever were to the Indians.

In the first surge of the period of discovery the Spaniards harried the major islands of the Antilles. Disillusioned as to the wealth which they expected to find, and their sadistic instincts aroused by the very gentleness of the natives, many of them followed the example of the callous Roldán. As the depopulation of Hispaniola by mistreatment and disease proceeded, slaves were brought in from the Spanish Main to fill the gaps in the manpower of the colony. Las Casas, himself a lay colonist and employer of Indian labor before he became a Dominican friar, witnessed this phase of the Conquest and was inspired by what he saw to deliver his burning polemic against his fellow Spaniards.

As the process of Conquest spread to the mainland, the Spaniards encountered the resistance of large numbers of warlike Indians who aroused their respect by their fighting qualities. In the violence of the wars that followed the invasion of the continent, no quarter was given on either side and each treated the other with complete disregard of any rules or principles of humanity or fair play. The ferocity of the Indians invited retaliation in kind, as it did in Colombia or when the Aztecs sacrificed their Spanish prisoners to the war god in the sight of their comrades. The various conquistadores differed greatly in their treatment of the Indians. Nuño de Guzmán, who overran the Pánuco country of northern Mexico, was a killer and slave hunter, who was called to account for his crimes by Bishop Zumárraga. Cortés, severe from military necessity during the period of actual fighting, later won the confidence of the Indian peoples of Mexico by his moderation.

Similarly, Balboa, after the initial rigors of hostilities were over, kept the peace throughout the Darien region by his fair treatment of the various tribal chiefs, only to have his work undone by Pedrarias Dávila. Although the Spanish Main was long a lethal hornet's nest of poisoned Carib arrows for any Spaniard who ventured ashore, Pedro de Heredia, founder of Cartagena, managed to establish satisfactory working relationships with the Indians of the neighborhood.[34] In Peru, but particularly in the coastal part of the country, the Indians suffered greatly during the Conquest and the civil wars which accompanied them. After Cajamarca, they always expected the worst from Francisco Pizarro and were seldom disappointed. Gonzalo enjoyed a much better reputation with the Indians than did his brother, and Pizarro's partner, Almagro, "had a way" with the Indians, as he did with his own men.[35]

If the Spaniard was often cruel to the Indian in the heat of the Conquest, once the fighting had ceased and the conqueror turned colonist, the lot of the Indians generally improved. If he settled down on an encomienda, the Indians who dwelt on the land became *his* people. As their *patrón,* he felt a responsibility for their welfare and he preferred to see them happy around him, because their happiness contributed to his own peace of mind. In the new relationship, the basic justice and humanity of the Spaniard tended to assert itself, and though there were individual exceptions, the institution of the encomienda with the safeguards established by the new laws was probably as satisfactory a framework as was possible for reconciling the interests of conqueror and conquered in that imperfect age.[36]

When there were abuses, first to protest against them were Spaniards, both clerics and laymen. It is to the everlasting credit of Spain that there were priests like Montesinos and Las Casas and the early Dominicans and Franciscans in Mexico, and men among the conquerors themselves, like Cieza and Oviedo and Cabeza de Vaca to raise their voices on behalf of the Indians. And no other nation had so humane a code of laws to protect a subject people as had Spain. Among them all, there was none who undertook with so much wisdom and devotion and good sense to preserve the values and institutions of the native civilization against the impact of the new forces as Vasco de Quiroga, Bishop of Michoacán and disciple of Thomas More. The fundamental fact remains that most of the blood in over half the Latin American republics is still Indian blood.

THE QUEST FOR GOLD

Much has been written about the conquerors' consuming passion for gold, as though greed were a vice only of Spaniards. But the basic motivation of conquest was not so simple. The economics of the conquerors was uncomplicated. Except for a few of the leaders, most of them were penniless and landless adventurers. If they appeared to place an extravagant value on the possession of gold, it was because the metal encompassed all their elemental concepts of wealth, and the riches of the Indies promised them release from the poverty they had always known. When gold fell into their hands as their share of the spoils of conquest, they spent it as eagerly as they had sought for it and on the morrow they were often as poor as when they had left Seville.[37] When wealth suddenly came to them, they were prodigal with it, and when they had gambled away the loot of Cuzco before the next dawn, they then gambled away the golden images from the temple of the Sun as if they were pitching *reales* in a roadside inn in Estremadura.[38] Of the Spaniards' contempt for money, once they had it, Cieza said that "if they required anything they thought nothing of it. They bought pigs in the sow's belly, before they were born, for a hundred pesos and more." [39]

Many of the conquerors of Peru became rich men for a time, but few lived to benefit from their riches, for wealth, like life itself, was highly ephemeral in that environment. Almagro financed his expedition to Chile from his share of the original Inca booty and advanced gold to many of his followers so that they could equip themselves. Then, when they arrived in the Valley of Chile, he canceled all their obligation to him in a gesture of liberality that was typical of him. Soto carried off with him the fortune with which he organized his disastrous expedition into the southern part of what is now the United States. Even those who were calculating in their greed, like Luís de Lugo, early Governor of New Granada, who was a virtual highwayman, did not live to enjoy their gains over a long life.[40] But when the booty of Vadillo's expedition was divided at Cali, young Cieza's share was five and a half pesos. "Such," he said, "was the reward for discoveries so laboriously made." [41] At the other extreme, when Atahualpa's ransom was apportioned among Pizarro's men at Cajamarca, each foot soldier received 440 pesos of gold and 181 marcos of silver, and each horse soldier twice as much. Bernal Díaz said that the common soldiers of Cortés were dissatisfied at the distribution of the Aztec treasure.[42] Of "Montezuma's gold, badly divided, and worse employed," he wrote, "Our captains got chains of gold made for them by the King's workmen; Cortés also had similar works executed for him, together with a service of plate. Many of our soldiers who had lined their pockets well did the same, and deep gaming went on day and night . . . and thus we passed our time in Mexico." After the final capture of the Aztec capital, the soldiers celebrated the event with a big and riotous party at Coyoacán. A cargo of wine and pork had arrived from Cuba in time for the festivities, and as the merriment increased, "the private soldiers swore they would buy horses with golden harness; the crossbowmen would use none but golden arrows; all were to have their fortunes made. When the tables were taken away, the soldiers danced in their armor with the ladies, as many as there were of them, but the dispro-portion in numbers was very great." [43] Good Father Olmedo, the Chaplain, was very scandalized by the goings-on. The division of the spoils was followed by a wave of inflation, as had occurred in Peru, and most of the soldiers were soon as poor as when they had arrived in Mexico. To ease their situation, Cortés declared a two-year moratorium on all debts among his men.[44]

More than gold, the conquerors wanted power and self-expres-sion, a fit field of action for their wild egos. All Spain was in a ferment and a deep restlessness reached into the farthest re-cesses of the nation. Men needed a wider theater for their surplus energies than was offered by the local round of petty activities. One day was liable to be much like another in Badajoz or Medel-lín, where the past ruled the present and there was no future, and their young men craved adventure and relief from the bore-dom and monotony of life in a dull provincial town. So, often with their sword their only baggage, they drifted down to the waterside at Seville, from which ships sailed to the Indies—per-haps to carry them to power and riches, but always to adventure and romance.

"The Conquistadores," wrote Fernando de los Rios, "repre-sent the most outstanding example of the will to power known at the tumultuous epoch of renascence. In that period of exaltation of individuals, of unlimited faith in the value of every human action, the appetite for power and glory is embodied in the conquistadores. Perhaps a comparable display of will has never been made in history . . . the incredible firmness and recklessness with which they undertook the most audacious feats. Abandoned in a milieu unknown, savage, and often horribly hostile, they looked dauntlessly at the eyes of the Sphinx, at the silent horizon of the future. Instead of intimidation, they felt the attraction of the mystery; consequently they went ahead, be-cause they had a blind faith in the value of their force of will, of the *'eroici furori'* that they incarnated and of the transcendent mission which, sometimes unconsciously, they felt that they were performing." [45]

THE BUSINESS OF CONQUEST

For the most part, the Conquest was organized and financed like any business venture.[46] Though a partner in any profits to the extent of one-fifth of the gross, the crown seldom contributed to the original capital of the enterprise. The initial funds were generally raised by the leader of the expedition, who might pledge any property which he held or give the lender a lien against the proceeds. Pedro de Mendoza financed his large expedition to the River Plate by his share in the sack of Rome. As capital accumulated in each successive step of the Conquest, it provided a revolving fund for further advances. Thus, in order, Santo Domingo, Cuba, and Mexico to the north, and Panama, Peru, and Chile to the south, became recruiting grounds and banking centers for new sallies into virgin territory. Pedro de Alvarado drew on his earnings from the conquest of Mexico to finance the conquest of Guatemala; then, from the profits of that piece of business he organized an army to join in the conquest of Peru, which he sold for 100,000 pesos cash to the conquerors already on the ground. The conquest of Peru had been underwritten by local capital on the Isthmus, which was raised by the priest, Luque, a silent partner of Almagro and Pizarro. Later, Hernando de Soto, a major shareholder in the Peruvian company, utilized his capital gains to pay the costs of his expedition on the mainland of North America, as Pedro de Valdivia did in the conquest of Chile.

The conditions under which each conquering expedition was to operate were set down in a formal document known as a "capitulation." This was a concession for conquest, but was not a license for hunting Indians, for the king always impressed on the concessionaires the necessity for showing a Christian spirit towards the aborigines. The raising and outfitting of the expeditionary force was the exclusive responsibility of the adelantado, as the leader was generally denominated in the contract. While the "capitulation" contained the customary waiver of the crown for any of the liabilities incident to the business of conquest, it made it clear that the king would expect one-fifth of any receipts on the credit side of the venture. It also defined the area, usually with great vagueness, within which the conquering expedition was to operate. The confusion on this point, which was inevitable in view of the geographical ignorance of the time, furnished the initial provocation for the break between Almagro and Pizarro, that precipitated the tragic civil wars of Peru. Titles of nobility were given very sparingly, and generally as reward rather than inducement. In this respect at least, Columbus was the most generously rewarded of all the discoverers and conquerors. For he was not only made Admiral of the Ocean Sea, but Duke of Veragua, a title that is still borne by his descendants in the Spanish peerage. His son, Diego, was the first Viceroy in the Indies. Both Cortés and Francisco Pizarro received a marquisate. Jiménez de Quesada was awarded the high-sounding, but empty, title of Marshal of the Kingdom of New Granada. The vanity of others was satisfied with a patent of knighthood in one of the military orders. Some were awarded a coat of arms, which in the case of a few, like Sebastián Elcano, the first circumnavigator, and Diego Mendez, the stout canoeman of Columbus, was sufficient glory for the pride of any man.[47]

After the first news of the conquest of Mexico reached Spain, the recruiting of volunteers for other expeditions presented few problems. For the inns of Seville usually swarmed with swaggering young blades eager for a place in the ranks of some new Cortés. Cortés raised his own force in Cuba from those who, like himself, had already returned to civilian life in the new colony. Many of those who followed him to Mexico were later to take part in the conquest of Peru and of even more distant lands. But by then a steady stream of fresh adventurers was pouring into the Indies from the Peninsula.

The conquest of the New World was the work of Castile, and the favored mother of conquerors was the Castilian province of Estremadura, which lies on the side of the kingdom next to Portugal.[48] Among the major Conquistadores, Cortés and the Pizarros, Valdivia and the fighting Alvarados, Balboa and Soto, were Estremeños. So were Sandoval and Orellana, and, of other captains in the conquest of Peru, Centeno, Hinojosa, Garcilaso de la Vega, Gómez de Tordoya, and Perálvarez Holguín. And last, but by no means least, of them was Bernal Díaz of Medina del Campo, source of many conquerors. From other parts of Castile came Ojeda, Montejo, Narvaez, Vásquez de Coronado, Velás-

quez de León, and Gil González Dávila. Jiménez de Quesada was
from Granada and Cabeza de Vaca was from Jeréz de la Fron-
tera. Martínez de Irala and Juan de Garay were Basques. There
were a few Basques and Portuguese in most of the expeditions.
There were three Portuguese among the original conquerors of
Mexico—"brave men," Bernal Díaz called them. As might have
been expected, the largest element among the rank and file of the
conquering armies was Andalusian—Sevillanos and men from
other towns in the valley of the Guadalquivir.

In addition to the important "camp master," the "captains,"
and ordinary men-at-arms, who comprised the bulk of every
company, efforts were generally made to recruit a few specialists
whose services would be particularly useful to the expedition. No
force was complete without an armorer, who also did duty as
blacksmith for the cavalry attached to the army. A Basque boat-
builder might comprise the rest of the engineers' corps. As in
most armies of the time, the medical department was always
badly served. Sometimes the soldier who did the barbering for his
comrades when beards got out of control also acted as *sangrador*
or bloodletter, after the therapeutic tradition of the Middle Ages.
After all, the medico's job was largely one of tying up wounds,
leaving recovery to time and strong constitutions. Bernal Díaz
tells of the Bachelor Escobar, "apothecary, surgeon and physician" to Cortés's little host. He adds briefly that "he went mad,"
which was no wonder in view of the patients he had to tend.

There was always a notary to record the actions and decisions
of a formal and suspicious people. He was guardian of their legal
conscience, as the priest who accompanied each expedition was
of its moral conscience. These chaplains usually took their responsibilities very seriously, and were often a restraining force
on the anarchical wills of their pious parishioners. Bernal Díaz
speaks very highly of Fray Bartolomé de Olmedo, who accompanied Cortés in the conquest of Mexico and apparently survived
all the hazards of the campaign against the Aztecs. According to
Bernal Díaz, he was not only a "great theologian" and a holy
man, but he sang well and was a good comrade.

In dealings with the Indians the need of interpreters was always keenly felt. Sometimes an Indian was kidnaped in advance
and given a quick course in Spanish, often only to find that he

spoke the wrong language and that his instructors had wasted their time on him. Much more useful were interpreters like the famous Doña Marina, who performed invaluable services in the conquest of Mexico, and Spaniards who had lived for years among the Indians, like Jerónimo Aguilar, whom Cortés picked up in Yucatán. Similarly, as a campaign progressed, and lines of communication lengthened, messengers and scouts assumed special importance in the tenuous logistics of conquest. Several messengers became well-known in the conquest of Peru and the time of troubles that followed. Of Pero Gallego, one of them, Cieza said: "He was a very swift walker and knew the country well." [49] Another was Alonso García, who, disguised as an Indian, carried letters from Vaca de Castro to Almagro. He was later tracked down by Juan Diente, most famous of the messenger-spies, and captured.

THE JUSTICE OF THE CONQUEST

A feature of any well-ordered *entrada,* or conquering expedition, was the reading of the *requerimiento,* or requisition, to the first party of Indians encountered.[50] If the Indians left the scene before the ceremony started or became bored by the proceedings and decamped while it was still in progress, the reading continued anyway. This extraordinary and typically Spanish document was part of the protocol or official formula of conquest, and was designed to introduce its listeners to the new facts of life as represented by the conquerors and so to prepare them for what was to come on earth, if not in heaven. This quixotic exercise in dialectics began at the beginning with an account of the creation, and from that point proceeded through the Old Testament well into the New. Along the way, the doctrine of the Trinity, incomprehensible even to Spanish laymen, was introduced, and the history of the papacy was outlined at some length. It was then made clear that the pope had deeded the New World to the king of Spain as his authorized agent and that the Spaniards present had come to take possession of the property and its usufruct, human and material, and, incidentally, to make good Christians out of its misguided inhabitants. To the bewilderment and consternation of the hearers, this long-winded farrago of theology and jurisprudence was delivered in Spanish. The Spanish soldiers kept a straight face while the notary was reading, but after the meeting had broken up, they were often given to outbursts of Homeric laughter, as Oviedo relates of his own experience. If the Indians did not appear to be duly impressed by the sonorous, but unintelligible, proclamation, as was likely to be the case, the Spaniards felt that they were now free to go about the business for which they had come.

In spite of what would have appeared to any other people as only an exhibition of Spanish quixotism, the *requerimiento* was symptomatic of the deep and sincere concern of the Spanish nation over the basic justice of the Conquest. The question of its righteousness or morality weighed heavily on the conscience of Spain and there was much searching of heart and mind as to the ethics of the great enterprise on which Spaniards had embarked with so much fervor and high hopes.[51] That they paused to consider in all seriousness the rightness or wrongness of what they were about to do is as much to the eternal glory of Spain as was the consummation of the epic adventure itself. It was not only the Church which raised its powerful voice on behalf of the Indians, but jurists and statesmen examined the issue calmly and objectively in a vain effort to find some way that would reconcile the interests of the two peoples. It was not enough that a Spanish pope had divided the New World between Spain and Portugal without consulting its inhabitants, and Spaniards as far apart as Francisco de Vitoria, who was probably the ablest political thinker of his time, and Admiral Diego Flores de Valdés questioned the papal prerogative. Men bluntly asked themselves what right they had to dispossess the Indians of what was theirs and to impose on them the law and faith of Spain. These Indian communities, they reasoned, may have titles to their lands as valid as those of Castile to the kingdom of Granada, and to quiet his own doubts the Viceroy Toledo ordered extensive research made into the manner in which the Incas had acquired dominion over their subject peoples. It was significant of the restraining force of Spanish legalism that the apologists of conquest attempted to fix on both the Incas and the Aztec lords the stigma of usurper and tyrant.

There were thoughtful Spaniards who refused to accept the comforting thesis that the Indians were barbarians and therefore had no rights which they were bound to respect. The conquerors, and the friars who accompanied them, learned early that there were Indians and Indians, and that not all of them were cannibals or brothers to the beasts. Most of them seemed true *gente de razón*, people endowed with reason and souls like themselves. They had highly organized states, like the English and the French, and in some respects their civilization appeared superior to that of Europe, as Bernal Díaz observed in Tenochtitlán.[52] Some of these peoples, they found, had an orderly society and gentle manners and a deep sense of beauty and elevated concepts of the difference between right and wrong. Such peoples deserved a better fate than was to come to them with the brutalities of conquest.[53] For the conquerors had the last word in the controversy, and in the iron path of conquest the ruins of truncated civilizations were strewn over the New World.

THE CONQUEST AS WAR

The military problem of the Conquest was very different from the conventional pattern of warfare to which Spaniards were accustomed in Europe. It is to the credit of their flexibility and ingenuity, as well as to their stamina and dogged resolution, that they adjusted their fighting habits to the new conditions so successfully and sometimes even proved superior to the Indians at their own style of warfare. The individualism, resourcefulness, and self-sufficiency of the Spanish soldier fitted him admirably for the every-man-for-himself style of combat that was the rule in the New World, where battles generally resolved themselves early into a wild and planless melee. The other most important assets of the Spaniards were steel weapons, gunpowder, horses, and dogs.

The pattern of warfare in the New World was as varied as the terrain and as the military habits and prowess of the native races. In spite of the picture drawn by Las Casas, war was endemic in the pre-Columbian world of the Americas. Whatever the motive—the excitement of combat, plunder, women, competition for hunting grounds, the greater glory of the warrior caste and captives for sacrifice to an insatiable war god, as among the Aztecs, meat for a cannibalistic bill of fare, or an imperial urge, as among the Incas—the peoples of the continent were always fighting one another. The Spaniard did not interrupt any idyllic rule of peace. A strange and unconventional enemy, he only injected the novelty of new weapons and tactics into the customary arena of their bellicosity.

The Conquest was not a miracle, wrought by the intercession of Santiago, the patron, as some of the clerical chroniclers would have us believe, of Spanish arms, nor even the work of an invincible soldiery. If in the end, most of the Indian peoples were conquered by the newcomers, it was not so much because of any disparity of individual fighting qualities as of a combination of many circumstances which favored the aggressors. Man for man —the Aztec and Chichimec of Mexico, the Carib of the Spanish Main, the Calchaquí of northern Argentina, the Guaraní of the River Plate lands, the Araucanian of Chile, and his kinsman on the Pampa—he was a worthy adversary of the redoubtable Spaniard. But the battle was seldom drawn so simply, and factors extraneous to human valor were to decide the issue.

In the conquest of Mexico, the relative weight of military strength was seriously disturbed by psychological factors of a supernatural character. The legend of the return of the "white god" Quetzalcoatl from out of the east fitted providentially into the designs of Cortés, who was quick to take advantage of any chance circumstance that might favor his daring and precarious enterprise. While Montezuma, demoralized by his fears, consulted the official necromancers, and omens and rumors filled the uneasy air of the Aztec capital, the will and power of a strong and warlike people were paralyzed with indecision. By the time the Aztecs were convinced that the Spaniards were not divine beings of their own pantheon but mortals set on their undoing, they had lost the initiative and much precious time. In Peru, old Huayna Cápac, last of the great Inca emperors, had persistent forebodings of disaster for his nation, which may have been prompted by reports of the mysterious strangers who had appeared in other parts of the continent.

At critical moments in the Conquest, a chain of fortuitous events played into the hands of the Spaniards. Thus, they arrived in Peru in the midst of a civil war, in which they were to be the only winners. Huayna Cápac had dismembered his own empire and prepared the way for its destruction by partitioning it between two of his sons, Huascar and Atahualpa.[54] Into this atmosphere of broken unity and divided loyalties the invaders brought a note of ruthless single-mindedness that was decisive. In Mexico, too, luck had been on the side of the conquerors. When Cortés learned that all was not well in Anahuac, and that the independence of the belligerent Tlascalans was a perennial canker in the Aztec body, he turned the hatred of Tlascala for its oppressors to account. He thereby gained an ally whose aid was to prove indispensable in the bitter and doubtful struggle that lay ahead. Wherever they found them in the New World, as in the rivalry of the Chibcha chieftains in Colombia, the Spaniards capitalized on the divisions among their adversaries. For there was generally one side in the local struggles which was willing to buy the efficient assistance of the Spaniards as the price of its co-operation against their own enemies. One of the conquerors once remarked that native auxiliaries had become as important in the prosecution of the Conquest as dogs were to a hunting party.

The Spaniards quickly found the weak spot in the hierarchical structure of society and as it affected the military strength of government in the more advanced Indian states. This was the helplessness of the mass of soldiery and subjects, once their exalted leader was captured or killed, as was demonstrated at Otumba and Cajamarca and on other occasions. In the same circumstances, the highly individualistic Spanish soldier went on fighting on his own responsibility.

Another advantage of the Spaniards was the superiority of their generalship. Against the military genius of Cortés and the masterly leadership of Balboa, the Pizarros, Almagro, Benalcazar, and even of an amateurish captain like Jiménez de Quesada,[55] the best of the native lords of battle generally had little more to offer than valor and devotion. Even Cuauhtemoc and Manco Capac, whose heroism is commemorated by monuments in Mexico and Lima, lacked the extra touch of greatness that was needed in the ultimate test on "the causeway" and at the siege of Cuzco. So, like Vercingetorix, the Gaul, Lobengula of the Zulus, another Indian, Pontiac, and the Spaniards' own Cid, they go down in history as superior leaders of lost causes. Probably of tougher fiber were the redoubtable Araucanian chieftains, Lautaro and Caupolicán, though as unfortunate in the final reckoning with the Spaniards.

The superior ingenuity and resourcefulness of the Spanish soldier weighed heavily on his side. Though the young *chapetones* fresh out of Spain were scorned by the veterans of the islands, they were quick to learn from experience, and learning the new ways of war was the only chance for survival. Oviedo says that the jungle campaigns of Balboa were a veritable school of conquerors. As in the particularly dangerous fighting along the Spanish Main, the Spaniard mastered the forestcraft of the Indian and learned how to take care of himself on this most trying of battlefields. Here the Conquest was an endless succession of guerrilla skirmishes, in which all the rules of conventional warfare had to be forgotten. There was no glory and little hope of reward from this kind of fighting, where hundreds of Spaniards died in agony of tetanus carried by the poisoned arrows of the Caribs, whom they seldom saw, or were horribly crippled by the effects of venom-tipped barbs which the Indians planted in the rotting mulch of their jungle paths.[56] The Spanish soldier wrapped his body in thick cotton quilting as protection against the most effective arm of the Indian. For the Indian bow could be a terrifying weapon, whether it delivered the "witches' brew" of the Caribs into the veins of the Spaniard or the Agincourt shafts with which the Indians of "Florida" impaled men and horses in Soto's expedition. On the other hand, the Indian never found adequate protection from the steel weapons of the Spaniards. When he borrowed the weapons of his enemy, he seldom learned to use them very successfully. He got little but a big noise from the harquebus when it fell into his hands, and he never became a good swordsman, though he could swing his own war club with devastating effect in close combat. The Araucanians and some of the plains Indians in Argentina adopted the Spanish lance and lengthened it. The Araucanians, who showed much skill in turning the arms and tactics of the Spaniards to their own use, used the lance in serried ranks as defense against the Spanish cavalry. The Pampas, once they tamed and mounted the wild horses about them, employed the lance as an offensive weapon in their raids. For defense, they depended on the ubiquitous bow-and-arrows and on the bolas, with which they tangled the legs of the Spaniards' horses or lassoed the riders in their saddles.

The Spaniard was quick to change his weapons as the situation demanded.[57] In jungle fighting, he tended to abandon the traditional sword and pike for the cutlasslike Basque machete, still the one indispensable tool in the rain forests of Latin America. At such times, he always carried a dagger in his belt, for use in hand-to-hand tussles or as protection against attack in the dark. He nĕver had much confidence in the clumsy firearms of the day, though he valued them for their psychological effect on the Indian and used them against his own kind in the open battles of the civil wars in Peru.

Not since Hannibal's elephants or the Mongol ponies had animals played such an important role in warfare as the horse did in the conquest of the New World. Whereas only the Spaniards' coloring was a novelty, the horse was as strange and monstrous a beast as a unicorn would have been in Spain. The Indians were awestruck by its very size and strength, and when it neighed or snorted, they would take to cover. They tried to placate its anger with gift offerings and with food which it could not eat.[58] In battle the first shock caused by the horse was as much psychological as physical, the effect of the stark terror which it inspired. Even after the initial impression of the centaur, of the identity of horse and rider, had vanished, the horse long remained a frightening thing, to be avoided or courted.

The Spaniard made the most of the Indian's attitude toward the horse. In the fury of battle his cavalry rode down the defenseless Indians without mercy and between times he cultivated the Indian's myth of the horse as a supernatural being endowed with reason and a wide range of emotion. He encouraged the Indian to remain at a distance, so that he could not familiarize himself with the limitations of the horse and learn the secret of his domination. He prohibited the civilized tribes from riding the horse, but could not prevent the roving tribes of the southern part of the continent from mastering the wild herds and turning them against their Spanish enemies.

The hippology of the Conquest is one of the most interesting phases of the early history of the Spaniard in the New World.[59] In all equine history there is probably no such roster of distinguished horses as Bernal Díaz' catalogue of the mounts of his captains and comrades.[60] The old soldier remembered their names and color and their temperaments as vividly as he recalled the idiosyncracies of his fellow men-at-arms. The Spaniard not only valued his horse as a means of transportation and reinforcement to his own strong arm, but cherished it as an inseparable companion of his wanderings and adventures. As a leader, he was liable to lavish more care and attention on his horse than on the soldiers in his command, who as Spaniards were rightly assumed to be self-reliant and able to look after their own needs.

As the Spaniard has always had the Arab's fondness for his horse, he also shared his contempt for the dog. Dogs were an auxiliary force in the Conquest, like the Indian allies and work batallions, and when some of them were alloted a share of the spoils, as Balboa's *Becerrillo* was, it was in payment for services performed. There was little sentimental attachment for these savage mastiffs and hounds, who were trained to attack hostile Indians and tear them to pieces, to track down captives who escaped, and to guard the camp at night.[61] When the fighting was over, packs of these unemployed dogs turned wild and were a scourge to the herds and flocks of the Spanish encomenderos. Then, by a strange irony, the Indian, with his penchant for pets, captured and brought up the pups to keep him company and follow him to the hunt. The ancestors of many of the mongrels whom we see about Indian settlements today came over with the conquerors.

The Spanish conquerors seem always to have been preoccupied with the problem of *ranchería* or food supply. It is a recurring obsession in the chronicle of Oviedo, who had had much practical experience with the subject. Sometimes hunger became so acute, that food was more important for the moment than gold. Balboa wrote to the king: "So far we have been more concerned with food than with gold, because we had more gold than health, and often we were more pleased to find a basket of corn than one of gold." In the more loosely organized expeditions into rough country, each soldier was liable to be his own commissary department. They quickly became very skilled at foraging and rustling for food. They operated on a feast or famine routine, but the fat days were much fewer than the lean ones. Often they never had enough to eat for months at a time, only because there was little to eat in their hungry paths, and many died of starvation. At first they hoped to solve their provisioning problem at the expense of the Indians. Sometimes, when the Indians were friendly and hospitable, the soldiers fared well as long as their hosts' food supplies lasted. But as their guests literally ate them out of house and home, the Indians took to hiding what they had and urged these human locusts to raid the stores of their neighbors. One of the Spaniard's most radiacal breaks with old habits was in the matter of eating. He learned to eat whatever was edible and early borrowed heavily from the cuisine of the aborigines. Where there was game or fish, he supplemented his food supply from those sources. In order to have fresh meat, some of the armies of the Conquest moved large droves of hogs along with them. On his long march north from Peru into the Cauca country of Colombia, Benalcázar herded over three hundred pregnant sows with him, and these roving larders became a regular feature of the better organized and more provident forays.

There was four major independent areas of the Conquest: Mexico, Peru, the Tierra Firme, and the River Plate. The two most important of the secondary areas of Conquest were Chile and Central America. There were also peripheral zones, like the Calchaquí country of northern Argentina, where the conquering movements overlapped and sometimes came into open conflict. In fact, the conquest of Central America degenerated for a time into a three-sided civil war between bands of conquerors coming from the north, the islands, and the Isthmus, or the followers, respectively of Cristóbal de Olid, Gil González Dávila, and Pedrarias.

THE CONQUEST OF MEXICO

The conquest of Mexico had a high dramatic quality unique in the over-all epic of the Conquest.[62] It was all of one piece, as the Greeks would have written it, unlike its parallel in Peru. The motif of the plot was possession of a rich and powerful state, and the argument was clear-cut and unified. The characters were worthy of Aeschylus. The rising concatenation of episode was a work of genius—the burning of the ships, the masterly stroke at Tlascala, the entrance into Tenochtitlán, the seizure of Montezuma, the seduction of Narvaez' punitive force, the flight over the causeway on "the melancholy night," the rising to the impossible at Otumba, the return, and the Homeric battles for the beleaguered and doomed city.

The conquest of Mexico was dominated by the transcendent personality of Cortés.[63] Bold, imaginative, and resourceful beyond others, with an army of half a thousand men he became one of the great captains of history. His lieutenants—Alvarado, Ordaz, and Sandoval—were brilliant soldiers, but they followed his leadership implicitly, and so long as they were within his reach, he controlled the wild ones, like Olid and Alonso de Avila. A chain of unerring decisions, made so quickly sometimes that with lesser men they would have seemed only foolhardy, marked the course of conquest under his command.[64] There was something imperial about him, even in the manner of his vanities and indulgences.[65] Later he could proudly address his own emperor as an equal, and he was the only one of the conquerors in whose presence Charles might have felt a certain uneasiness. He was certainly the ablest man that modern Spain has produced—maybe the ablest the New World has known. He was much more than the first of the conquerors. A many-sided man, he had the gifts of the states-man and he set the pattern which ruled Mexico until independence, as the efficient ghost of the Viceroy Toledo governed Peru until Ayacucho.[66] None of the other conquerors ranked his company. Valdivia approached nearest, though still afar, and Balboa might have reached the same high level if he had not been cut off so early.

Though Bernal Díaz resented Gómara's hero worship of Cortés, he was as ungrudging as the official historian in his tributes to his captain.[67] His "resources were inexhaustible," he said, and "He also possessed the heart and mind, which is the principal part of the business." Though "he was very affable with all his captains and soldiers . . . he was a strict disciplinarian" and "when Cortés ordered, no remonstrances availed," so that "never was a captain in the world better obeyed." "When we had to erect a fortress," Bernal Díaz says, "Cortés was the hardest worker in the trenches; when we went into battle, he was as forward as any of us." Here was, indeed, a man one could follow anywhere. And they followed him even to the end of his futile expedition to Honduras, which was the supreme test of his leadership. When even Sandoval threatened for a moment to turn back to Mexico,

Cortés answered that if his men refused to follow him, "there still remained soldiers in Castile." As he himself wrote to the emperor, "Fortune is always on the side of the daring." [68]

THE CONQUEST OF PERU

The conquest of Peru was less classical and more truly Spanish in its execution. There was the same superhuman daring and valor. The terrain was more difficult and there was more of it. Distances were far and the range of altitude was great and very trying to men's bodies. There was a four-dimensional quality about it all and there must have been times when it seemed to the Spaniards as though they were wandering on another planet, so unfamiliar and unreal was the face of the world about them. Peru turned out to be both more lucrative and more lethal for its conquerors. The conquest of Peru was also more confused and disorderly than that of Mexico, for soon after it attained its principal objective, the capture of Cuzco, it rapidly lost whatever unity it had and dissolved into a scramble for power. The unity of the enterprise was, in fact, doomed beforehand by its divided command.

After the intrepid dash to Cajamarca and the march up into the high heart of the dead Inca's empire, the Spaniards—only a few hundred in all—spread out over the dazed country in search of more treasure. Except for Manco Capac's long siege of Cuzco, the conquest was over. The conquerors had overthrown a vast state and dealt the death blow to one of the most intriguing civilizations men have ever come upon, but they were unable to put the fragments together again or to appreciate the value of what they had destroyed so effectively.

For a long time, Peru was a vast well of energy that often spilled over the edges in every direction. It was as though there were not enough to do in Peru and it were overcrowded with a few thousand men. So it became a secondary center of conquest, as the islands and Mexico and the Isthmus had been. From the old Tahuintinsuyu of the Incas men moved north with Benalcázar and his hogs by the Quito country over into the valley of the Cauca and across the ranges into Chibcha territory, where there were other Spaniards. South of the Lake they spread over the high Collao, where in time the Audiencia of Charcas was to rule over

Upper Peru and where they founded towns that were to became cities like La Paz and Chuquisaca or Sucre and Cochabamba and, above all, Potosí. Bands of them poured down the *quebradas* or deep ravines off the plateau and out onto the *pampa* and over to the Platine rivers, where they found the men of Paraguay. To the west of the Tucumán and Cuyo foothills and beyond the giant wall of the Cordillera, Almagro made his epic raid into the far vale of Chile and later Valdivia crossed the Atacama to lay the foundations of a proud new province for Spain. The matted green wilderness to the east of the mountains seemed to exert an almost morbid fascination on the conquerors. Several of them yielded to the spell of the jungle, as Jiménez de Quesada did far to the north, and all of them with the same tragic results, for they refused to learn from experience as the Incas did. Only Alonso de Alvarado, a man very capable and reliable, showed any judgment and good sense when he ventured out of the high sierra in the direction of the Amazon. For he kept to the semitropical *montaña,* where nature still observed some rules that a Spaniard could understand, and did not allow himself to get lost in the low country beyond the ridges. And he left towns, like Chachapoyas and Moyobamba, that have endured to this day and whose inhabitants are still more Spanish than those of most of the towns of Peru. The others, including Gonzalo Pizarro and Peranzures and Pedro de Candia, the stubborn and slow-witted Greek artilleryman, left only their delusions and the bones of most of their followers.[69] They plunged headlong into the jungle with their Indian carriers —some with gentle Inca women or *coyas*—and with horses and dogs. In the extremity of their hunger they ate their horses. The Indians melted away in the forest from starvation or because their bodies were not made for the heavy atmosphere of the lowlands, or they disappeared and reverted to savagery. Those who came back to the mountains were tattered ghosts of men. Of those who did not return were Francisco de Orellana, Gonzalo's lieutenant, and some fifty others, who discovered the Amazon and crossed the continent on its waters.

With the end of the Conquest, no peace came to the conquered land. Instead, the high adventure of conquest degenerated into the anarchy of civil war, into a brutal free-for-all among men of the same race. The dragon's teeth of discord were sowed and the harvest was hate and treason and death. At first, it was the Almagristas, "the men of Chile," against the Pizarros or against Vaca de Castro, the king's man; then the rebellion of Gonzalo Pizarro against the royal power, that was represented by the Viceroy Núñez Vela and by Pedro de la Gasca; and, finally, the flare-up of the malcontents under Hernández Girón, with his armed company of black slaves and his circus train of fortune-tellers, oracles, astrologers, palmists and necromancers.[70] The Conquest had come to a sorry end, and it was high time for the great Viceroy Toledo to set things right, though the spirit of disorder of the civil wars was to survive the repression of Gasca and Toledo to find a perennial outlet in the turbulent life of Potosí.

Cieza de León has told the story of chaos and demoralization. "From that time," he wrote, "began the period when confidence and faith were overthrown and men looked upon cruel civil war as a profitable occupation."[71] He said that the soldiers in Peru joined the rebellion of Gonzalo Pizarro "because they delighted in war and hated peace." "This land is the Devil!" cried the tragic Núñez Vela; "Great are the evils which surround it. Never are those who live in it at peace with one another." Then he asked in despair: "In whom can I put trust?"[72] The factions hated each other with a ferocious hatred. After the disaster of Las Salinas, Almagro said to his jailer, Alonso de Toro: "At last you are going to drink my blood"; to which his enemy replied: "And that is the greatest good fortune that God could grant me."[73] Of the savage battle of Chupas, where men became feral in their hate, Cieza wrote: "Swords clashed down on helmets, stunning their bearers, and cut through coats of mail; then, pausing for a short space, men glared at each other like bulls in the rutting season."[74] At night, marauding Indians would strip the wounded of their clothes on the battlefield and leave them to die of the cold. Gradually, as the years went on, nearly all the leaders of the Conquest were immolated in the fury of their own passions and violence—executed, assassinated, or killed in battle. Soto went off to the north and Valdivia to the south, and each died before his time. By some strange chance—or divine mercy?—the three captains who survived the multiple hazards of Peru—Lorenzo de Aldana, Alonso de Alvarado, and the father of the Inca Garcilaso—were among the noblest of the conquerors.

Except in his iron resolution, Francisco Pizarro was a lesser figure than Cortés.[75] Once the pressure of the common danger was relaxed, he could neither dominate the centrifugal forces that inevitably asserted themselves in his command, nor win these wild wills to him by the magic of his person, as Cortés could have—or as Balboa might have done, if Pizarro had not arrested him that night in Darien so long ago. For the land he had taken, he had no policy. His contemporaries had little good to say of him. Oviedo, for example, while not questioning his personal valor, said that he was not suited to govern others, and that he lacked the skill and mental equipment needed for his high position in Peru. According to Herrera, "his thoughts were strangers to his promises."

Of the Pizarro brothers, the ablest was Hernando, who was removed from circulation early in the course of the Conquest and immured in the strongest castle in Spain. However, he was in Peru long enough to become its evil genius. A swaggering and decisive man, burly of body, arrogant, ruthless, and faithless, as sharp of tongue as of wits, he alienated his companions and looked down his red bulbous nose at his older half-brother, the pig-driving bastard who had become a Marquis of Spain.[76]

According to Oviedo, the Pizarros had come out of Spain "as proud as they were poor." [77] Except for young Juan, who was a general favorite of his comrades and was killed at the siege of Cuzco, Gonzalo was the most attractive of the brothers.[78] There was a certain magnanimity about him, and there was a knightly splendor about his person, as there was about Pedro de Alvarado. The Indians generally warmed to him, which was high praise for any of the conquerors of Peru. He bedeviled the land with his rebellions, but it might have been better in the end if he had set up his independent Kingdom of Peru, half Spanish, half Incaic. It was a daring conception, whether it was his or Carbajal's, and though the ratio would probably have changed, it might have saved more of what was worth preserving of the native civilization. But because he lacked the moral courage and the imagination to take the ultimate step, and because he, too, in the final reckoning was only a soldier, though a very magnificent one, he failed and Peru became instead a Spanish satrapy for nearly three hundred years.

Diego de Almagro, Adelantado of New Toledo and original partner of the Marquis, was a natural leader of men, a great soldier's soldier, an earth-bound Ulysses.[79] But all that was not enough, either for his own salvation or the good of Peru. He trusted in bonds of old comradeship that no longer held and lacked the guile to meet the Pizarros on their own ground. He was strangled by orders of Hernando after the Battle of Las Salinas, and his death set off the gigantic vendetta among the conquerors that poisoned the atmosphere of Peru for many years.

Rodrigo Orgóñez, Almagro's loyal and devoted captain, and a mighty man of war, who had urged his chief to do away with Hernando and Gonzalo when he had them in his power, died, too, at Las Salinas, beheaded on the spot by the soldiers to whom he surrendered. "Many surrounded him," said Herrera, "and he fought against all of them, wounding many." [80]

Francisco Carbajal had been a soldier long before most of his fellow conquerors were born and had become infinitely wise in the ways of war. Only Valdivia of those who fought in Peru was his peer as a captain, and though the doughty Centeno was an adversary to be respected, he was never the equal of the terrible old battler. Known to his diabolical generation as "the Demon of the Andes," and "Enemy of the human race," the implacable Carbajal was cruel and pitiless to all who were on the other side, whether at the time it was the king's side or the side of rebellion. Strong men dreaded his domineering presence, the quick play of his wits made them seem to themselves dumb clods, and his blistering tongue left men strangely stripped of their pride and self-confidence.[81] The only person on earth whose remonstrances he ever heeded was his Portuguese wife. He was given to grim jests, even on the most tragic occasions, including that of his own execution. At eighty-four, when his end came, he was still a man of tireless energy and prodigious fortitude, who slept when he had to, in a hard chair or nodded in the saddle while he drove his men through the mountains by night like someone possessed. His unconventional appearance set him apart from his fellows. He did not wear a shining helmet and armor, but a slouch hat with rooster feathers for a panache and an old black cape. And he did not ride an Arab charger, as any Spanish *caballero* of position would insist on, but a mule, who, like his master, was not interested in fanfare and paraphernalia, but only in arriving intact at wherever he had set out for.

THE FAR COUNTRIES

The conquest of the Tierra Firme, or Spanish Main, from the Isthmus around to the Peninsula of Paría, and its hinterland began with the expeditions of Ojeda and Nicuesa in 1509. It continued as a series of disconnected ventures until the various Indian tribes had been exterminated, pacified, or otherwise reconciled to Spanish rule.[82] Considering its extent, the nature of the terrain, and the lack of a strong native state ruling over a large territory, there could be no unity to the conquest of this wide area. The series of disjointed *entradas* proceeded inland from some point on the long coast, like Darien, Urabá, Cartagena, Santa Marta, Coro, or Cumaná. The most impressive and generally successful expedition was that of Jiménez de Quesada into the Colombian highlands. Much of this phase of the Conquest was jungle and hill fighting at its worst. As a rule, the Indians were extremely savage and belligerent, and the warfare was correspondingly bitter and pitiless on both sides. It was in this area and its backlands that Balboa and Andagoya, Bastidas and Heredia, César and Vadillo and Robledo, operated.

Of this select company, Balboa was easily first. Oviedo, who knew him well, said that on the Isthmus "Vasco Nuñez was everything. . . . He was much superior to all the others."[83] He was ambitious and "had his thoughts directed towards power." "He was not given to spending his time in idleness." Reading Balboa's long letter to the king, written on January 20, 1513, one is aware how much Spain and her empire in the New World lost with the early death of this very wise and strong leader.

The River Plate lands comprehend an area of vast extent in what is now Argentina, Uruguay, Paraguay, and Bolivia. Spaniards moved into this vacuum from various directions—northward by way of the main river itself, overland from the Brazilian coast, down out of the high Charcas country of Upper Peru or Bolivia, and from over the Andes in Chile. After the initial failure at Buenos Aires, Asuncíon became the center from which bands radiated out far and wide to found new towns, like Sante Fé and Santa Cruz de la Sierra, or to refound old ones, like Buenos Aires.

There were no large and highly organized Indian nations to contend with and Spaniards and Indians sometimes learned to live peaceably together after the initial hostilities, as they did in Paraguay. From very early the Spaniards were as much colonizers as conquerors in this open frontier country. The gold and silver for which they had originally come had proven a delusion, so they tended to settle down in some pleasant spot to enjoy the rustic satisfactions of an unconfined existence, and where they were free to wander aimlessly when the old mood was upon them.[84] For the country was open and the rivers ran invitingly across the land and horses were plentiful.

The conquest of Chile was an extension of that of Peru. Almagro's expedition—down behind the east side of the mountains, then over the passes into the Mapocho country, and back across the implacable desert to Cuzco—was only a raid, a reconnoitering foray, but the greatest of all the Conquest. The real work of conquest was done, or at least initiated, by Pedro de Valdivia and his lieutenants and successors—Aguirre, Villagra, Monroy of the golden stirrups, and Hurtado de Mendoza. It was never quite finished.

This was the ultima Thule of the Conquest. Here, on the far edge of the world, the Vale of Chile was in reality an alluring island, bounded on four sides by desert, mountains, forest, and ocean. The forest was the habitat of the Araucanians, but into the gale-swept region of the archipelago not even they would go. For a long time it offered little but dangers and hardships to those who came into it. There was little reward except in strength of character—and the conquerors brought that with them. In the end they were to possess something more valuable than gold or silver in the favored land itself. But for many years the price of survival was constant vigilance and alarms. There were only a handful of Spaniards at any time, but their desperate position called forth a courage beyond the ordinary meed of their race. Their settlements were destroyed by their relentless enemies and their isolated garrison posts were wiped out, but by some miracle of Spanish tenacity, the little community was never overwhelmed by the numbers that threatened to engulf it time and again. Finally, its roots were too deep in the land for it ever to be driven from it.

There were only 150 men in the original band and one woman, Inés Suárez, Valdivia's mistress, as brave as the rest.[85] Fourteen of these immortals of Chile including the Negro, Juan Valiente, a fugitive slave from Mexico, and one of Almagro's host. One third of them died in battle with the Indians. Seven of them were hanged and two more were beheaded. Four others died violent deaths. Fourteen of them left Chile, most of them for Peru, and did not return. The rest of them lived out their lives in the colony they had founded. Valdivia came to Chile in 1540, five years after Almagro's expedition. A quarter of a century later, in 1565, there were not over 1,500 Spaniards in Chile. The ratio of those killed in battle had remained the same. At that time, according to a Chilean writer, there were probably some 20,000 mestizos in the land. A Spanish resident of Santiago wrote in that year that there were from two to eight mestizos in each house in the town.

Archetype of the conquerors of Chile was Francisco de Aguirre.[86] This prodigious figure was an hidalgo of Estremadura, and when he left for the Indies he was already a veteran soldier of the Italian wars and had been *corregidor* of his home town, Talavera de la Reina. He took his six-year-old son with him to the New World, where he was joined twenty-three years later by his wife and four other children. In the meantime, as the father of at least fifty mestizo children, he did much to make the new Chilean race. Arrived in Peru, he joined lustily in the work of conquest and when Valdivia set out for Chile, Aguirre met him in the Atacama with twenty-five horsemen and went along with him. He was one of the founders—and first Alcalde, of Santiago, Lieutenant-Governor of the Colony, founder of La Serena, and Governor of Tucumán on the other side of the mountains. More cultivated than most of his fellows, he was belligerent and indomitable. He lived and fought with enormous gusto. War was a game to him and Chile and much of Argentina his playground. He made a fortress of his home, wherever it was, with a cannon on the roof, but he was not a reposeful person and preferred to spend his time on the warpath with a small troop of his retainers, striking terror into his enemies, Indian or Spanish. His last warlike deed was to defeat and drive back to their ship a company of Drake's men, who had sacked Valparaiso. Three years later he passed away in the pleasant town of La Serena, with as much serenity as he was capable of. That was in 1581, over forty years after he had come to Chile with Valdivia. He was then well along in his seventies. He was loud-mouthed and blasphemous, and his terrible oaths got him into long trouble with the Inquisition, from whose clutches he always emerged more irreverent than before. Before he died he had lost in the king's service three of his four Spanish sons, a son-in-law, a brother, three nephews—and a princely fortune.

THE WORK OF COLONIZATION

The Conquest was burned out and so were the men who had made it. They had spent their energies in a thousand battles and exhausting marches through desert, mountains, and jungles. They had earned a rest, and it was well for the future of the new Spanish empire that they were ready to retire. From the very beginning, when ever there had been a lull in the fighting for long and no gold was in prospect, they had turned to farming or stock raising or trading. The animals multiplied rapidly in the islands, and when the call went out for a new expedition, there were plenty of horses to take along and pork and *charqui* to feed the force in the initial stages of the *entrada*. Now all this was over, and they settled down for good. Some of them went back to the land, for which they always felt a strong attachment, and if they had received an encomienda as a reward for their services, they lived with their Indian retainers and tenants about them. Sometimes they followed again a trade which they had practiced before the wars. At any rate, the conquistadores were the first *pobladores* or colonizers. They gradually fell into the ways of the new civilian order of things and became an integral part of it. When Juan Jufre, one of Valvidia's lieutenants, asked the king in 1553 for a piece of land at the foot of the Cerro de San Cristóbal on which to build a mill, he wrote: "I am conqueror, colonist, and sustainer—of the first who served your Majesty in this Province—and I have married in this land, and I wish to perpetuate myself in it." [87] However, like the proud and cantankerous old veterans they were, they always continued to carp at the way the new officialdom from Spain ran things.

There may have been times when the conquerors had as deep a

satisfaction from the plants and animals which they introduced into the country as they did from their military exploits.[88] Bernal Díaz was very proud to have planted the first orange trees in Mexico.[89] His concern for such things was one of the redeeming features of Pizarro's career. Cieza tells of the visit of the conqueror's future assassin to the garden of Pizarro's home in Lima: "Then the Marquis, with his own hand, plucked half a dozen oranges from the tree, being the first that were borne in that country and gave them to Juan de Herrada." [90] This incident was symbolic of the change that had come over Peru since the break between the Pizarros and Almagro's "men of Chile." For a brief spell, there was promise of peace in Peru and, in the work of Herrera, "there began to be harvests of wheat and barley and many other crops of Castile—and there was good order and quietude in the towns of the Castilians." The first wheat was brought to Peru by Doña María de Escobar, wife of one of the conquerors.[91] For several years she nurtured the increase from her few seed grains, until she had enough to distribute to encomenderos in the neighborhood. Grapes were first grown in Peru by Francisco de Caravantes. Later Captain Bartolomé de Terrazas planted vines near Cuzco and when they had grown to a good size, he sent thirty Indians, loaded with the grapes, to the father of the Inca Garcilaso.

From the earliest period of the Conquest, men came to the New World, not as soldiers, but as civilians. Columbus tried to bring over farmers who would devote their full time to work on the land and Las Casas attempted to found an agricultural colony of Spaniards. The registers of persons licensed to go to the Indies reveal the names and trades of many artisans and craftsmen, and illustrate the growing complexity of the civilian societies that were already springing up in the colonies.[92] Among those who received permits to cross the Atlantic in 1509 were Jorge de Vitoria, farmer; Diego Pérez, farmer and muleteer; Pero Cid, merchant; and Antonio Ruíz, horticulturist. The next year's list included a druggist, four shoemakers, a cutler, and a Flemish smelter and assayist. Thereafter the occupational index becomes steadily more diversified. In 1511, a carpenter, a barber, an engraver, a tailor, a painter, a blacksmith, and a bootmaker were granted permission to migrate to the colonies. A hosier and a cartmaker were added the next year. In 1513, the following occupations appear for the first time on the registers: silversmith, money-changer, candlemaker, miner, plasterer, cloth shearer. Other passengers were Master Jerónimo, "surgeon toothpuller," and his son, assistant, and servant. The same year, Diego García, of Seville, took out a company that consisted of his sister Inés; Inés Fernández as duenna; Sebastían de Mendoza, probably the first professional *vaquero* to come to the New World; Alonso Martín, shepherd; Alonso de Andújar, fruit farmer; Francisco, a mule driver; and two others. In 1514, Miguel Ruíz, barber of Seville, crossed over with another barber and three carpenters. Many stonemasons were needed to construct the solid new towns, and in 1510 eight masons went out "to build and erect the churches of Hispaniola." Other trades which show up in the lists are turners, embroiderers, locksmiths, bakers, potmakers, tankers, armorers, and swordsmiths. In 1535, Master Hernando, fencing master, went out to the Tierra Firme. The same year, Master Esteban, probably the first printer in South America, was licensed to accompany Mendoza's expedition to the River Plate. As Mendoza's personal physician there also went Dr. Hernando de Zamora. When García de Lerma was appointed Governor of Santa Marta in 1528, his company included five stonemasons, a carpenter, two plasterers, a swordsmith, a druggist, a barber, a tailor, a chef, and a pastry cook.[93]

The evolution of a settled society in Paraguay offers an interesting example of the transition between conquest and colony. Asunción was founded by the hardy survivors of Mendoza's ambitious project, who worked their way up the river until they found a site that suited their fancy. For a while they carried on rather aimless warfare with the various Guaraní tribes up and down the river and in and out the back country. However, the Indians had nothing except women which the Spaniards particularly coveted, and since there were women enough to go around and ample space to live in, both sides came to accept one another's presence without further ado. Among themselves, the new colonists were a quarrelsome and complaining lot, but it was a rich and inviting country they had come to, and eventually age and their gentle womenfolk and the charm of the land tamed the old wildness in them. "It is a very pleasant land," wrote Herrera, "of many waters and woods, and it is fertile and lovely." For many years they lived in this pleasant eddy of the Conquest isolated from the world they had left. They forgot all their dreams of glory and riches and their memories of Spain grew dim with the years. This was home to them and they made the most of it. There were no luxuries, but there was a rustic plenty and all the simple satisfactions of life were at hand. The finery they had originally brought with them was well worn out and they dressed in cotton trousers and broad-brimmed straw hats and shoes they made from the leather they had tanned. They took up again old trades they had long since abandoned and learned new skills that were necessary to the rudimentary economy of the colony. Among them there were carpenters and coopers, sawyers and shipwrights, cordage makers and basketweavers, blacksmiths and shoemakers.[94] One of the most useful citizens of Asunción was Richard Lincoln, of Plymouth, England, one of its three blacksmiths, in whose shop there was a forge, an anvil, three hammers, and two pairs of tongs. He and his fellows made nails and fishhooks and other light hardware for the daily needs of the colonists, as well as shoes for their horses and spurs for their stirrups. When Cabeza de Vaca was Governor, he petitioned that no lawyers be allowed to come out to the colony, "because in newly settled countries they encourage dissensions and litigation among the people." [95] Balboa was as insistent that the king keep all lawyers out of Darien and for the same reason. Bernal Díaz also says that a memorial from the conquerors of Mexico asked "that his Majesty would be pleased not to suffer any scholars or men of letters to come into this country, to throw us into confusion with their learning, quibbling and books." [96]

In time the colony took on the special character which the country still has. The mestizo children whom the conquerors begat in such profusion grew up about them and took over with new vitality and enterprise where their fathers had left off. Eventually there were no longer Spaniards or Guaranís, but only Paraguayans and the process was complete.

Though seldom with the same finality and usually with many variations according to the particular local ingredients, a similar process went on in other parts of the New World. As a rule, a Spanish minority, steadily replenished by immigration from the

Peninsula, maintained its identity as a ruling class. Costa Rica, where the Spaniards were a majority, vegetated uneventfully for centuries, a forgotten Arcadia off the beaten track of colonial travel. As miscegenation proceeded along with the interminable tensions with the Araucanians, Chile, too, assumed the form it was to keep. In Mexico and Peru, the structure of colonial society remained much more complex, like their social composition and economic organization. Whatever the ethnic and cultural elements in the situation, the pressure of Spain on custom was always greater in centers of authority like Mexico City and Lima than it was in towns that were creole or frankly Indian in their atmosphere and temper, like Asunción or Cuzco. But the pressure never could be heavy or persistent enough to make over these mixed communities in the image of Spain, even if she had been so unwise as to will it so. So they kept enough variety to identify them from one another, even though their law and religion and the dominant language became Spanish and the peculiar genius of Spain entered deep into their thinking and their ways of doing.

THE PORTUGUESE IN BRAZIL

The Portuguese taking of Brazil was more an affair of occupation and colonization than of outright conquest.[97] It was no more a conquest, in fact, than was our opening of the West, and for much the same reasons. There were immense spaces of land only sparsely inhabited by primitive Indians, so that no large-scale military operations were necessary. The Portuguese only wanted to get on with the business of living off the land as quickly—and profitably—as possible. They were few in numbers and did not want to advertise to the world what they were doing, as the Spaniards did in their sublime indifference to all other peoples. They had trouble enough keeping the French off the premises. Nor did they trust their Spanish cousins to observe the Line of Demarcation, so they pushed out across the wilderness and marked their frontiers with incongruous stone forts in the jungle.

They had had their great experience in the Orient, and now they expected no glamorous returns in riches or adventure from this land of dyewoods and parrots and naked women who greeted them on the long beaches. They were a practical people and had not crossed the Atlantic for the fun of it. They set out to make a paying investment of their great raw colony with sugar and other unromantic goods for which there was a steady and profitable market in Europe. In the process they set up a rural society, founded on Negro slavery after trial of Indian labor had failed, that was singularly successful in serving the purpose for which it was founded. Those who had the inclination for adventure struck across into the unknown wastes as the Bandeirantes, the tough frontiersmen who really sealed the future of Brazil as one country.

NOTES

1. Bernal Díaz del Castillo, *The True History of the Conquest of Mexico*, p. 549. Written in Guatemala in 1568, the *Verdadera Relación* was published in an abridged form in 1632, and in its entirety in Mexico City in 1904–5. The Hakluyt Society issued an English translation in 5 volumes between 1908 and 1916. References are to the Maurice Keating translation (1 vol., New York, 1927).

2. *Ibid.*, p. 562.

3. *Ibid.*, p. 160.

4. *Ibid.*, p. 165.

5. *The Discovery of America* (2 vols., Boston, 1895), II, 260.

6. *Letters of Cortés* (tr. from the Spanish, 2 vols., New York, 1908), I, 225.

7. Garcilaso de la Vega, *Historia General del Perú* (3 vols., Buenos Aires, 1946), I, 43.

8. Gonzalo Fernández de Oviedo y Valdés, *Historia General y Natural de las Indias, Islas y Tierra Firme del Mar Océano* (4 vols., Madrid, 1851–55), IV, 185. An interesting sidelight on the economics of the Conquest is related by Oviedo. The total value of Atahualpa's ransom was calculated at 1,326,539 pesos for the gold, plus 51,610 *marcos* of silver. As examples of the inflated prices which resulted from the suddenly accumulated buying power of the conquerors: a horse sold for from 2,500 to 35,000 gold pesos; a jug of wine, 60 pesos; a Flemish cape, 100 to 120 pesos; a sword, 40 to 50 pesos; a clove of garlic, ½ peso. *Ibid.*, pp. 200-01.

9. *Ibid.*, p. 202.

10. *De Orbe Novo* (tr. from the Latin, 2 vols., New York, 1912), I, 247. The first part of this work was published at Alcalá in 1516, and the first complete version appeared in 1530. "Cabotto (Sebastian Cabot) frequents my house, and I have him sometimes at my table." *Ibid.*, p. 348.

11. Bernal Díaz, *op. cit.*, p. xxvi.

12. Cieza de León, *Civil Wars of Peru: The War of Las Salinas* (tr. from the Spanish, London, 1923), p. 88. Two other books in the same series are *The War of Chupas* (London, 1918), and *The War of Quito* (London, p. 1913). References are to the Hakluyt Society editions.

13. Oviedo, *op. cit.*, I, 73.

14. *Ibid.*, p. 5.

15. Probably the best one-volume history of the Spanish conquest is F. A. Kirkpatrick, *The Spanish Conquistadores* (London, 1934). For an interesting analysis of the character and motives of the conquerors, see Rufino Blanco Fombona, *El Conquistador Español del Siglo XVI* (Madrid, 1922), especially pp. 15, 201, 241-44, 263-64.

16. See Walter Prescott Webb, *The Great Frontier* (Boston, 1952).

17. Oviedo tells of the fate of the large company that came out to the Isthmus with Pedrarias. Many died in the *entradas* against the Indians—"this hellish hunt and chase." In the port town of Santa María del Antigua de Darién, which Balboa had established, many fell down dead in the streets from starvation. Fifteen to twenty died each day in the miserable town, until in a little while over 500 had perished. *Op. cit.*, III, 37.

18. According to Ulrich Schmidel, the German soldier, who was one of the survivors, when Juan de Ayolas took the remainder of Mendoza's force upriver to Paraguay, only 560 were left of the original 2,500, and half of these died on the river voyage. *Viaje al Rio de la Plata* (tr. from the German, Buenos Aires, 1942), pp. 22, 23. Later, on a long expedition to the west of the Paraguay River, Ayolas, with about 80 Spaniards, was beaten to death by Indians who had assured them of their friendship.

19. Oviedo lists the names of twenty who suffered "the curse of the adelantados" and the manner of their passing. *Op. cit.*, II, 189.

20. One of the mutinous soldiers who killed Bastidas was a son of the great Castilian linguist and humanist, Antonio de Lebrija. Oviedo called the dishonor to his illustrious father "a monstrous thing of infamy." *Op. cit.*, II, 343.

21. "Dying of leprosy, he willed funds for the perpetual supply of water to travellers athirst on the mountain trail to Bogotá." John Eoghan Kelly, *Pedro de Alvarado, Conquistador* (Princeton, N. J., 1932), p. VII.

22. *Compendium and Description of the West Indies* (tr. from the Spanish, Washington, D. C., 1942), p. 96.

23. "He was a man the like of whom never appeared again in all the annals of the conquest, and, but for an evil turn of fortune and the ill-will that he evoked by his protection of the Indians, he would have gone down to history as the first figure amongst all the conquerors." Robert Bontine Cunninghame Graham, *The Conquest of the River Plate* (New York, 1924), p. 5. See also *ibid.*, p. 158. Of his overland march from the Brazilian coast to the Paraguay River, Oviedo wrote: "On so long a journey he did not lose a single man nor did he fight with the Indians of these provinces, so that he arrived with his force intact at Asuncion." *Op. cit.*, ii, 189. According to Herrera, "Alvar Núñez took particular care to keep the Indians contented. . . . He understood well the nature of the barbarians."

24. *Op. cit.*, II, 265.

25. Bernal Díaz, *op. cit.*, *passim*.

26. *"Ojos de cascabel."* See Fray Pedro Simón, *Historia de la Expedición de Pedro de Ursua al Marañón y de las Aventuras de Lope de Aguirre* (reprint, Lima, 1942; originally published in 1627), p. 180. See also Adolph F. Bandelier, *The Gilded Man and Other Pictures of the Spanish Occupancy of America* (New York,

1893), p. 95; and "Letter of Lope de Aguirre to Philip II (1561)," in A. Curtis Wilgus, ed., *Readings in Latin American Civilization* (New York, 1946), p. 49.

27. Cieza de León said of Almagro that "his lineage began and ended with himself." *The War of Las Salinas, op. cit.,* p. 223.

28. "These discoverers of new countries ruined and exhausted themselves by their own folly and civil strife." Peter Martyr, *op. cit.,* I, 217. "But for the jealousy of the Spaniards, who can never agree amongst themselves . . . all these countries would already be conquered. . . . Each is the declared enemy of his companions in this dusty squabble of ambition, which blinds them." *Ibid.,* p. 340. In respect to the three-cornered civil war in Central America between Cristóbal de Olid, Gil González Dávila, and the lieutenants of Pedrarias, he says: "The Spaniards, who cannot bear to work together, kill one another as soon as they meet." II, 413.

29. Oviedo, *op. cit.,* II, 383.

30. *The War of Chupas, op. cit.,* p. 29.

31. *Ibid.,* p. 57.

32. Oviedo, *op. cit.,* I, 179.

33. *Ibid.,* II, 313. Sir Walter Raleigh, who underwent many hardships on the Orinoco, wrote: "Neither am I so farre in love with that lodging, watching, care, perill, diseases, ill savours, bad fare, and many other mischiefes that accompany these voyages, as to woo my selfe againe into any of them, were I not assured that the Sunne covereth not so much riches in any part of the earth." In Hakluyt, *Voyages* (Everyman's Library), VII, 327.

34. Heredia was an extremely competent conqueror. See Oviedo, *op. cit.,* II, 451.

35. After his execution, "The Indians all mourned, saying that Almagro was a good captain, from whom they always received kind treatment." Cieza de León, *The War of Las Salinas, op. cit.,* p. 222. Of Gonzalo Pizarro, Cieza said: "Always just and inclined to mercy, he never put anyone to death without trial. On his return to Lima he enacted some excellent laws for the protection of the Indians. Gasca (who had him executed) confessed that Gonzalo Pizarro was a good governor." *The War of Quito, op. cit.,* p. 158.

36. When Lorenzo de Aldana, one of the better conquerors of Peru, died in 1571, he left all his wealth to be invested for the payment of the tribute or poll tax levied by the crown on the Indians who lived on his estates. *Ibid.,* p. 74.

37. Don Quixote said: "War is a school where the covetous grow free, and the free prodigal; to see a soldier a miser is a kind of prodigy which happens but seldom."

38. "That image and statue of the Sun (made out of a huge slab of gold) fell by lot at the capture of that imperial city by the Spaniards, to a valiant pioneer by the name of Mancio Sierra de Leguisamo. They say he was a great gambler and he gambled it away in one night, which gave rise to the saying: He gambles the sun away before it rises." Vázquez de Espinosa, *op. cit.,* p. 561.

39. *The Travels of Pedro de Cieza de León, A.D. 1532–50* (tr. from the Spanish, London, 1864), p. 95.

40. Bernard Moses, *The Spanish Dependencies in South America* (2 vols., New York, 1914), I, 153.

41. *The War of Las Salinas, op. cit.*, p. 201.

42. Bernal Díaz, *op. cit.*, p. 207.

43. *Ibid.*, p. 358.

44. Of the financial troubles of the conquerors, Bernal Díaz wrote: "Among the soldiers of our army very heavy debts were contracted; a crossbow was sold for 50 crowns, a musket cost 100, a horse 800, 1,000, and even more; and everything else was in proportion. Then one surgeon, Maestre Juan, charged high, as did a Doctor Murcia, who was an apothecary and barber. There were besides various other money traps, all of which were to be satisfied out of our dividends." *Ibid.*, p. 365.

45. In Charles C. Griffin, ed., *Concerning Latin-American Culture* (New York, 1940), p. 53. "The soul of the conquistador combined audacity with covetousness, superstition with cruelty, the pride of the hidalgo with the rigour of the ascetic, a rigid individualism and a thirst for glory with an infallible faith in the greatness of his own destiny." Francisco García Calderón, *Latin America: Its Rise and Progress* (tr. from the French, London, 1915), p. 45.

46. "A captain of conquistadores had to be, above all, a man of business, with capital and credit and enterprise." Carlos Pereyra, *Las Huellas de los Conquistadores* (Madrid, n. d.), p. 89. Sir Arthur Helps called Cortés "a consummate man of business." *The Spanish Conquest in America* (4 vols., London, 1855), III, 10. Germán Arciniegas lists the following "capitalists" among the early discoverers and conquerors: Diego Velásquez, whom Cortés left in the lurch in Cuba; Bastidas and Fernández de Lugo, on the Spanish Main; Pedro de Mendoza, in the River Plate; the Pinzón brothers, backers and colleagues of Columbus; and the German concessionaires of Charles V. *El Estudiante de la Mesa Redonda* (Santiago, Chile, 1936), p. 93. After Juan de Vadillo had spent over 50,000 gold pesos in outfitting his expedition into the interior of Colombia, his men deserted him at Cali to join Benalcázar, and he went on to Peru to try his fortune anew. Oviedo, *op. cit.*, II, 462.

47. The coat of arms of Elcano consisted of a globe, with the inscription, "You first sailed around me." Diego Méndez, when Columbus was shipwrecked on Jamaica, crossed to Hispaniola in an Indian canoe and walked from its west coast to the city of Santo Domingo, to bring help for the Admiral. "As a reward for his loyalty, the King gave him a coat of arms with the same canoe on it." Oviedo, *op. cit.*, I, 79.

48. See Garcilaso de la Vega, *Historia General, op. cit.*, II, 378; Pereyra, *op. cit.*, pp. 266-7; Charles Edward Chapman, *Hispanic America: Colonial and Republican* (New York, 1937). p. 32. Oviedo lists the names and places of origin of the 54 men who first descended the Amazon. Among the Estremeños, Orellana and three others were of Trujillo, the home town of the Pizarros, two of Badajoz, and two of the locality of Medellín. There were eight from the southwest corner of Andalusia including three from Palos and four from Moguer. There were three Basques, three Asturianos, two Gallegos, and two Portuguese. *Op. cit.*, IV, 384-5.

49. *The War of Las Salinas, op. cit.*, p. 40.

50. Of the experience of Cortés with the *requerimiento*, see his letters to the emperor, *op. cit.*, I, 147, 150, 156.

51. "The Spanish conquest of America was far more than a remarkable mili-

tary and political exploit. . . . It was also one of the greatest attempts the world has seen to make Christian precepts prevail in the relations between peoples. This attempt became basically a spirited defense of the rights of the Indians, which rested on two of the most fundamental assumptions a Christian can make: namely, that all men are equal before God, and that a Christian has a responsibility for the welfare of his brothers, no matter how alien or lowly they may be. . . . No other European people, before or since the conquest of America, plunged into such a struggle for justice as developed among Spaniards shortly after the discovery of America and persisted throughout the 16th century. The struggle occurred because of the widespread concern felt by soldiers, ecclesiastics, and the crown that all Spain's laws and actions in America be just." Lewis Hanke, *The Spanish Struggle for Justice in the Conquest of America* (Philadelphia, 1949), p. 1. On the question of *right* in the Spanish title of conquest, see also Silvio Zavala, *Ensayos sobre la Colonización Española en América* (Buenos Aires, 1944).

52. Cortés said of the Aztecs: "They live civilly and reasonably," that is, according to European standards of living and the dictates of reason. *Op. cit.,* I, 165.

53. Of his siege of the Aztec capital, Cortés wrote: "Seeing that the people of the city were so rebellious, and displayed such determination to die as no race had ever shown, I knew not what means to adopt . . . to avoid utterly destroying their city, which was the most beautiful thing in the world." *Ibid.,* II, 107.

54. "And had this Guaincapa (Huayna Capac) been alive when we Spaniards entered this land, it would have been impossible for us to win it, for he was much beloved by all his vassals." Pedro Pizarro, *Relation of the Discovery and Conquest of the Kingdoms of Peru* (tr. from the Spanish, 2 vols., New York, 1921), I, 199.

55. On Jiménez de Quesada, see Germán Arciniegas, *The Knight of El Dorado* (tr. from the Spanish, New York, 1942); Robert Bontine Cunninghame Graham, *The Conquest of New Granada* (London, 1922). Oviedo called him an "honorable man, of gentle understanding, and very able." *Op. cit.,* II, 378.

56. Juan de la Cosa and seventy or eighty of his men were killed by poisoned arrows at Turbaco on the Gulf of Urabá. Alonso de Ojeda, one of the most daring of the first conquistadores, was also shot by a poisoned arrow and had red-hot irons put on the wound to cauterize it. Pereyra, *op. cit.,* p. 170. Ojeda, noted for his great physical prowess, ultimately died on Hispaniola as a result of his wounds and hardships. "When he knew he was going to die, he wrapped himself in the robe of a Franciscan friar, very tired and sick and angry at all the trials and ill fortune which he had suffered." Oviedo, *op. cit.,* II, 423.

57. On the weapons employed by both sides, see Alberto Mario Salas, *Las Armas de la Conquista* (Buenos Aires, 1950).

58. On his expedition into Honduras, Cortés abandoned a lame horse among the Indians of northern Guatemala. "The Itzá treated the horse as a god, offering it fowl, meats, and garlands of flowers, on which diet the horse died. The Itzá, terrified at the death of a god on their hnads, made a stone idol in likeness of the horse, which they worshipped in order to prove that they were not responsible for its death." A priest, who found it in 1618, broke it to pieces as sacrilegious. Sylvanus G. Morley, *Tht Ancient Maya* (Stanford University, California, 1946), p. 123.

59. See Robert Bontine Cunninghame Graham, *The Horses of the Conquest*

(London, 1930; republished, Norman, Oklahoma, 1949); Robert Moorman Denhart, *the Horse of the Americas* (Norman, Oklahoma, 1947); Edward Larocque Tinker, *The Horsemen of the Americas* (New York, 1953). On the loss of a mare, killed by Indians, Cortés said: "We grieved exceedingly at it, for the horses and mares gave life to us." *Op. cit.*, II, 112. He also wrote: "After God, our only security was the horses." *Ibid.*, I, 301.

60. Bernal Díaz, *op. cit.*, p. 475.

61. According to Herrera, an order sent to Vaca de Castro by the Council of the Indies in 1541 forbade the use of *"perros bravos carniceros"* against the Indians. Antonio de Herrera, *Historia General de los Hechos de los Castellanos en las Islas i Tierra Firme del Mar Océano* (5 vols., Madrid, 1726–30), *decada* VI, *libro* 8, p. 185.

62. See William Hickling Prescott, *The Conquest of Mexico,* various editions.

63. There are biographies of Cortés by H. D. Sedgwick, *Cortés the Conqueror* (Indianapolis, 1926); Salvador de Madariaga, *Hernán Cortés* (Buenos Aires, 1941); Sir Arthur Helps, *Life of Hernando Cortes* (2 vols., London. 1871); F. A. MacNutt, *Fernando Cortés* (New York, 1909).

64. "Perhaps the most supremely audacious act which history records is the seizure of Montezuma in the midst of his own court, and his conveyance to the Spanish quarters; an undertaking so stupefying in its conception and so incredible in its execution that only the multitude and unanimity of testimony serve to remove it from the sphere of fable into that of history." F. A. MacNutt, introduction, *Letters of Cortés, op. cit.*, I, 34. Bernal Díaz wrote: "Now let the curious consider upon our heroic actions: first, in destroying our ships and therewith all hope of retreat; secondly, in entering the city of Mexico after the alarming warnings that we had received; thirdly, in daring to make prisoner the great Montezuma, King of all that country, and in the center of his own palace, surrounded by his numerous guards; and fourthly, in publicly burning his officers in front of his palace, and putting the king in irons during the execution." *Op. cit.*, pp. 191-2. The fame of Cortés's skill spread throughout the New World. To Cieza de León in Peru, he was "the mirror of governors and captains in the Indies." *The War of Chupas, op. cit.*, p. 370.

65. On his daring expedition into the jungles of southern Mexico and the northern part of Central America, his personal retinue consisted of "a steward and paymaster, a keeper of the plate, a major-domo, a butler, a confectioner, a chamberlain, a physician, a surgeon, a number of pages, two armor bearers, eight grooms, two falconers, five musicians, a stage dancer, a juggler and puppet player, a master of the horse, and three Spanish muleteers." Bernal Díaz, *op. cit.,* p. 439. The dancer died of fatigue, worn out by the walking. "As for our poor musicians," wrote Bernal Díaz, "with their instruments, their sackbuts and dulcimers, they felt the loss of the regalements and feasts of Castile, and now their harmony was stopped, excepting one only, whom the soldiers used to curse whenever he struck up, saying that it was maize and not music they wanted." *Ibid.*, p. 444.

66. "The policy of Cortés became the policy of its [Mexico's] rulers for three centuries." Lesley Byrd Simpson, *Many Mexicos* (New York, 1941), p. 23.

67. Bernal Díaz, *op. cit., passim.* Francisco López de Gómara wrote *La Historia*

de las Indias y Conquista de México (Zaragoza, 1552), which presumed to be the official story of the conquest.

68. Cortés, *Letters, op. cit.,* I, 305.

69. On Gonzalo Pizarro's disastrous expedition in search of "the Land of Cinnamon," see Herrera, *op. cit., decada* VI, *libro* 8, pp. 180 ff.

70. Garcilaso de la Vega, *Historia General, op. cit.,* III, 103, 157. Hernández Girón claimed to possess supernatural powers, in order to increase his hold on the superstitious people. Among his retinue were one Valladares, who presumed to read the "inclinations" of men by their faces and physiognomies; Urquizú, who had the "Pythagorean wheel" painted on a piece of paper, with which he hoaxed men; Lucia the Moor, "a great witch, who claimed to receive revelations"; Becerra the oracle, who answered all questions; and Vázquez the priest, who was an astrologer and necromancer (*nigromántico*). He was also a palmist and claimed to predict the future by "signs of the hand."

71. *The War of Las Salinas, op. cit.,* p. 42.

72. *Ibid.,* p. 57.

73. See Blanco Fombona, *op. cit.,* p. 287.

74. *The War of Chupas, op. cit.,* p. 280. Of the night before the battle of Las Salinas, Cieza wrote: "When the night came on, all remained under arms, with such hopes and fears as the reader may imagine. But never, either on one side or the other, came any proposal of peace, such was the hatred by which they were actuated." *The War of Las Salinas, op. cit.,* p. 198. Cieza quotes Cicero's remark that he had "never known a peace so bad but it was better than a good war." *The War of Chupas, op. cit.,* p. 254. He adds that "peace has such excellent and singular power that without it the world could no longer exist." *The War of Las Salinas, op. cit.,* p. 1. In another place he wrote: "The conquerors and settlers of these parts should not pass their time in fighting battles and marching in chase of each other, but in planting and sowing, which would be more profitable." *Travels, op. cit.,* p. 402.

75. Frank Shay, *Incredible Pizarro, Conqueror of Peru* (New York, 1932); Hoffman Birney, *Brothers of Doom: The Story of the Pizarros of Peru* (New York, 1942); Philip Ainsworth Means, *Fall of the Inca Empire and the Spanish Rule in Peru* (New York, 1932).

76. Oviedo remarks on "the terribleness and arrogance" of Hernando Pizarro. *Op. cit.,* IV, 234.

77. *Ibid.,* IV, 148.

78. Garcilaso called Juan Pizarro "a man so generous, so valiant, so affable, so beloved for all the virtues that could be desired in a caballero." *Historia General, op. cit.,* p. 185.

79. Oviedo called him "the most beloved captain who has ever been seen in these parts." *Op. cit.,* IV, 341.

80. Herrera, *op. cit., decada* VI, *libro* 2, p. 39. "So brave a soldier," Cieza said of him. *The War of Las Salinas, op. cit.,* p. 204.

81. "He got the best of and triumphed over those who thought they could dominate him, for never, even in his days of greatest power, did he show so much authority, dignity, and so commanding a presence as on that day of his imprison-

ment" Garcilaso de la Vega, *Historia General, op. cit.*, II, 261. See *ibid.*, pp. 88, 98, 133, 200, 268.

82. "The longest, the most toilsome, and the most imperfect of the Spanish conquests. Every cacique waged a separate war, a war of stratagem and ambuscade." F. Depons, *A Voyage to the Eastern Part of Terra Firma, or the Spanish Main, in South America, during the Years 1801, 1802, 1803, and 1804* (tr. from the French, 3 vols., New York, 1806), I, 6.

83. Oviedo, *op. cit.*, III, 6, 15; II, 426. See Charles L. G. Anderson, *Life and letters of Vasco Núñez de Balboa* (New York, 1916); and Kathleen Romoli, *Balboa of Darien: Discoverer of the Pacific* (Garden City, New York, 1953).

84. See Agustín Zapata Gollán, *Las Puertas de la Tierra: Jornadas del Litoral* (Santa Fé, Argentina, 1941), pp. 27, 35-37.

85. Tomás Thayer Ojeda and Carlos J. Larraín, *Valdivia y sus Compañeros* (Santiago, Chile, 1950).

86. See Bernard Moses, *op. cit.*, I, 170 ff.; II, 27-37.

87. Carlos Pereyra, *op. cit.*, p. 377.

88. "I have also explained to your Caesarian Majesty the need for plants of all kinds; for every species of agriculture may flourish here; but nothing has so far been provided, and I again pray your Majesty to order a provision from the Casa de Contratación at Seville, so that no ship be allowed to sail without bringing a certain number of plants which would favor the population and prosperity of the country." Cortés, *Letters, op. cit.*, II, 218.

89. Bernal Díaz, *op. cit.*, p. 49.

90. *The War of Chupas, op. cit.*, p. 15.

91. Garcilaso de la Vega, *Comentarios Reales de los Incas* (2 vols., Buenos Aires, 1943), II, 267. The *Comentarios* were first published at Lisbon in 1609. The olive tree was introduced into Peru in 1560 by Antonio de Rivera, one of the founders of the city. He brought in three seedlings from Spain and planted them in his gardens, from which he sold grapes, figs, melons, pomegranates, oranges, limes, and other Spanish fruits and vegetables in the Lima market to an annual value of over 200,000 pesos. He had Negro slaves and a pack of dogs to guard the olive trees, but, in spite of all his precautions, one was stolen and carried to Chile, where shoots were taken from it. Three years later it was brought back to Lima and secretly replanted in Rivera's gardens. Garcilaso says that in the early days three olives were presented with much ceremony to each guest in the home of Rivera. *Ibid.*, p. 271. Garcilaso tells of how García de Melo, the royal treasurer in Cuzco, once sent three stocks of asparagus as a gift to his father. "My father," he wrote, "for greater solemnity in honor of this Spanish vegetable, ordered it to be cooked on the brasier in his quarters, before seven or eight gentlemen who were dining with him. When the asparagus were cooked, oil and vinegar were brought, and Garcilaso, my father, passed around the two largest stocks, giving each one a bite. He kept the third stock for himself, saying that, if they would pardon him, since they were a thing of Spain, he would keep the lion's share for himself this time. So they ate the asparagus with more rejoicing and festivity than if they were eating the phoenix bird, and although I served the table and brought the makings for the sauce, I got none of it." *Ibid.*, p. 277.

92. Cristóbal Bermúdez Plata and others, eds., *Catálogo de pasajeros a Indias* (2 vols., Seville, 1940, 1942), *passim*.

93. García de Lerma was one of the worst of the early governors. Oviedo called him a "notorious and insupportable tyrant," who put on the airs of a great prince. He was tried by the Audiencia of Santo Domingo for the crimes of his administration and died before the *residencia* or investigation of his term of office was finished. Cowardly, as well as avaricious, he was not respected by the Indians who called him a *gallina* (hen). *Op. cit.*, II, 351.

94. See Harris Gaylord Warren, *Paraguay: an Informal History* (Norman, Oklahoma, 1949), pp. 125-30.

95. Quoted from Herrera, *op. cit.*

96. Bernal Díaz, *op. cit.*, p. 392.

97. See Robert Southey, *History of Brazil* (3 vols., London, 1810-19), I, *passim;* João Pandiá Calogeras, *History of Brazil* (tr. from the Portuguese, Chapel Hill, N. C., 1930), *passim;* Caio Prado Junior, *Formação do Brasil Contemporaneo: Colonia* (São Paulo, 1942), pp. 13-78.

Chapter V

THE NEGRO

SINGLY, AS slave or servant, Negroes came to the New World with the first of the conquerors. A Negro, Ñuflo de Olano, was with Balboa when he discovered the Pacific.[1] Another, of Narváez' party, was said to have introduced smallpox into Mexico. Bernal Díaz tells of a Negro, "a comical fellow," who, after the defeat of Narváez by Cortés, "danced and shouted for joy, crying: 'Where are the Romans who with such numbers have ever achieved such a glorious victory?' "[2] When Francisco Pizarro

made his initial reconnaissance of northern Peru, he left a Negro
with the Indians at Tumbes, along with a Spanish soldier, a sow,
and a rooster and hen. Later, when Pizarro's companion, Diego
de Almagro, was beheaded during the civil wars in Peru, it was a
Negro who took his body to church for burial.[3] Alvar Nuñez
Cabeza de Vaca was accompanied on his long journey through
what is now the southern part of the United States by a Negro
named Estevanico, or "Little Steve," who later served as interpreter for Friar Marcos de Niza, the precursor of Coronado's
expedition into the southwest.

During the Conquest, Negroes were frequently employed as
verdugos, or executioners. Carbajal, "the Demon of the Andes,"
always had three or four of "these Ethiopian soldiers" with him
and used them for that purpose.[4] Domingo, a Negro, served in
the dual capacity of executioner and town crier for the Santiago
of Valdivia's time.[5] Long afterward, when Humboldt was in
Venezuela, the public headsman at Cumaná was a Negro.[6]

In the last phase of the wars between the conquerors in the
Andes, Francisco Hernández Girón formed a company of over
three hundred soldiers, whom he had impressed from the house-
holds and estates of their owners among the loyalist faction in
the country.

THE SLAVE TRADE

Much more important than these isolated cases were the slaves
who were systematically imported into the Indies as workers in
the mines and on the plantations. This movement began about
1502, only ten years after the discovery. The Spaniards in the
islands were already disillusioned as to the value of the aborigines
as a labor force, and the Dominican friars, in their guise of protectors of the Indians, recommended the introduction of Negro
slaves as the lesser of two evils. Permission was first given to introduce European-born slaves into the Antilles in 1501 during the
governorship of Obando. In 1511, fifty slaves were brought in
directly from Africa. After some indecision on the part of the
authorities in Spain as to the propriety of the business, the gates
were opened wide to the importation of Negroes in 1517. At that
time, an *asiento* or monopoly agreement was granted to a Fleming

for the introduction of 4,000 slaves a year, one third of whom must be women for breeding purposes.

During one period or another, the *asiento*, or monopoly for the importation of slaves into the Spanish colonies, was held by Genoese, Flemings, Portuguese, Dutch, and English.[7] At all times, there was considerable smuggling of slaves, often connived at by Spanish officials. Hakluyt says of John Hawkins's voyage of 1562: "Being amongst other particulars assured that Negroes were very good merchandise in Hispaniola, and that store of Negroes might easily be had upon the coast of Guinea, [he] resolved to make triall thereof."[8] The venture proved very profitable, and on his third voyage Hawkins sold 200 Negroes in one night at Rio de la Hacha on the Spanish Main.[9] "In all other places where we traded," he said, "the Spanish inhabitants were glad of us and traded willingly." In 1591, Christopher Newport, another of the Elizabethan sea dogs, captured a Portuguese slaver bound out of Guinea for Cartagena with 300 Negroes on board, and later disposed of them for Spanish pieces of eight.[10] When William Dampier, that literary buccaneer, lay in Guayaquil harbor, he saw three Spanish ships in the stream with a thousand slaves on board, "all lusty young Men and Women," and only regretted that his crew was not in sufficient force to carry them off to Darien to work for gold.[11]

At the time of the discovery of America, Negro slavery had already existed in Portugal for a half-century. Antonio Gonçalves brought the first slaves to Lisbon in 1441 or 1442,[12] and a company was shortly formed to carry on the trade with the west coast of Africa. In the Algarves, to the south of the Tagus, where Moorish blood had long since been predominant, the influx of Negroes further changed the ethnic and chromatic complexion of the population. Lisbon itself received an imprint which it has never lost, as the only European city with a considerable Negroid element among the inhabitants.

The Portuguese also found a ready market for slaves in southern Spain, and for a time Seville was a flourishing center of the trade. It was from this pool of slaves that the first Negroes were taken to the New World. However, Negro slavery never took deep roots in Spain, though Spaniards were accustomed to the enslavement of Moors, Jews, and other white peoples.[13] Voluntary manumission of slaves was common, and Negro or mulatto freedmen early began to appear in the lists of persons licensed by the *Casa de Contratación* to go to the colonies. One such, Francisco, took ship for Santo Domingo in 1510.[14] In 1512, the female mulatto, Juana, who declared herself to be the daughter of Francisco Martín de Cazella, and a freedwoman, named Cristina, with her three-year-old daughter, received permits for passage to the islands. The register of passengers for the next year includes the names of six freed persons of color. In 1527, a former slave of the Archbishop of Tarragona crossed the Atlantic with his wife, Francisca. In 1536, "Maestre Jorge," with his wife, María López, and his son Jerónimo, received permission to return to Santo Domingo, where he had been a slave of the bishop.

The Portuguese were much laxer than the Spaniards in the reporting and documentation of their overseas enterprises so that there are few dates in the early movement of slaves to Brazil. Moreover, at the time of emancipation in 1888, the Brazilian abolitionists destroyed all existing records of the slave trade that they could find in Bahia and Rio. The first slaves to be imported directly from Africa reached Brazil in 1538, where they aroused the protests of the famous Father Nobrega. According to his fellow Jesuit, Father Anchieta, there were more than 14,000 slaves in Brazil by 1585, at which time the non-Indian population of the colony was about 57,000. From then on the trade increased steadily until it was ended by imperial decree in 1850. In the forty-four years between 1759 and 1803, 642,000 Negroes were imported from Angola alone. At that time the colored population of Brazil was measured by the millions and was the largest agglomeration of blacks in the Western Hemisphere.

The slaves came from the Portuguese trading stations that extended from Forte de el Mina and São João de Ajudá (Whydah) on the Guinea coast around the Cape to Mozambique. In point of numbers, the principal source of slaves was the widespread Bantu stock of central and southern Africa—Congos, Angolas, and Mozambiques, as they were known from the regions of their origins. Docile and faithful, they were particularly desired as field hands, and were always in demand in the markets of Pernambuco, Maranhão, and Rio. Except as general purpose workers, Bahia always preferred Negroes from the western Sudan or from the Islamized tribes of the Guinea hinterland. The Negroes of this general area were handsomer and more intelligent than the Bantu slaves. However, they were usually less manageable, and some of them, like the superior Hausas and Fulas, could never be taken for granted, much less mistreated. The Portuguese of Bahia favored especially the Sudanese Yorubas, who had a reputation for being more hard-working and better tempered than the other peoples of that part of Africa, which included the Ashantis and Dahomans, as well as the Moslem Mandingos.

By 1600 Negro slaves formed the basis of the colonial economy over large areas.[15] This was particularly true in the more tropical regions. Wherever sugar cane was grown, as in northern Brazil, in the irrigated valleys of the Peruvian coast, in the *tierra caliente* of Mexico, and in Santo Domingo, they were the indispensable labor element. In Cuba the Negro has been a racial factor of major importance. As the last of Spain's colonies to gain its independence, Cuba was long immune to the liberalizing influences which benefited the man of color in the republics. Since the basis of its economy was sugar, it was uncommonly dependent on Negro labor. Later, when the local labor supply proved unequal to the demands of the great industry, Haitians were to be brought in for the duration of the *zafra* or cane harvest.

The Indian, much less the Spaniard, would not submit to the grueling work of the cane fields. On the coastal plain of northern Peru and thence up into the valleys among the foothills of the Andes, the Negro early supplanted the original Indian population, as he had done long since in the islands. Though the Negro was out of his natural element in the colder climate of the high mountains, many of them were used in the mines, particularly in Colombia.

While the Negro always had his champions among the clergy, and even among the laity, the religious orders were among the largest slaveowners. In the seventeenth century, Thomas Gage, the English Dominican, visited a large property belonging to one of the orders in the Chiapas country of southern Mexico, where "near 200 blackamoors" worked in the cane fields and the grinding mill.[16] Near Puebla he found as many slaves on an hacienda of his own order. An English ship encountered two Portuguese sail off the mouth of the River Plate in 1587. Between them they carried eighty Negro slaves, then worth 400 ducats apiece in Peru; a large shipment of religious books and other articles; four or five friars, including an Irishman, and four Portuguese women. The ships and cargo had been bought in Brazil by an agent of the Bishop of Tucumán, who was then building a new monastery.[17] The Jesuit Father Gervasoni reported that in 1729 the college of his order in Buenos Aires had over 300 slaves.[18] At that time, he estimated that a third of the city's population of 24,000 consisted of Negro slaves. In the latter part of the same century, the itinerant "Inca" Concolorcorvo wrote that in Córdoba he witnessed an auction of 2,000 blacks from two properties of the religious colleges who were sold in family lots.[19] Among them were many musicians and others with special skills. The nuns of Santa Teresa had a farm in the neighborhood with 300 slaves, and some families possessed 300 slaves, and some families possessed thirty or forty domestic slaves. The learned Indian added the comment that the female slaves were famed as laundresses. Writing long afterwards of the same locality, the anticlerical Sarmiento said: "Each convent and monastery owned an adjoining property, on which there were bred eight hundred slaves of the Order, Negros, Zambos, and mulattoes." [20] The young female mulattoes, the testy Argentine president described as "blue-eyed, fair-haired, slow-moving, with legs polished like marble; real Circassians, endowed with all the graces, who served as a whip to the human passions, all for the greater honor and profit of the convent to which these houris belonged."

During the latter decades of the colonial period, several foreign and creole observers took stock of the racial composition of the population and made apparently credible estimates of its components.[21] By the beginning of the nineteenth century, the population of Brazil, Cuba, and Santo Domingo was predominantly Negro or mulatto. At that time there were an estimated 72,000 slaves and 400,000 mulattoes in Venezuela, or about forty-seven per cent of the inhabitants of the captaincy-general. Of an estimated population of 3,250,000 in Brazil in 1798, there were 406,000 freedmen and 1,582,000 slaves, of whom 211,000 were mulattoes. An official estimate made twenty years later gave the total population as 3,817,000, the number of freedmen as

585,000, and of slaves as 1,930,000, including 202,000 mulattoes. The decline in the number of persons classified as mulattoes represents the tendency of the octoroons and lighter colored quadroons to disappear into the category of whites, a process which continues to be accentuated by the ethnic fluidity of the Brazilian population. Alexander von Humboldt, who spent several years in Spanish America during this period, estimated the black population of the West Indies at 1,300,000, of whom 230,000 were slaves in Cuba. On the basis of data submitted to the Cortes of Cadiz, Humboldt gives a figure of 114,000 for the free "colored" population of that island. However, the proportions of black blood were insignificant in Chile, Costa Rica, and Paraguay, and in the mountain cities like Bogotá, Quito, Cuzco, and Potosí. In the coastal cities, from Vera Cruz around by Cartagena, Bahia, Rio de Janerio, Buenos Aires, Lima, and Guayaquil, to Panama, the Negro and mulatto population was everywhere heavy, save in Valparaiso.

THE NEGRO IN BRAZIL

Nowhere else, save in the western end of Hispaniola, did the Negro influence so profoundly the shape of civilization as in northern Brazil.[22] This was due not only to the weight of his numbers, but to the receptivity of his Portuguese masters. Unlike the Spaniards, the Portuguese were socially among the most plastic of people.

By the time she undertook the colonization of Brazil, Portugal had already spread thin the more dynamic part of her sparse population over the vast area of her enterprises in Asia. The mortality rate of maritime imperialism was very high, and the Portuguese now felt the need for conserving their dwindling manpower. In brief, their aim was to reduce the occasions of their exposure to the inevitable risks of tropical pioneering. As entrepreneurs in a system of large-scale plantation agriculture, they had to find a cheap and numerous labor supply. Early convinced of the unsuitability of the forest Indians for their purpose, they gradually turned to the Negro slave, with whom they were already familiar in Portugal.

The Negro worked in the cane fields and at the sugar mill. He was blacksmith, carpenter, and general mechanic in the self-contained community of the "big house." In the towns that grew up along the coast, the scope of his labors comprised nearly all the menial and skilled manual occupations, from porter and stevedore to tailor and barber. Dressed in gaudy uniform, he formed part of the ornamental retinue of his master on his comings and goings about Bahia and Olinda. In the manor houses there swarmed a noisy and garrulous company of black female slaves in a loose hierarchy of ages, skills, and responsibilities, with the cook and the personal maid of the *donna da casa* in the top echelons of authority and prestige. Their naked and uninhibited children constantly streamed in and out, to add to the din and confusion—and the merriment—of the pullulating and inefficient household.

From the standpoint of the whites, one of the most demoralizing phases of slavery was that represented in Brazil by the so-called *Negro de ganho,* whose counterpart was also found in the Spanish colonial cities. The *Negro de ganho* was a slave who performed "odd jobs" about the city. Sometimes he was an unskilled laborer who might work as a porter or stevedore or at even more menial tasks; sometimes he had some skill which was in demand, so that his earnings were correspondingly greater. In either event, he was required to turn over to his master a fixed sum at the end of each day; anything which he made in excess of this "quota" was generally his own. Many citizens of Bahia and Pernambuco who could raise enough capital to buy one or more slaves lived in idleness on income from this source. Among this class of petty slaveowners were Negroes who had themselves been slaves.

Though many features of this slave society bear a resemblance to the system in our ante-bellum South, the differences were many and far-reaching. Certainly the lot of the Negro was much superior in Brazil. In no other part of the world where black men were kept in servitude was their treatment so humane or the bonds so lightly worn.[23] The Portuguese planter was generally too easygoing to be cruel. Punishments were mild and outbursts of sadism were rare. The personal relationship between master and slave was a very intimate one, unclouded by pride of race or prejudices of color. For the Portuguese had been conditioned against racial intolerance by centuries of experience in living

with dark-skinned peoples. The southern Portuguese, particularly
those from the Algarves and Alemtejo, were well mesticized from
long practice of intermarriage with Moors during the Middle
Ages. In the century preceding the colonization of Brazil, Negro
slaves added another ethnic element to the existing hybridization to be absorbed into the blood stream and all-embracing society of Portugal. Meanwhile, their adventures in the Orient had
widened their contacts with peoples of color, toward whom,
whether dusky Tamils of the Malabar Coast or brown Malays
of the islands, they exhibited the same racial open-mindedness
and generative catholicity.

In Brazil, miscegenation went on, unrestrained by moral
taboos or social traditions, to produce a new race.[24] This process
was favored by a combination of circumstances: the concupiscence
of the Portuguese male; [25] the stimulation of the tropical climate;
the freedom of a new society whose rules of conduct he made; the
lack of women of his own among the early colonists, and the relative frigidity of his too repressed and sheltered womankind; the
easy compliance—or resignation—of the Negroes; and the sexual
allurements of the light-skinned quadroon or octoroon, as successive stages of miscegenation progressively accelerated the ferment
of racial creation.[26] The favored instrument in the process of
miscegenation was the "Mina" woman from the Sudan, stately,
intelligent, competent, and affectionate, in her dual role of mis-
tress-housekeeper for the many unattached males of the colony.[27]
The lowlier and more primitive Congolese and Angolas also contributed much to the seething *olla podrida* in which the ultimate
Brazilian race was being prepared.

The great mixing served unwittingly the purposes of state-
craft, for it created people where there had been no people.[28]
And more population than was available from Portugal was ur-
gently needed to fill the demographic vacuum of the Brazilian
wilderness. It was the fecundity of the Negro woman and the
strong arm and patient endurance of the Negro man which enabled Portugal to hold and develop northern Brazil and the
coastal plain that shut off the interior highlands from the sea in
the south of the vast colony. But for them the French and the
Dutch would have taken over the Brazils from the Portuguese.

The Negro adjusted himself very quickly to the demands of his life in Brazil. He was at home in the blazing sun.[29] His food was simple and, though lacking variety, it made a better diet than his master had. In a physical sense he flourished in his new environment. He had been torn loose from his cultural roots in Africa. He had been sold into bondage by men of his own race. He had suffered the terrible ordeal of the ocean crossing in the crowded holds of the slave ships. It is no wonder that at times he was brooding and melancholy. But his spirit was naturally so resilient that, once he had recovered from the effects of the "central passage" and had fallen into the rhythm and routine of his new existence, he was prone to make the best of what was far from the worst possible of worlds. If he sang at his work, it was not always to ease the burden in his heart, but oftener to express his animal joy at the compensations which his new condition offered to him for what he had lost.[30] Everywhere he gave a lighter touch to life on the edge of the great forest. The Portuguese was given to sentimental melancholy, and the Negro took him out of his dark moods by his laughter and his songs. His influence still permeates the popular music of Brazil, that is so different from the mournful *fados* of Portuguese folk music. He set the pattern of festivity for Brazil and, in spite of the Pierrots and Columbines among its more aristocratic revelers, the Carnival at Rio, that supreme fete of the world, is his barbaric saturnalia.

Though he arrived in the New World with only a breech-cloth he brought with him in his black head the whole treasury of his folklore, his body of superstitions and demonology, and the rites of his jungle cults. Like their northern counterparts, *Vodun* or voodoo, in Haiti, and *Ñañigo* in Cuba, *macumba* or *candomblé* in Brazil gave a familiar form and meaning to his relationship with the supernatural forces which crowded the little cosmos of his primitive mind. Mingled with his own "superstitions" were borrowings from the lush animism and mythology of the Indian. The Hausas and other tribes of the southern Sudan brought with them their Moslem faith and knowledge of the Koran.

The Negro accepted Christianity as readily as did the Indian. And, like the Indian, he accepted of it only what he could understand, and what was congenial to his simple soul—the Savior (the *Bom Jesus*), the Madonna, the saints, and the colorful ritual of the Catholic Church. He learned the catechism, but theology was

beyond him. The Church was much concerned for his religious
welfare, and his Portuguese masters encouraged his instruction
in the rudiments of the faith. More than that, no one, priest or
master, expected of him. The Jesuits, who were a great power
in the colony, were more concerned with the salvation of the
Indian, and the religious ministrations of the Negro were largely
left in the hands of the priest who served as chaplain of the "big
house," and who was liable to be neither very learned nor very
exigent in matters of dogma. In this society, which took its religion as easily as it accepted the facts of racial difference, the
Negro added to the gentle Christianity of Portugal a special
warmth and sensuousness. He further softened and paganized the
observances of a faith that was already pliant and tolerant beyond the other branches of Christiandom.

The emancipation of the slaves in Brazil was progressive.[31]
It was not cataclysmic and attended by civil war and its punitive
aftermath, as it was in the United States. Manumission was inherent in the very nature of Brazilian slavery, and the process of
liberation was virtually contemporaneous with the history of the
institution itself. For the slave, the door to freedom was always
ajar and there were many occasions and pretexts, founded in
humane custom and law, for opening it wide.

The master generally freed his own mulatto children when his
parentage left no doubts. It was also customary to free a favorite
slave at special family festivals, such as the celebration of a birth
or christening or marriage, on the master's birthday, or on a religious holiday.[32] A slave could buy his freedom by offering his
master the amount of his original purchase price; sometimes he
redeemed his liberty by installment payments. The children born
to a Negro slave and a freedwoman were free. Any slave, man or
woman, who had ten children, or even less, could be freed. For
a town slave who was industrious and possessed some skill, it
was not difficult to accumulate the equivalent of his original
purchase money. Besides Sundays, there were as many as eighty-
four holidays, religious and official, on which his time was his own.
To this extent, slavery in Brazil might have some of the temporary nature of indentured servitude in the English colonies,
under which the white servant worked off the cost of his passage
to the New World. Finally, there were always slaveowners who

questioned the justice of chattel slavery, and whom considerations of conscience led to free their bondsmen.

It was from this group that came part of the impulse for the abolitionist movement in the nineteenth century, though, as in the United States, many of the members of the abolitionist societies did not own slaves. This was particularly true of the abolitionist element in the southern provinces of the empire, whose economy was increasingly dependent on free labor. The abolitionists in the last century not only financed the manumission of many slaves, but they worked for emancipation through the imperial parliament and the household of the imperial family, which was very susceptible to humanitarian influences.

It was this powerful and persistent pressure group which by a series of political acts prepared the way for the final emancipation of all remaining slaves in 1888. By the enforced liberation of all children born to slave mothers, the automatic emancipation of all slaves on reaching the age of sixty, and the suppression of the slave trade, slavery was doomed anyway before the Regent, the Princess Leopoldina, issued the ultimate decree of emancipation.

Though the position of the Negro was never hopeless, yet he was a slave, and slavery at its best, as it was in Brazil, was still slavery. Bondage bore heavily on the spirit of the prouder and more sensitive slaves. Many fled deep into the backlands, where they were beyond the reach of the regular hunters of fugitive slaves, who were themselves sometimes freedmen, but usually were Indians. In the seventeenth century a large number of renegade slaves formed the so-called "Republic of Palmares," with all the political and ecclesiastical machinery of a sovereign state. The proximity of this refuge community was so great a temptation to discontented slaves that all the armed authority of the north was invoked against it. It was only destroyed after long resistance when the redoubtable Paulista frontiersmen were brought in from the south and thrown against its barricades. In the early decades of the last century there was a succession of isolated slave revolts in the coastal regions, particularly in the Bahian Reconcavo. Generally led by the haughty Haussas or other "Mina" Negroes, they were all put down with severity. While all these slave uprisings were abortive, they served to strengthen the hands of the growing abolitionist element in the

empire by emphasizing the harsher aspects and the basic injustice of the system.

The completion of the process of emancipation dealt a heavy
blow to the traditional economic and social system of northern
Brazil. Although some of the new freedmen, particularly the
older ones, chose to remain on the lands of their former masters
as wageworkers, the old relationships were widely disrupted except where the force of inertia and habit proved too strong to
break. Many of the newly liberated Negroes moved into the
cities, to swell their slums and to create fresh social problems, or
they wandered aimlessly through the country to add to the weight
of Brazil's perennial problem of a nomadic population.

Under the stimulus of the new freedom, and the mobility of
movement which it encouraged, miscegenation increased apace.
The trend toward the eventual absorption of all ethnic elements
in a single race was too strong to be withstood short of the old
white aristocracy, and even some of its members could not boast
an unbroken lineage out of Portugal. Brazilians, reluctant to
admit the tensions of a "race problem" in their country, generally
accepted the inevitable, and even made efforts to rationalize a
situation which they could not prevent if they would. On the
theory that unrestricted miscegenation would ultimately obliterate
the characteristic physical marks of the three component races,
they tended to consider the progressive *branquemento,* or whitening, of the population as a national ideal.[33] Observation of the
gradual lightening of the Brazilian complexion during this century would go far to confirm this assumption. In other words, the
Brazilians contend that they are breeding the Negro, with his
peculiar stigmata, out of the race. They do not want a racial
minority in their country to plague their internal peace.

Meanwhile, outsiders in Brazil are impressed by the absence
of the stresses which exist in other countries where the Negro
exists alongside the white man. There is little *racial* discrimination where the man of color is concerned.[34] Brazilians tend to
avoid the use of the word "Negro," or even of the word "mulatto," and resort to softer terms when they refer to those with
African origins.

If there is little racial intolerance, there *is* color discrimination in Brazil. Its basis is economic or social, since the Negro or

dark-skinned mulatto is liable to have a lower living standard than the average white Brazilian or light-complexioned end product of the miscegenetic process. He may be discriminated against as lines are drawn against the white poor. If he observes the rules of good breeding on which Brazilians set heavy store, if he has succeeded in rising above the handicaps that beset his group, and has obtained an education and a respected place in one of the professions, most of the doors of society are opened to him.

Many men of color have attained to fame and high place in Brazil. Machado de Assís, its great classical novelist, was the son of a Portuguese father and a Negro woman of the Rio slums. However, he was ashamed of his African blood and shunned the company of other mulattoes. Others include the poets Gonçalves Dias, Castro Alves, and Olavo Bilac; the journalist and abolitionist, José de Patrocinio; the engineer, André Rebouças; a president of the Republic, Nilo Peçanha; the senator and viscount of the empire, Francisco Gé Acabaya de Montezuma. One of the most famous of Brazilian mulattoes was the brilliant eighteenth century architect and sculptor, Antonio Francisco Lisboa, better known as Aleijadinho. Though severely crippled and deformed by leprosy, he designed or decorated many of the churches of Minas Geraes, and created a school of colonial art whose best examples are seen in the old prominent capital of Ouro Preto.

Brazil is not a paradise for people of color. Discrimination is probably on the increase in the more populous and progressive south. Fast-moving São Paulo finds the dark-skinned laborer from the north too slow for its pace. Some influential circles are sensitive to the good opinion of foreigners who bring their racial prejudices to Brazil with them. The better hotels which cater to the tourist trade are liable to draw color lines on occasion. And the officer corps of the Navy is still recruited from the class of white Brazilians. Yet there is no country on earth where the relationship between white men and black men is generally so civilized.

THE NEGRO IN THE SPANISH COLONIES

In the Spanish Colonies, Negro slavery lacked some of the benignant quality that was the rule in Brazil, where it tended to atone for the basic injustice of the institution. In general, the

Spaniard did not succeed in establishing the intimate relationship which usually existed between the Portuguese master and his
slaves. The slave society always seemed to be less peaceful and
more explosive. The Spaniard had not been conditioned for living
with the Negro, as the Portuguese had been by his long contacts
with the peoples of the African coasts. In spite of his racial tolerance, he harbored within him a greater pride of blood, that was
liable to assert itself whenever his dominance was challenged.
There were other provocations peculiar to Spanish colonial society.
The use of Negro slaves in the difficult work of the mines created
an inflammable situation that sometimes led to rebellion or wholesale flight. Foreign marauders frequently played on the discontent
of the Negro slaves and turned their grudges to use against their
Spanish masters, so that the Spaniards could seldom be sure of
the loyalty of this numerous element in the population.[35] Also,
the presence alongside the Negro of large masses of docile Indians
in both New Spain and Peru complicated the relations of the
three races. The Indian was an alternative and competitive source
of labor, to whom the Spaniard could turn if necessary. And in
the Indian the more agressive Negro found an object on which
he could give vent to his own frustrations. The Spaniards claimed
that the Negro either bullied or corrupted the Indian, and there
were severe, if inffectual, laws designed to isolate the two races
from each other.

The *Zambo,* mixture of Indian and Negro, was early considered to be the one insoluble—and completely undesirable— ingredient in the racial melting pot of the colonies. Bitter and truculent, and spurned by the two peoples responsible for his hybrid
soul, as well as by the Spaniard, he was a hopeless pariah and a
potential enemy of the society that would have none of him. In
time, as the conflicting elements in his personality became reconciled, the Zambo and his descendants occasionally found a certain—and sometimes important—place in the local hierarchy of
classes. His numbers were probably greatest in the coastal areas
of Peru, the Ecuadoran lowlands, on the Spanish Main, and in
the Amazon Valley.[36]

At least before the nineteenth century, slave revolts were
more common in the Spanish colonies than they were in Brazil.
Spanish chroniclers and observers frequently complained of the

turbulence and disorderliness of the Negro population. Sometimes cities were thrown into panic by rumors of a Negro uprising that did not materialize. Thomas Gage wrote of the Negroes in Guatemala that "They are so desperate that the City of Guatemala hath often been afraid of them, and the masters of their own slaves and servants."[37] By the middle of the sixteenth century there were 20,000 African slaves in the hot country about Cuernavaca and Veracruz. They caused the Spaniards more uneasiness than did the far more numerous Indians. The Viceroy Mendoza hanged a number of them as an example, but the Spaniards never took the Negroes for granted. Early in the next century, the rumor spread through Mexico City that the Negroes were going to rise and slaughter all the Spaniards on a certain day. One night the nervous Spaniards mistook the noise of a herd of runaway hogs in the streets for the ominous sound of barefoot Negroes bent on their destruction, and the next day they executed over thirty blacks in sheer panic.[38]

The first slave revolt in the Spanish colonies probably occurred in 1522. It was started by Negroes who belonged to Diego Columbus, the discoverer's son, who was then Governor of Santo Domingo.[39] Other slaves joined the uprising, which was put down with great severity, and thereafter bands of armed Spaniards patrolled the island to prevent a recurrence of the trouble. In 1550 Negroes burned the town of Santa Marta on the north coast of South America, and committed widespread outrages in the region.[40] The Negro "republic" of Palmares in the backlands of northern Brazil had its counterpart in Venezuela in the middle of the sixteenth century. A Negro named Miguel, who worked in the mines, escaped to the hills, where he rallied about him a large number of slaves. He set up the machinery of a state, had himself crowned king, and later attacked the coast town of Nueva Segovia or Barquisimeto with his desperate band of followers. He was repulsed and killed, and the survivors of his company were returned to a slavery that was made more intolerable than ever by their Spanish masters.[41]

Thereafter punitive laws of savage rigor were issued by the Council of the Indies to discourage future revolts by the slaves. A graduated scale of penalties was fixed for fugitive slaves, ranging from fifty lashes and the pillory for an absence of four days to hanging for those who remained away for six months in the company of "seditious Negroes." [42] After Spaniards had resorted to the cruel punishment of mutilation, one law ordered that "in no case is there to be carried out against fugitive Negroes the penalty of cutting off their parts, which out of decency cannot be named." During the period of disorders that followed the civil wars between the conquerors in Peru, the Negroes got out of hand and were only brought under control again by the stern Viceroy Toledo. [43] By this time the curfew which aimed to keep Negroes off the streets of cities after nightfall had become general. In 1598, several thousand Negroes who worked in the rich gold mines near Zaragoza in Nueva Granada (now Colombia) suddenly went berserk, wrecking the mines, and killing the Spanish administrators and miners. [44] Then they defied the Spanish authorities from behind palisades which they had thrown up, but, as happened with all these desperate and forlorn insurrections, the rebellion was suppressed with systematic ruthlessness by the colonial government. When the Negro slaves rose in their successful revolt against their French masters in Santo Domingo in the latter eighteenth century, the Spaniards in Cuba expected their own slaves to follow suit. Some of the French planters who had escaped the fury of the rebellious Negroes arranged to escape to eastern Cuba, where they spread the story of the bloody insurrection on the neighboring island. Governor General O'Donnell instituted terroristic measures that prevented Cuban blacks from imitating their fellow slaves on the other side of the Windward Channel. It is interesting to note that when the Spaniards had recovered from their panic, the French planters who had taken refuge in Cuba became a moderating influence in the treatment of slaves.

Fugitive slaves always gave the Spaniards much concern, not so much for the economic loss to their owners which they represented, as for their potential threat to the peace and security of the community. As a rule, the renegade slave or *cimarrón* was satisfied only to escape from his bondage and to find a safe refuge in "the bush" or in the hills, where he might be secure from the long arm of Spain. Spanish authorities sometimes even made arrangements with the older refugee communities to capture and turn in fugitive slaves from the nearby towns and plantations.

Gemilli Careri, the globe-trotting Italian druggist, passed through a well-behaved *cimarrón* village (San Lorenzo de los Negros) on the way between Mexico City and Veracruz in 1698. "This place," he wrote, "being all inhabited by Blacks, looks like some part of Guinea,[45] but they are all handsome, and apply themselves to husbandry." There were also several colonies of runaway slaves in the Panama country.[46]

Spaniards generally wavered between strict observance of the laws which forbade the arming of the Negro, and an opportunistic policy of utilizing him to supplement the slender defenses of the colonies.[47] Sometimes bands of Negroes resisted landing parties of foreigners on their own initiative; sometimes, particularly along the Spanish Main, companies of Negro militia were incorporated into the royal forces. In the seventeenth century there was a black artillery company of 600 men at Cartagena. The Negro relished the fanfare and panoply of military service and was an effective fighter in the rough-and-tumble style of warfare that was the vogue along the Spanish-American coasts. A lone Negro settler, known as Captain Juan Beltrán, became a legendary figure in southern Chile by his one-man war against the redoubtable Araucanian Indians. Brazilian Negroes played an important part in the war of liberation from the Dutch in the seventeenth century. Later, many blacks served in the armies of Bolívar during the wars of independence, and a big Negro lancer was the special bodyguard of Paez, chief of the *llaneros*, the wild irregular cavalry from the Venezuelan plains. The Brazilians used large numbers of Negro soldiers in the war of Paraguay, and it was a Negro lancer who killed López, the Paraguayan dictator, to put an end to that long and bloody struggle. In the Cuban insurrections against Spain in the last century, Negroes were always in the forefront of the fighting, and General Antonio Maceo, a dashing cavalry leader of the insurgents, is one of the national heroes of Cuba.

For personal service, the Spaniard generally preferred the Negro to the Indian. He found his company more congenial. The Negro himself was always happiest in the city, while the Indian was at heart a villager.[48] Whereas the Indian was disposed to be taciturn and introverted, the Negro added a light touch to the rather staid atmosphere of colonial life by his capacity for laughter and mimicry, and by his very garrulousness. Because they amused him, and sometimes comforted him in his distress, the Spaniard condoned the occasional impudence of his slaves and the other liberties which they might take with him.[49] As in our ante-bellum South, the domestic servants exerted a great influence over the affairs of the household and the lives of its members, and the young creoles were accustomed to spend much of their childhood in the company of the little Negro boys whose mothers served in the house of their parents. The Englishman Stevenson, who spent some time in Lima in the early part of the last century, remarked that "the African Negroes, owing to the kind treatment they receive, appear to be completely happy." [50] And he added: "When they are treated with compassionate kindness, they are generally faithful and honest; they frequently become personally attached to their master, and though they may be sometimes loath to exert themselves in laborious tasks to serve him, yet in an emergency of danger they would die for him. On the contrary, when treated harshly and unjustly they become stubborn in greatest degree, and the master is only secure from personal violence through the irresolute temper of the slave and his fear of punishment."

The Negro in Colonial Society

Wherever the Negro lived, there was music. Sometimes he sang to ease the burden of his servitude; generally he sang because there was song in him. At any rate, he was given to singing, whatever his mood.[51] It might be the music of the liturgy of the Church, the ballads of Spain or Portugal, the lays of the land where he lived, the wild rhythms that his people had brought with them from Africa, or his own improvisations. Those who labored in the fields or as porters or dockworkers in the cities or as boatmen on the rivers sang or chanted to the rhythm of their bodies. Kidder listened to the Negroes in northern Brazil as they sang Stephen Foster's "Oh, Susanna!",[52] and Captain Basil Hall, of the British Navy, heard slaves in Panama singing a patriot song of the wars of independence, in which the word "liberty" was repeated over and over again.[53] "There was something discordant to the feelings in all this," he remarked, "and it was painful to hear these poor people singing in praise of that liberty acquired by their masters, from whose thoughts nothing certainly was farther removed than any idea of extending the same boon to their slaves."

As they sang, so, too, did they play any instrument that came to hand or on anything on which they could beat out a tune. Travelers were alternately delighted by their harmonies or horrified by their cacophonies. Mrs. Agassiz, wife of the famous scientist, was charmed by the orchestra of small Negro boys who entertained the family at dinner on a large Brazilian fazenda. Theodore Haenke wrote of the "noisy and discordant" music of a Negro orchestra in Lima;[54] and Humboldt, who was in Venezuela during the same era, complained that the "wild gaiety" of the Negro slaves in the courtyard outside kept him from sleeping. Colonel Mansilla found among the haughty Ranqueles on the outer pampas a Negro accordionist who went among the Indians, singing, capering, and, for background, eternally playing his accordion, making jokes at the expense of everyone.[55] The itinerant "Inca" Concolorcorvo, who observed the goings-on of the Negroes in the country between Tucumán and Potosí, compared the din of their barbaric discords to the soft and melancholy music of his own people.[56] He said that the infernal racket which they produced with the jawbone of an ass, and their big drums caused even the burros, "the most stolid and least timid of animals," to run away. "Their singing is only howling," he added, and as for their dances, their motions "are reduced to wriggling the belly and hips with much dishonesty." However, he concluded impartially: "The diversions of both Negroes and Indians begin and wind up in drunken orgies."

The Negro, in the Spanish colonies, as in Brazil, owed much to the Church. It tried conscientiously to protect him from the worst abuses incident to his servile condition. One of the noblest figures in the history of the colonial Church was the Jesuit priest, Father Pedro Claver, a Catalan, known as "the Apostle to the Negroes." For forty years Father Claver labored at Cartagena, the principal port of entry for the slave ships of the *Asiento,* to mitigate the horrors of the trade at its worst. And when he died in 1654, the grief-stricken blacks who had been the objects of his devotion wailed in the streets: "The Saint is dead!" Though the religious orders were themselves slaveowners, they were noted for the humanity with which they treated their charges. For example, they refused to break up the slave families, so that the Negroes considered themselves fortunate to belong to the friars.

The Church also took very seriously the law of 1538 which prescribed that "the slaves, free Negroes and mulattoes be instructed in the Holy Catholic Faith." [57] As with the Indian, it had no illusion about the Negro's ability to absorb the theology of Roman Christianity, but limited its teachings to the catechism and the simpler elements of the Catholic dogma. It treated him as a human being, for whom the gates of Heaven were open as wide as for the white man. The impressive solemnity of the Mass, the administration of the sacraments, the festivals of the saints, and the pomp and pageantry of the ritual enriched his life and appealed to his deeply emotional and religious nature. If he often mixed survivals of African demonolatry and folklore with the faith of Spain and Rome, the Church learned to be tolerant of his spiritual vagaries. Sometimes, though, any Christian elements in his worship became unrecognizable, as his heterodoxy took the form of pagan sorcery, and he became a devotee of the various regional forms of the voodoo cult.

The Negro's propensity for display caused his Spanish overlords great annoyance, and led to much sumptuary regulation and legislation. The Negro woman's penchant for parade was particularly distasteful to the ladies of the ruling class, who refused to brook any rivalry in ostentation from their social inferiors. If her means permitted, she dressed flamboyantly, decked herself in gaudy jewelry, and perfumed herself with the most penetrating scents, and in this finery, she was accustomed to appear in public places that were frequented by the *grandes dames* of the colony. Indignant protests to the Council of the Indies resulted in decrees that were sometimes very explicit in their provisions. Thus, a law of 1571 reads: "No Negress, whether free or slave, or mulatto woman, may wear gold, pearls or silk; however, if a free Negress or *mulata* is married to a Spaniard, she may wear gold earrings with pearls, and a small necklace, and on her skirt a fringe of velvet. None may wear *mantos* of *burato* or of any other material, except short cloaks, which may reach to a little below the waist, under the penalty of having them, as well as any gold jewelry or silk clothing, taken away from them." [58] A similar, and even more stringent ordinance was issued by the Portuguese crown in 1749 to govern the garb of the colored population in Brazil.[59] Though offenders were occasionally beaten or stripped of their elegancies, these laws appear to have been enforced only lightly.[60] The Negroes continued to dress as they could, and in the middle of the eighteenth century, Juan and Ulloa commented that the black inhabitants of Cartagena wore only "a small piece of cotton stuff about their waist." However, they added: "Some Mulattoes and Negroes dress like the Spaniards and great men of the country." [61]

In spite of the greater stresses and strains which characterized Negro slavery in the Spanish colonies, conditions were favorable to emancipation.[62] The various processes and occasions of manumission were similar to those in Brazil, and the high ratio of freedom to bondsmen at the end of the colonial regime is testimony to their effectiveness.[63] Spanish jurisprudence had long been predisposed against the institution, and the *Siete Partidas*, the famous code of Alfonso IX of Castile, had clearly expressed the basic Spanish abhorrence of slavery.

Though the letter of the regulatory laws that governed Negro slavery in the colonies appears harsh at times, the potential menace of large-scale slave insurrections to Spanish authority and to the lives of the small body of Spanish settlers was always present. Under the circumstances, little mercy was to be expected anywhere in the world in that age. The institution itself was evil, and responsible Spaniards did not apologize for slavery. The spirit of leniency in which the most Draconian laws were often applied, and the tendency to ignore them altogether once the period of crisis was past reflects the aversion of the Spaniard to extreme measures. His humane instincts and the sense of equity which always moderated the rigors of Spanish law asserted themselves in normal times. As with the Portuguese, Spanish opinion treated the slave, not as a chattel to be held in perpetuity, but as a human being whose unfortunate condition was temporary. Under such a philosophy the logical end of slavery was freedom, so that the conscience of Spain made it easy for the slave to become a free man, and once he was free it attached no stigma to his past. If there were deliberate impediments to his future, they were the work of groups or individuals whose pride or self-interest preferred the order of things as it was. But the government was solicitous for his welfare, and one of the *Laws of the Indies* provided that "the Audiencias are to hear and to provide justice to those whose liberty is proclaimed." [64]

For those who remained in slavery, there were laws to protect them from cruel treatment. Most comprehensive of these was the slave code which was issued by the king in 1789.[65] While the royal order of that year restated some of the earlier legislation, there were new and advanced features which reflected the spirit of the "age of enlightenment" in Europe. Provision was made for the health and morals of the slaves, for the security of family ties, for the care of slaves too old to work, and for recourse to the courts against arbitrary and inhuman punishments. Though much good was doubtless accomplished especially through the intervention of the *abogado de los pobres,* or "lawyer of the poor," the reforms came too late to affect seriously the deep-seated abuses that were inherent in the institution itself.

The Mulatto

The mulatto early became an important element in the life of the Spanish colonies. He grew steadily in numbers and social influence through the colonial period and into the republics. The progressive desirability of the mulatto, after the initial crossing of white man and black woman, to the light-colored octoroon, beyond which step in the chromatic evolution there was no longer a question of color, accentuated the process of miscegenation.[66] Either as wife or concubine or as agent in a more casual mating, the woman of color co-operated, if not always fervently, at least passively, in the making of a new race that knew no distinctions of pigmentation.[67] In cities like Lima and Buenos Aires and Mexico, which had once had considerable slave populations, the Negro had almost completely disappeared as a separate and recognizable factor by the beginning of this century. In Cuba, the man of color was, and still is, in much evidence. And in the hot lands everywhere, as around the coasts of the Caribbean, where the whites had always been in the minority, the universal preponderance of the blacks ultimately produced a people with pronounced Negroid features and characteristics. They make up a large part of the population in cities like La Guaira and Santa Marta on the Spanish Main, the port towns of Central America; Acapulco [68] and Veracruz in Mexico, Santo Domingo in Hispaniola, and Guayaquil in Ecuador. In the tropical lowlands they have greatly influenced the tone of living, adding a certain insouciance and volatility and sensuousness to the general atmosphere of the community.[69] One observes how the limits of their influence are fixed by altitude as he goes up the valley of the Magdalena into the cool Colombian highlands, where the graver temper of the Indian takes over. Again one notes the change in reverse as he moves from Bogotá over into the lighter mood of Cali, lying in the warm and sunny Cauca Valley. There the Negro long ago found a congenial home, only to be absorbed eventually into the body of the population, but leaving his mark on the spirit of the place. No large city has reflected more the influence of the Negro than does Havana, with the readiness of its inhabitants for laughter and indulgence, the singsong rhythms of their speech, their devil-may-care attitude toward things, and their glibness of tongue. The *choteo,* which is an unforgettable feature of Cuban life—a gift for rough-and-ready ridicule and satire in the give-and-take of ordinary conversation—has its roots in the sprightly irreverence of the Negro.[70]

The mulatto as a separate element in society came into his own during the century after 1750. Whatever prejudices may have existed in the early history of the colonies had softened by then. Though grudgingly at first, the magnificoes of the colonies and their womenfolk had come to accept their presence as part of the local scheme of things. Their economic status had been greatly improved. They dominated some of the skilled trades in the cities, and some of them were later destined to make substantial fortunes in business. They took every opportunity to avail themselves of the education that opened the way to the professions and to the position of prestige which the professions provided. They developed the social graces, including a snobbish hauteur toward those who were darker-skinned than they were. They cultivated the art of conversation and were frequently better company than the original elite of the cities.[71] They proved to be skilled at ingratiating themselves into the favor of those who were recognized sources of power and position in the community. At last a society which had lost much of its forbidding stiffness and exclusiveness took them more and more to itself for what they were—often attractive and gifted individuals—and treated them as such. The political life of the republics afforded an ample and inviting arena for their ambitions and talents. Their sharp wit and ready tongue, their bent for fluid oratory, the suppleness that enabled them to bend easily to the sudden winds of politics or to take quick advantage of a favorable opening— all these proved valuable assets in this new field—and they made the most of their opportunities.[72]

THE NEGRO IN HAITI

The Negro of Haiti is a very special case. The Haitian Republic is *his* country, though a mulatto minority serves as the ruling class. It was founded by Negroes as a result of the only successful slave revolt in the history of the Western Hemisphere. Whites are insignificant in number and are latecomers, with only shallow—or no—roots in the land. The foreign element in the national culture is French instead of Hispanic.

In most of its details, the slave society of Haiti followed the traditional pattern of the plantation system in the tropics. Like that of Brazil and Cuba, it was based on the large-scale production of sugar. In the latter part of the seventeenth century, French buccaneers moved over to the western end of Hispaniola from their base on the nearby island of Tortuga and settled there. The title of France to the area was founded on its occupation by these retired seafarers, just as England laid claim to Belize when her own buccaneers found mahogany cutting a better—and safer— business than piracy. As soon as their claims were recognized in the cynical give-and-take of the Peace of Ryswick in 1697, the French began in earnest the development of their new colony of Saint Domingue. The colony gained in wealth and respectability as capital poured in from France and slaves from Africa.

In spite of its prosperity and the glamour of its social life, the situation in the richest of France's colonies was inherently explosive. The colony came too late, for the "Enlightenment" in Europe was laying the philosophical groundwork for a consideration of human rights that would shortly question the very principle of slavery. Moreover, the French, new to the responsibilities of slaveholding, had much to learn, which the Spaniards and, more particularly, the Portuguese had learned by two centuries of experience. The disparity between slaves and whites was dangerously high—over ten to one near the end of the regime in 1790. To relieve the inevitable tensions latent in such a situation, the Frenchman never learned how to bridge the crucial gap of sentiment which provided a safety valve in the relationship between master and slaves in Brazil. In other words, he never learned how to live with his Negroes as so many men and women. The critical class of the *affranchis* or freedmen, most of whom were mulattoes and many of whom were cultivated individuals, was alternately coddled and repressed. As a result of their social insecurity and frustrations of this intermediate group, the French beneficiaries of the system could not depend on their loyalty, and when the crisis came most of them threw in their lot with the slaves.

The French Revolution brought the fundamental issues to a head by its vacillating policies. After the French had lost the support of the mulattoes, the plantation slaves took advantage of the charged atmosphere in the colony to break out in open revolt in 1791. There followed over a decade of great confusion and violence, aggravated by a prolonged English invasion. It was during this chaotic interim that Spain ceded the eastern part of the island to France, but events moved too fast to allow the French to avail themselves of their new possession. The rise of Toussaint l'Ouverture, a Negro of extraordinary capacity for leadership,[73] appeared to offer a prospect for peace in 1801, but Bonaparte's abrogation of the agreements made with the Negro leader by the Directory reopened all the issues. The failure of General Leclerc's [74] efforts at armed suppression of the rebels and the treachery of the French in their dealings with Toussaint l'Ouverture ended the last chance of France to recover her rich colony. Under the ruthless direction of Jean Jacques Dessalines, the insurrection took on a new ferocity. Late in 1803 the last French troops left the island and early the next year the Republic of Haiti was born to a troubled life. Dessalines, self-appointed ruler in perpetuity, early simplified his administrative problems by exterminating the whites who had not managed to leave the island in time.

The ground was cleared for a free Negro state and society. The outside world looked with horror or contempt on the new republic that had been founded with so much bloodshed.[75] No one

extended a helping hand to it, and it was long before France, the
spiritual mother of its tenuous top-layer culture, deigned to accept its company. Spurned by foreign chancelleries, its black masters deliberately utilized the natural mulatto aristocracy as a
front of respectability in their dealings with other governments.
Left otherwise to their own resources in default of all political
experience, the founders of the republic had little to go by except
their own elemental instincts and native shrewdness.

In view of such a background, it was no wonder that for a
century the history of Haiti was so stormy and its evolution so
agonizing a process.[76] There were periods of anarchy when civilization seemed on the point of reverting to the jungle. However,
the welter of half-barbarous despotisms, like those of Christophe [77] and Soulouque, was relieved at intervals by the benevolent rule of some superior figure who revealed the promise of a
better future for the nation. This promise was not realized until
after the American occupation in this century. For while the
American intervention offended the national patriotism, and those
who benefited from the abuses of the old order, it provided a
foundation of political order, financial stability, and technical
knowledge, without which the country could never have risen to
its possibilities.[78]

The class structure of Haitian society is very simple. About
ninety-seven per cent of the population is made up of the black
peasantry; the small remainder consists of the elite, which is predominantly mulatto.[79] Among themselves, Haitians avoid any reference to color as a social line of demarcation. The Negro gives
little thought to his color, but the mulatto is extremely sensitive
to the prejudices of the "white" world on the outside. The fairer
skinned are secretly fond of their lighter pigmentation, yet they
realize that, unlike Brazil, the white leaven in Haiti is too small
ever to change materially the general complexion of the population. When they travel abroad, as they do frequently, the members
of the elite prefer to visit countries where color of skin is not a
social issue. For only then can they lose their self-consciousness
and feel at ease as the very agreeable human beings they generally are.

The great mass of the Haitian people live close to the earth.
It is no longer a good earth, in spite of the beauty of the land-

scape. The peasant grubs a poor living from the niggardly soil, which has been worn by centuries of erosion and indifferent cultivation. There are far too many of his kind for the land that is available, and the plot of ground which he works can give him only the barest necessities of life. They are a kindly and gentle folk,[80] who have evolved a simple philosophy of life that accords with the restricted circumstances of their existence. Their principal concern is to avoid the incidence of trouble. That is, they try to keep on good terms with their neighbors, with the unseen spirits who have the power to affect their lives, and with the agents of authority. They are careful to follow the time-honored rules of community living as they find them. They propitiate the spirits by the rites of voodoo, or Vodun, whose more sensational aspects have been greatly exaggerated. At the same time, they pay the proper respect to any priest of the Catholic Church who may reside in the neighborhood. As for the agents of government, they shun them as far as possible and try to avoid falling afoul of those who represent authority. They are conservative and suspicious of change and of strange ideas that are outside their limited ken. In short, they desire only to keep the little they have. For language, they speak "Creole," a grammarless farrago of words from French, Spanish, Carib, and various African tongues. Since Creole is virtually without a literature, they live outside the influence of the written word and within the bounds of a closed culture.

In very few countries does there remain so true an aristocracy as the Haitian elite. It represents the nation before the rest of the world. It is the exclusive repository of political and economic power. It is Society, as the cities of Haiti know it. It has a monopoly of all but the most elementary level of education. It speaks French, and this barrier of language separates it intellectually from the primitive world of the peasantry. It has a decorative culture which exists in a functional vacuum, far removed from the material problems of Haitian life. It is highly literate and indulges in good conversation as a mental exercise. It is intensely Francophile in its cultural leanings and discusses endlessly the current fashions of philosophical thought as they come from Paris. Its better-to-do members live well, if not luxuriously, in the pleasant mansions above Port-au-Prince. They have gracious manners and dress well, though conservatively. They profess the Roman Catholic faith and are married according to the rites of the Church, unlike the peasants, who customarily dispense with formal marriage as a needless expense, a dangerous concession to authority, and an impediment to freedom of action.

Yet, with all the advantages of its position in the social hierarchy of the country and the amenities of its daily life, this attractive and cultivated group is full of a deep discontent and restlessness. In spite of its studied cosmopolitanism, its provincial outlook only hides a great uneasiness about its little country's place in the world. The values on which it sets so much store are unhappily outmoded or ignored in an age of power politics and material achievement. It feels that it has no place in a world dominated by cataclysmic and cyclopean forces, in which the refinements of the human spirit seem to be in suspense. Meanwhile, it plays decorously at its way of life. It reads Proust and Maurras and argues the merits of Sartre as though he were the new bearer of "the Word." It holds an International Exposition, which it can ill afford, and a World Congress of Philosophy, in whose dialectics it revels for a brief spell. And while it displays a plaintive anxiety to be accepted by the rest of the civilized world at its own valuation, it cocks an ear toward the drums that beat in the hills at night, where the earthy substance of Haiti goes its primitive way.

THE NEGRO IN LATIN AMERICAN CIVILIZATION

The countries in which the Negroid element is most important today are Haiti, Brazil, and Cuba. It is also a substantial factor in the population of the Dominican Republic, Panama, and Venezuela, and to a somewhat lesser extent in Colombia, Honduras, and Nicaragua. In the lowlands of Central America, the original Negroid element has been considerably increased by the influx of Negroes from the British islands in the Caribbean, who were brought in as laborers in the Canal Zone or in the plantation enterprises in the coastal area to the north of Panama. Negroes of the same origin had penetrated much earlier into the belt of rain forest along the coasts of Honduras and Nicaragua in what became known as the Mosquito Territory. Here they intermingled with the sparse Indian population along the rivers to form a new Zambo race of hybrid culture.

In varying degrees, depending on his relative numbers, the duration of his residence, and the prevailing attitudes of the dominant European stock, he has influenced greatly the culture of these countries. He has left an indelible mark on life, sometimes limited to localities where he was most numerous, sometimes only in certain fields where his own potential contributions were naturally greatest, as in music and the dance and other expressions of his deep sense of rhythm. To the reserve of the Spaniard and Portuguese and the lower key of the Indian temperatment, he added a demonstrative and unrestrained emotional nature. For good or bad, he gave freer play to his strong feelings. Where the Indian could smile at most, the Negro could laugh uproariously. Where the Indian was taciturn or soft-spoken, he was glib and garrulous. Warmhearted and affectionate, he was capable of great loyalty and devotion. Though given to big talk and braggadocio, he could be as dignified as the Spaniard or the more stolid Indian. Moody and mercurial, his passions were quicker spent than those of the less volatile Indian. He was a creature of his impulses, rather than of rules or principles, and his slavery made of him a born opportunist. He had highly developed sensory feelings and was generally a fine human animal very conscious of his body and what it could contribute to his enjoyment of life. High-strung and inflammable, his capacity for disorderliness gave particular concern to the Spaniards. These qualities and values of the Negro have been thoroughly integrated into the regional character and civilization of Latin America. Except for those who were influenced by the "racist" philosophy of the Comte de Gobineau,[81] few Latin Americans of our time have questioned the net worth of the Negro as an ingredient in the national society of their countries.

NOTES

1. Oviedo, *Historia General*, III, 12. Peter Martyr reported that in 1513 the Spaniards heard of a Negro community in the Isthmus, whose members were descendants of shipwrecked Ethiopian pirates! *De Orbe Novo*, I, 286.

2. Bernal Díaz, *The True History*, p. 240.

3. Garcilaso de la Vega, *Historia General*, I, 235.

4. *Ibid.*, II, 274.

5. Vernon, *Pedro de Valdivia, Conquistador of Chile* (Austin, Texas, 1946), p. 63. According to Agustín Edwards, the first Negro to reach Chile landed from a shipwreck in 1544. The Indians captured him and washed him with boiling water. Then they scoured his skin with corn husks and opened him to see what was inside. *My Native Land* (London, 1928), p. 129.

6. Alexander von Humboldt, *Personal Narrative of Travels to the Equinoctial Regions of the New Continent, during the Years 1799–1804* (tr. from the German, 7 vols., London, 1814–29), IV, 70.

7. Moses, *The Spanish Dependencies in South America* (2 vols., New York, 1914), II, 264-6.

8. Hakluyt, *Voyages*, VII, 5.

9. *Ibid.*, p. 55.

10. *Ibid.*, p. 159.

11. Dampier, *A New Voyage Round the World* (London, 1937), p. 114.

12. Arthur Ramos, *The Negro in Brazil* (tr. from the Portuguese, Washington, D. C., 1939), p. 1.

13. Hernando Pizarro was granted permission to own four white slaves.

14. Cristóbal Bermúdez Plata, and others, eds., *Catálogo de Pasajeros a Indias* (2 vols., Seville, 1940–42).

15. The Italian, Girolamo Benzoni, who was in the Indies in the middle of the sixteenth century, said that many Spaniards then living in Santo Domingo predicted that the island would be taken over by the Negroes—"questri Mori di Guinea." *Istoria del mondo nuovo*, quoted by Humboldt, *op. cit.*, p. 158. "The Spaniards lacking men to worke in their Ingenios, and to looke unto their cattell, they are forced to bring Negroes out of Guinea, where they have so increased that the Island is nowe as full of them, as it was of the naturell inhabitantes; so that the Spaniards carrie Negroes from this Island to the maineland and there sell them." Lopes Vaz, in Hakluyt, *op. cit.*, VIII, 164.

16. Thomas Gage, *A New Survey of the West Indies, 1648* (New York, 1929), p. 166.

17. Hakluyt, *op. cit.*, VIII, 137.

18. Frank Tannenbaum, *Slave and Citizen: The Negro in the Americas* (New York, 1947), p. 9.

19. Concolorcorvo, *El Lazarillo de Ciegos Caminantes, desde Buenos Aires hasta Lima* (Buenos Aires, 1946), p. 58.

20. Domingo Faustino Sarmiento, *Facundo: Civilización y Barbarie* (Buenos Aires, 1938), p. 76.

21. E.g., Alexander von Humboldt and F. Depons.

22. The outstanding work on the slave society of northern Brazil is Gilberto Freyre, *The Masters and the Slaves* (New York, 1946), translated by Samuel Putnam from the Portuguese, *Casa Grande e Senzala*. See also, by the same author, *Sobrados e Mucambos;* and *Brazil: an Interpretation* (New York, 1945).

23. Johan Baptist von Spix, the German scientist who visited Brazil during the Empire, wrote: "The condition of these slaves is much less unfortunate than is the general belief in Europe; they do not suffer from a lack of food, they dress in conformity with the demands of the climate, and they are rarely overworked." Spix

and Martius, *Viagem pelo Brasil* (tr. from the German, 3 vols., Rio de Janeiro, 1938), II, 301. Cf. the comments of other writers and observers: "Nowhere, even in oriental countries, has the 'bitter draught' so little of gall in it." Richard F. Burton, *Explorations of the Highlands of the Brazil* (2 vols., London, 1869), I, 270: "Humane and intimate relations between master and slave were . . . in all likelihood . . . the general rule." Donald Pierson, *Negroes in Brazil* (Chicago, 1942), p. 50: "The Negroes whether free blacks, or slaves, look cheerful and happy at their labors." Maria Graham, *Journal of a Voyage to Brazil* (London, 1824), p. 170.

24. "The dynamics of race contact and self-interest were stronger than prejudice, theory, law or belief. The difference was that in Brazil it was accepted as a matter of course and has come to be, to a certain extent, a point of pride." Frank Tannenbaum, *op. cit.*, p. 121.

25. Freyre, who has much to say on this subject, speaks of the "procreative fervor" of these "unbridled stallions." *The Masters and the Slaves*, pp. 10, 29. The Brazilian historian, Caio Prado Junior, writes of the "profound crossbreeding of the three races (Portuguese, Indian, and Negro) . . . mixing without limit, in an orgy of unrestrained sexualism, which was to make the population of Brazil one of the most variegated ethnic compounds that humanity has ever known." *Formação do Brasil Contemporáneo* (São Paulo, 1942), p. 102.

26. Afranio Peixoto, the distinguished Brazilian physician and writer, tells of a luncheon at Columbia University at which John Dewey remarked to him: "The seduction of the woman of color is irresistible." To this Peixoto remarks: "We never heard that expressed so explicitly in Bahia." *Breviario da Bahia* (Rio de Janeiro, 1925), p. 325. He then continues with comments on the sexual attractions of the mulatto women: "Custa a conquista de uma branca. Êstes ídolos parados condescendem, mas não se dão, não sabem retribuir. Deixam-se amar. Se amam, escondem-se, envergonhadas. Algumas se arrependem ou resmungam. O amor lhes é uma posição social, o casamento é um sacrifício, imposto pela necessidade. O êxtase é substituido por um frêmito. Se atraem, não retem. . . . A outra não, sente-se exaltada com o amor do branco; dá-se-lhe sem reservas; humilha-se, abole-se totalmente, e tanto, que não se deixam amar apenas; são espontâneas, ativas, diligentes, provocando e oferecendo, irrestritamente, ao seu dono, dócil e plástica, nas mãos dêle, e, o que é mais, depois, agradecida." *Ibid.*, p. 326.

27. Descendants of these women, whom Freyre describes as "very tall, heraldic-appearing, aristocratic in bearing," *The Masters and the Slaves*, p. 319, are very common in Bahia today. Mrs. Agassiz, who visited Brazil in the sixties with her husband, the famous scientist, described the "Minas" whom she saw at Bahia, as "fine-looking athletic Negroes of a nobler type, at least physically, than any we see in the States. They are a very powerful-looking race, and the women especially are finely made and have quite a dignified presence." *A Journey in Brazil* (Boston, 1869), p. 82.

28. "From their first contact with women of color they mingled with them and procreated mestizo sons, and the result was that a few thousand daring males succeeded in establishing themselves firmly in possession of a vast territory and were able to compete with great and numerous peoples in the extension of their colonial domain and in the efficiency of their colonizing activity." Freyre, *op. cit.*, p. 11.

29. Lieuts. Herndon and Gibbon, U.S.N., who made a survey of the Amazon

Valley from the west, wrote: "Our experience with a black crew gives reason to believe the climate is more congenial to them than the red or white races. . . . The Indian enjoys the shade of the forest trees, while our Negroes rejoice in the heat of the sun." They remarked that whereas few Indian men seemed to live beyond forty, they found many old Negroes in Brazil who were still active and high-spirited. *Exploration of the Valley of the Amazon* (2 vols., Washington, D. C., 1854), I, 302. Cf. the comments of Freyre: "The Negroes were possessed of something like a biologic and psychic predisposition to life in the tropics. There was their greater fertility in hot regions, their taste for the sun, their energy, always fresh and new when in contact with the tropical jungle." *The Masters and the Slaves*, p. 282.

30. "The Negro slave seems very happy in Brazil. This is remarked by all foreigners." Herndon and Gibbon, *op. cit.*, I, 337.

31. "The rise of the mulatto, as also that of the slave, was further favored by the gradual, rather than catastrophic, character of the emancipation process, which in Brazil released most of the lower stratum of society from servile status gradually and as individuals, under circumstances favorable to the continuance of those intimate personal ties so highly advantageous to a 'new freeman'." Pierson, *op. cit.*, p. 171.

32. "The freeing of one's slaves was an honorific tradition, and men fulfilled it on numerous occasions." Tannenbaum, *op. cit.*, p. 58.

33. "Negroes are now rapidly disappearing in Brazil, merging into the white stock; in some areas the tendency seems to be towards the stabilization of mixed-bloods in a new ethnic type, similar to the Polynesian." Freyre, *Brazil: An Interpretation*, p. 96.

34. Frank Tannenbaum says of the traditional Brazilian tolerance of differences of color, "In Brazil the Negro, and especially the mulatto, had an access to the culture and a role in social life unknown in the United States. In politics, in the arts, and in society the mulatto found the door ajar, even if not fully open, and a markedly different social milieu has come into being. Even under the Empire the Negro and the mulatto—and socially, the attractive mulatto woman—had an acceptance unthinkable in the American scene." *Op. cit.*, p. 4.

35. Sometimes the Negroes told English landing parties of the location of the Spaniards; at other times they deliberately misled the invaders. "There is no trust or confidence in any of these Negroes, and therefore we must heed and beware of them; for they are our mortal enemies." Hakluyt, *op. cit.*, VII, 121.

36. "The Zambos are more robust than the mulattoes, they are morose and stubborn, partaking very much of the character of the African Negro, but prone to more vices. A greater number of robberies and murders are committed by this caste than by all the rest, except the Chino (mixture of Negro and Chinese), the worst mixed breed in existence: he is cruel, revengeful, and unforgiving, very ugly, as if his soul were expressed in his features; lazy, stupid, and provoking." W. B. Stevenson, *A Historical and Descriptive Narrative of Twenty Years' Residence in South America* (3 vols., London, 1825), I, 309. Fray Vázquez de Espinosa describes the interesting Zambo colony which he visited in the Esmeraldas region. These were believed to be descendants of shipwrecked slaves who killed off the Indian men of the locality and appropriated their women to themselves. Of these

he wrote: "They are good-looking and all wear gold nose-plugs in their nostrils, gold plaques on their breasts, and gold ear-loops." *Compendium and Description of the West Indies* (tr. from the Spanish, Washington, D. C., 1942), p. 375. Stevenson wrote of them over a century later, as "tall and rather slender, of lightish black colour, soft curly hair, large eyes, nose rather flat, and thick lips, possessing more of the Negro than of the Indian." *Op. cit.*, II, 387.

37. Gage, *op. cit.*, p. 205.

38. Henry Bamford Parkes, *A History of Mexico* (New York, 1938), p. 95 (note).

39. Oviedo, *op. cit.*, II, 109, 256.

40. Moses, *op. cit.*, II, 400.

41. Herrera, *op. cit.*, D. VIII, L. VI, 137.

42. *Leyes*, L. 7, t. 5, laws nos. 21, 22, 23.

43. Arthur Franklin Zimmerman, *Francisco de Toledo, Fifth Viceroy of Peru* (Caldwell, Idaho, 1938), p. 164.

44. Vázquez, *op. cit.*, p. 341.

45. Giovanni Gemelli Careri, in Churchill, *A Collection of Voyages and Travels* (4 vols., London, 1704).

46. Vázquez, *op. cit.*, p. 304; Juan and Ulloa, *A Voyage to South America* (tr. from the Spanish, 2 vols., London, 1806), I, 109, 134; William Dampier, *op. cit.*, p. 125.

47. *Leyes*, L. 7, t. 5, laws nos. 14, 15, 17. In view of their military value, one law (number 10) ordered the royal officials to "look to the good treatment of the free men of color, and to respect their privileges."

48. Salvador de Madariaga, *Cuadro Histórico de las Indias* (Buenos Aires, 1945), pp. 531-9.

49. Of a dinner ball which she attended in Havana Mme. Calderón de la Barca wrote: "After supper we were amused to see the Negroes and negresses helping themselves plentifully to the sweetmeats, uncorking and drinking fresh bottles of champagne, and devouring everything on the supper tables, without the slightest concern for the presence either of their master or mistress." *Life in Mexico during a Residence of Two Years in that Country* (Everyman Edition), p. 16.

50. Stevenson, *op. cit.*, I, 303.

51. "The Negro was a singer, an inveterate and incorrigible singer." Luis Alberto Sánchez, *Vida y Pasión de la Cultura en América* (Santiago, 1935), p. 53.

52. *Brazil and the Brazilians* (London and Boston, 1857).

53. Basil Hall, *Extracts from a Journal* (2 vols., Edinburgh, 1824), II, 152-43.

54. *Viage*, II, 295.

55. Lucio V. Mansilla, *Una Excursión a los Indios Ranqueles* (Buenos Aires, 1942), p. 151.

56. Concolorcorvo, *op. cit.*, pp. 200-1.

57. *Leyes*, L. I, t. 1, law no. 13.

58. *Leyes*, L. i, t. 5, law no. 28.

59. Luiz Edmundo, *Rio in the Time of the Viceroys*, p. 161, in Wilgus, ed., *Readings in Latin American Civilization* (New York, 1946), p. 153.

60. F. Depons, *A Voyage to the Eastern Part of Tierra Firme* (tr. from the French, 3 vols., New York, 1806), I, 194.

194 THIS NEW WORLD

61. Juan and Ulloa, *op. cit.*, I, 1, 31-32. Of some of the social effects of the prevailing styles of dress among the lower class of colored women in Mexico City, Thomas Gage wrote: "The attire of this baser sort of people of blackamoors and mulattoes is so light, and their carriage so enticing that many Spaniards, even of the better sort (who are too prone to venery) disclaim their wives for them." As a fashion note, he adds: "Their bare black and tawny breasts are covered with bobs hanging from chains of pearls." Gage, *op. cit.*, pp. 85-6.

62. "The number of freedmen is very considerable: Spanish laws and customs favor emancipation. A master cannot refuse his freedom to a slave who offers him the sum of 300 pesos, even though the slave may have cost double that. The number of persons who, in their wills, free a certain number of slaves is higher in the Province of Venezuela than elsewhere." Humboldt, *op. cit.*, IV, 161.

63. The Frenchman, Depons, who was in Venezuela during this period, said: "The Spanish possessions have more freedmen and descendants of freedmen than slaves." Depons, *op. cit.*, I, 168.

64. *Leyes,* L. 7, t. 15, law no. 8.

65. Moses, *op. cit.*, II, 404; Depons, *op. cit.*, I, 164-6.

66. Where the mulatto was the child of a white woman by a black man, the motivation of the woman·was generally revenge for the interracial philanderings of her husband. On various aspects of this problem, see Depons, *op. cit.*, I, 160.

67. The high social value of a light skin was a further stimulus to these unions. After cataloguing the successive gradations of the mulatto population of Cartagena, Juan and Ulloa wrote: "Every person is so jealous of the order of their tribe or cast, that if, through inadvertence, you call them by a degree lower than what they actually are, they are highly offended, never suffering themselves to be deprived of so valuable a gift of fortune." Juan and Ulloa, *op. cit.*, I, 29-30. After sacking Guayaquil, the English privateer, Capt. Woodes Rogers, remarked: "The King of Spain is able to match the skins of his Americans to any colour, with more variety and exactness than a Draper can match with his cloth and trimming." *A Cruising Voyage Round the World* (London, 1928), p. 150. Sometimes for a consideration, the royal authorities formally certified to the whiteness of mulattoes. M. Depons wrote: "During my stay at Caracas a whole family of colour obtained from the king all the privileges attaching to the whites." One of the most prized of these privileges was the right to kneel on a rug in church. Depons, *op. cit.*, I, 168.

68. "The climate is hot and deleterious, though healthy for Negroes and mulattoes, for that reason and because it is a wealthy port, many of them live there." Vázquez, *op. cit.*, p. 169.

69. The low-class mulatto, like the free Negro, also probably contributed more than his share to the disorders and crime of both the colonial and early republican periods. Herndon and Gibbon wrote: "The Negro murderers on the highways of Peru are more desperate and unmerciful than either the Spaniard or the mestizo." And again of their boat crews on the Amazon: "We were in hopes of getting rid of those impudent half-savage free Negroes who refused positively to obey the authorities of the town (Borba)." Herndon and Gibbon, *op. cit.*, I, 285, 312.

70. Richard Pattee, *Introducción a la Civilización Hispano-Americana* (Boston, 1945), p. 68.

71. French travelers who visited Cuba in the latter part of the eighteenth century commented that the only women in the island who could carry on an interesting conversation were the *mulatas*. On the place of the mulatto in Lima society in the early nineteenth century, see Stevenson, *op. cit.*, I, 307.

72. See Luís E. Valcarcel, *Ruta Cultural del Perú* (Mexico, D. F., 1945), p. 95, and Jorge Basadre, *Perú: Problema y Posibilidad* (Lima, 1931), p. 121.

73. He was the subject of a panegyric by Wendell Phillips, the famous American abolitionist.

74. General Leclerc, by his marriage to Pauline Bonaparte, was brother-in-law of Napoleon, who was at the time First Consul of the French Republic.

75. See Richard Pattee, in Charles C. Griffin, ed., *Concerning Latin American Culture* (New York, 1940), p. 23. Pattee is one of the best-informed and most understanding of American authorities on Haiti.

76. See H. P. Davis, *Black Democracy: the Story of Haiti* (New York, 1928); also, Spencer St. John, *Haiti* (London, 1889) and Dantes Bellegarde, *La Nation Haitienne* (Paris, 1938).

77. Three of the rulers of Haiti—Dessalines, Christophe, and Soulouque—had themselves proclaimed as king or emperor.

78. On the American occupation, see Charles E. Chapman, "The Development of Intervention in Haiti," *Hispanic American Historical Review*, August, 1927, and A. C. Millspaugh, "Our Haitian Problem," *Foreign Affairs,* July, 1929.

79. The most satisfactory work on this subject is James G. Leyburn, *The Haitian People* (New Haven, 1941).

80. "To know the average Haitian is to feel a warm affection for him. His life is never easy, yet he bears it with true beauty of spirit." Leyburn, *op. cit.*, 295.

81. French diplomat and scholar, author of *Essai sur l'inégalité des races humaines*. For an example of the influence which his "Aryanism" had on Latin American opinion, see Francisco García Calderón, *Latin America: Its Rise and Progress* (tr. from the French, London, 1915), pp. 355-62.

Chapter VI
THE FOREIGNER

ONE OF the Laws of the Indies provided that "no foreigner, or prohibited person, may trade in the Indies or go to them," unless he was first naturalized and then cleared by the *Casa de Contratación,* or House of Trade.[1] That was in 1592, a century after the discovery.[2] Rules for the exclusion or control of foreigners were in force from early times, but the body of anti-foreign legislation which was later codified in the *Recopilación* did not begin to appear as royal decrees, or *cédulas,* until after the middle of the sixteenth century. For the purpose of the restrictive laws, a foreigner could be naturalized if he had lived for twenty years in Spain or the Indies, provided that for half of that period he had possessed a house and property to the value of

4,000 ducats, and was married to a Spanish woman or to the Spanish-born daughter of a foreigner.[3]

The most severe of the exclusionist laws was that of 1614, prohibiting trade with foreigners in the Indies under pain of death and confiscation of property.[4] There is no record of this extreme penalty ever having been applied. A law of 1602 had ordered the colonial officials "to clean the land of foreigners and persons who were suspicious in matters of the Faith." [5] All such heretics were to be "thrown out of the Indies" as a menace to the orthodoxy of the aborigines and other "ignorant people." As a security measure, the viceregal authorities were also to use their efforts to prevent foreigners who resided in the Indies from informing their home governments of the state of the defenses of the Spanish colonies.[6] Foreigners who were permitted to go to the Indies were forbidden to remain in the port cities,[7] and unmarried foreigners who were found living on the Spanish-American coasts were to be summarily expelled from the Indies, unless they held licenses of residence from the government.[8]

The laws against foreigners were not applicable to artisans, whose skills were declared to be "valuable to the Republic," but were aimed largely at traders.[9] Their principal purpose was stated to be the "purging of the Republic of unsuitable persons, and keeping those who are useful and necessary, while guarding the integrity of our Holy Catholic Faith." Officials were to be lenient in applying them to foreigners of long residence, or to those who had performed useful services in the period of discovery or in the civil wars, or "alterations," of the Conquest, or to those who were married and had children or grandchildren.[10] Special concessions were always made to those who had established roots (*arraygados*) in the colonies. It was made easy for such persons to obtain the necessary permit or "composition" to remain in the Indies, though on condition that they live in the interior and refrain from moving from one viceroyalty to another. They could even hold Indians in encomienda. The Portuguese were long exempt from the legal provisions against foreigners, but from 1614 they were to be treated as outsiders.[11]

Such was the official policy of Spain. Its motives were compounded of three considerations, political, economic, and religious: the security of the colonial empire, the Spanish monopoly

of trade with the colonies, and the preservation of Catholic orthodoxy against the invasions of heresy. The laws which embodied
these policies appear to have been indifferently enforced by the
officials who were charged with their execution. Some colonies,
like Paraguay, were always hospitable to foreigners.[12] The colonial authorities were liable to be influenced by self-interest, by
mental reservations about the legislation itself, or by ties of
friendship, that potent motivation which among Spanish peoples
easily transcends more formal obligations. The government in
Spain eventually recognized the futility of its efforts to control
the entry of aliens into the New World, and in 1667 it issued another law, commanding the viceroys, *audiencias,* and governors
to round up all unlicensed foreigners in their jurisdictions and to
pack them off to the *Casa de Contratación* at Seville.[13] "There is
no prohibition oftener repeated," reads the law, "than that against
unlicensed foreigners going to the Indies, as has always been ordered by many decrees and ordinances." Then it adds, "Nothing
is so important as to put them into effect." Beyond a temporary
spurt in enforcement, there is nothing to indicate that the exclusion laws were generally any better observed than formerly,
though occasional high officials of the viceroyalties continued to
take the laws very seriously in their treatment of foreigners.[14]
By then, fear of the Inquisition was the most formidable deterrent to the presence of unauthorized foreigners in the Spanish
Indies. At least, the Inquisition was consistent in its zeal, and it
was not in the habit of making friends.

In the Middle Ages, Spaniards, like most Europeans, were
likely to be wary of outsiders. Politically fragmentized as it was,
Europe was parochial in its organization and its outlook, and, cut
off from the body of the Continent by the wall of the Pyrenees,
no people were more parochial-minded than the inhabitants of the
Iberian Peninsula. The Hispanic peoples were not only suspicious
of other peoples, but the natives of the various shifting kingdoms
distrusted each other, and well into the period of the colonial
empire, Basques and Catalans and Navarrese were treated as
strangers by the Castilians.

This universal xenophobia, which Spaniards shared with
Frenchmen and Germans, was the natural result of the conditions
of the times. In an age of disorder, like the Middle Ages, when

roving armies, whether Vikings out of Scandinavia or Mongol hordes out of Asia, or raiding parties from across the river, perpetually harried the little men in their path, it was natural for people to associate the stranger with the enemy. To the lower classes—and most of Europe was lower class—the concepts of universalism and the brotherhood of man represented by the Church were beyond their ken—or the range of their curiosity. As unfamiliar to them was the feeling of nationality or the spirit of patriotism, with its loyalty to an impersonal state and dislike of those who lived outside its boundaries.

The discovery and conquest of the New World coincided in time with a series of momentous changes in the life of Spain, that were to affect deeply the temper of its peoples. In the early sixteenth century the innate pride of the Spaniard took on an antiforeign turn. In 1513, Francesco Guicciardini, Ambassador of Venice at the court of Spain, and a shrewd observer of Spanish customs, said of the Spaniards: "They have little love for foreigners and are very uncivil toward them." At that time they had only recently expelled the last remnants of the Moors from the Peninsula, driven the recalcitrant part of the Jewish population into permanent exile, established a strong foothold in Italy, and opened up a new world beyond the Atlantic. The kingdoms of the Spains were at last unified under strong and wise monarchs who were capable of arousing the enthusiastic devotion of their subjects. It is no wonder that the famous pride of the race now asserted itself in a new arrogance and contempt for foreigners that grew with the widening circle of conquest. When the Sieur de Brantome saw the long invincible soldiery on the march, he said they carried themselves like princes. For Spaniards entered their "golden century" with their heads high, and on their haughty faces was disdain for other peoples.

The suspicion of foreigners assumed a much milder form among the Portuguese than it did among the Castilians. Their relations with the old and highly civilized peoples of Asia during the early part of the sixteenth century made the Portuguese remarkably tolerant of other races throughout the period of their expansion into the New World.[15] Like the Spaniards, they were an ethnically complex people and had received a considerable infusion of north European blood during the time of the Crusades.

However, they appear to have assimilated the various extraneous elements in their racial composition—Moorish, Jewish, Germanic, and, more recently, Negro—more successfully and with fewer consequent tensions than did the Spaniards. Moreover, their pride was not fortified by any consciousness of their country's power, about which they held no illusions. As a result, they were disposed, both in Europe and in Brazil, to show much less antagonism toward other people with whom they came in contact. In Brazil, the only standard applied to the admission of foreigners was a religious one.[16]

The Protestant Reformation and the attendant schism in the Christian world had the result of aggravating the national intransigence of the Spaniards as the special guardians of the Catholic faith. The stranger was now distrusted because he was a heretic or a religious suspect as well as a foreigner. As the number of dissidents multiplied in Europe, and heterodoxy in various guises appeared even in the Peninsula, the tendency of the Spaniard, who was never given to subtle distinctions, to confuse all outsiders with schismatics grew stronger. It was seldom that he drew a distinction between the two, as Pedro Menéndez de Áviles did when he wiped out the Huguenot colony in Florida, and served notice that he had dealt with his victims "not as Frenchmen, but as Lutherans." Meanwhile, the efforts of the Church, and particularly of the Inquisition, to combat heresy in the Spanish dominions had promoted the growing spirit of intolerance in the nation. The Inquisition was now to become the principal instrument in the government's campaign against foreigners, for heresy and treason to the mind of Spain were one and the same thing.

In practice, Spanish individualism tempered the belligerent racism of the nation. While inclined collectively to be hostile to foreigners, the Spaniard was accustomed to judge the lone foreigner on his merits as a man rather than as an alien, and to treat him accordingly. Moreover, his basic humanity made him very considerate of foreigners who were in distress, as was so widely demonstrated in Mexico by the merciful treatment of Hawkins's Englishmen by the Spanish civilians in the viceroyalty. It was only when they fell into the hands of royal officials, and especially of the Inquisition, that they suffered any indignities or cruelties at the hands of the Spaniards.

If the Inquisition, as part of the royal machinery of political control, was uncompromisingly antiforeign, the religious orders were likely to be cosmopolitan in their make-up and attitudes. This was particularly true of the Society of Jesus, whose international character was one of the factors which led to its ultimate suppression by the Spanish government. Among prominent Jesuit missionaries in the New World, one finds many such non-Hispanic names as Fritz, Sontag, Kino, Fields, and Gervasoni.

THE ITALIANS IN THE CONQUEST

In addition to the three Columbus brothers, Christopher, Bartholomew, and Diego, many other Italians took part in the discovery and conquest of the New World. As might have been expected, the majority of them were Genoese or men from other points on the Ligurian Coast. The influence of the Admiral, and, later, of his son Diego, was able, as the historian Peter Martyr observed, to obtain the necessary authorizations for their fellow Genoese.[17] Michele de Cuneo, of Savona, a friend of the Admiral, commanded the *Niña* on her second voyage across the Atlantic. Bartolomeo Fieschi, of Genoa, was in command of the *Vizcaina* on the third voyage of Columbus. Both were able navigators and men of character and courage. Another Genoese of the same stamp was Giovanni Batista de Pastene, "Pilot—and Lieutenant General of the South Sea," who performed invaluable service for Valdivia in the conquest of Chile by maintaining the ocean connection with Peru. Of landsmen, probably the most famous Genoese was Giuseppe della Doria, who was one of the early settlers at São Vicente in southern Brazil. Member of an illustrious house of the republic, he became a wealthy sugar planter and in a hazardous age lived to be a hundred years old. His daughter married John Whithal, an enterprising young Englishman, to whom she brought as dowry a sugar mill and a large number of slaves. Doria's hospitality to stray foreigners was legendary, as were his benefactions. Among his good works was the founding of the Carmelite order in the community. Another Genoese, known to the Spaniards as Blas Testanova, served as physician to the young colony of Asunción in Paraguay, as another Italian, Lorenzo Minangliotti, did a half century later.[18]

Of other Italians, those best known to history were Amerigo Vespucci and Sebastian Caboto or Cabot. Vespucci, after whom the New World was named, was a Florentine and first appeared in Spain in 1492, probably as an agent of the banking house of the Medici. His fame as a navigator was due to the four long voyages which he claimed to have made for Spain and Portugal. Though his own accounts of those voyages were sometimes so confused and vague as to arouse the incredulity of serious historians, he evidently spent enough time at sea to acquire a considerable reputation as navigator and oceanographer, as a result of which he was made Pilot Major of Spain. His nephew, Giovanni Vespucci, was pilot of the flagship in the fleet of Pedrarias Dávila which went to the Isthmus in 1513. According to Peter Martyr, Giovanni "had inherited his uncle's great ability in the art of navigation and taking reckonings."

As a result of his Genoese-born father's naturalization, Sebastian Cabot was of Venetian nationality. A sailor-of-fortune and, like his father, a consummate navigator, he alternated between the maritime service of England and Spain. For Spain he headed an expedition in 1525 which was intended to follow Magellan's route around South America, but was diverted into the River Plate and far up the Paraná by reports of great riches in the interior of the continent. On his return to Spain from a somewhat fruitless voyage he was out of favor for a while, but was eventually restored to the high post as Pilot Major, which had been filled earlier by the elder Vespucci.

Many years after Cabot had sailed up the Paraná, a Genoese merchant named Leo Pancaldo, who was bound for Peru with a cargo of merchandise, instead took his ship upriver to Asunción. There he sold his goods to the eager Spanish settlers and initiated Paraguay's foreign trade with the outside world. Among other Italians of various categories who were found in the New World in the time of the Conquest were Francesco de Lentin, a companion of Balboa in Darien;[19] Pietro de Umbria, commander of one of Nicuesa's brigantines in the Caribbean; Francesco Cotta, who accompanied the expedition of Pedrarias Dávila; "Nicholas the Florentine," barber to the bewhiskered Spanish soldiery in

Paraguay; and one "Codrus," a learned naturalist who studied the botany of the Indies. Antonio Pigafetta, a patrician of Venice, went along for the trip with Magellan and became the chronicler of that epic voyage.[20] One of the distinguished Florentine house of the Cavalcanti migrated to northern Brazil during the colonial period.

The records of the *Casa de Contratación* reveal the passage of more Italians to the Americas during the period of the Conquest.[21] In 1516, two Neapolitans were granted licenses to go to the Indies. Ten years later three Genoese were authorized to cross the Atlantic in Spanish ships—one of them to remain a maximum of ten years in the colonies. In 1534, two Genoese and one Neapolitan were licensed to make the voyage. The following year a company of seven Genoese were given specific permits for New Spain, and two more Genoese and a Milanese received authorization to accompany Mendoza's expedition to the River Plate. In 1536, a Florentine citizen was admitted to Santo Domingo.

Vázquez de Espinosa reported eleven Genoese and seven Corsicans as living in the mining center of Castrovirreina in the Peruvian Andes in 1610, and several merchants of the same origins in the city of Chuquisaca (now Sucre).[22] In 1808, toward the end of the colonial regime, thirteen Italians were residing in Santiago, the largest foreign colony in the provincial capital of Chile.[23] The persistence with which Italians migrated to the New World, in spite of all the Spanish prohibitions against the admission of foreigners, is testimony to the general favor with which Spaniards looked upon them as useful and adaptable colonists and to the circumstance that their presence as nationals of the relatively weak city-states of Italy represented no political threat to the security of the Spanish Empire.

THE FRENCH

With the French, it was otherwise. It is not surprising that the only Frenchmen known to have received licenses from the *Casa de Contratación* for passage to the Spanish colonies were five pastry cooks, who were authorized to proceed to New Spain in 1538. Listed only as Guillaume, Pierrot, Henri, Raymond, and Pierre, they were evidently considered innocuous enough not to threaten the security of the viceroyalty. Their admission to Mexico as *"maestros de hacer pastel"* is indicative of the changes which had already occurred in the style of living of the local Spaniards.[24] The French were citizens of a powerful and aggressive nation which had imperial designs of its own, and looked with scant respect on Spain's papal title to dominions in the New World. Spaniards and Frenchmen fought for the hegemony of Italy, and the Valois king, Francis I, and Charles V were rivals for control of the Continent. The acceptance of Calvinism by a large body of Frenchmen made the French people more suspect than ever to the highly orthodox governments of Portugal and Spain, especially after the efforts of the Huguenot heretics to establish colonies in Brazil and Florida. It was only during the *Decadencia* of Spain, which followed the reign of Philip II, that the French made much headway with their designs in the Americas. But by then they were preoccupied with their interests in Canada and India, and were primarily concerned with the commercial possibilities of the Spanish colonies. After the accession of a Bourbon prince to the Spanish throne as Philip V in 1700, the policy of Spain became more favorable to French interests. For a time the bold and enterprising merchants of Brittany and Normandy made trading voyages at will to the west coast of South America and to other parts of the Spanish Empire.[25] Though they generally confined their ventures to the coasts, an occasional French merchant traveled to the interior cities, as Acarrete du Biscay had done in 1658.[26] But Acarrete was in South America before the *rapprochement* between the two monarchies, and had to contend with the traditional suspicion of Spaniards toward foreigners. He crossed to the River Plate in a Spanish vessel under an assumed name, "because in Spain only native-born Spaniards are allowed to go in their ships to the Indies." In the port of Buenos Aires he found twenty Dutch and two English ships, loaded with hides, silver, and vicuña wool. He heard later that on their way out of the river the Dutch took a French frigate and put everybody on board to the sword, as one of the customary amenities of commercial competition in that age. He reported that at Buenos Aires there were "a few Frenchmen, Hollanders, and Genoese, but all of them pass for Spaniards, otherwise they could not reside here, especially those who differ in their religion from the Roman Catholic, since the Inquisition is established here." He found few foreigners at Potosí in upper Peru. In addition to Dutchmen, Irishmen, and the usual Genoese, there were some Frenchmen from St. Malo, Bayonne, and Provence who masqueraded as Navarrese and Basques.

In spite of long periods of open hostility between the two countries, the territorial gains of the French at the expense of Spain were very small. The most substantial of these was the western end of Hispaniola, which the French called Saint Domingue, but this acquistion was made by French buccaneers who presumably operated independently of the royal authority. Sometimes in company with Englishmen or Dutchmen, sometimes alone, French pirates harried Spanish shipping and port cities about the Caribbean during the latter part of the seventeenth century. In 1697, a French fleet with over 4,000 men on board captured Cartagena and held it for ransom. Since his force was already heavily decimated by disease, the French admiral then sailed away and made no effort to retain possession of the important city. After he had left, twelve hundred French buccaneers, who had served as auxiliaries in the expedition, mercilessly sacked the stricken city.[27]

French designs on Brazil were more serious and persistent than their efforts against the Spanish colonies. Though ships from Dieppe and St. Malo are believed to have visited Brazil soon after its discovery by the Portuguese, the first recorded voyage was made by Binot Paulmier de Gonneville of Honfleur in 1503. It was many years before the Portuguese began the active development of their vast colony which was neglected in favor of the rich commerce with the Orient. Meanwhile the French made regular trading voyages to the Brazilian coast, and by the time the Portuguese were ready to give their attention to Brazil they found the French traders well established the length of the land.[28] The crews of their half-piratical ships might contain a mixture of Portuguese, Basques, Genoese, and Catalans, as well as Bretons and Normans. In addition to the dyewood from which the country received its name, and which was the principal staple of the trade, these ships carried back with them to France monkeys and parrots for the amusement of the ladies at the court, the native variety of pepper, ginger and rosewood, tree cotton, the feathers of araras and other bright-plumaged birds, and other exotic merchandise that was then strange to the peoples of Europe.

Though the Portuguese made an effort to clean out the French intruders in 1516, the French continued their activities along the coast long after Martin Affonso de Souza laid the belated foundations of the colony in 1531. At the time the French already had a trading post near the present site of Recife. For many years more they held out in Maranhão farther to the north and also at the mouth of the Amazon, whose valley Louis XIV coveted for France. In the middle of the sixteenth century, the French established a settlement in Rio Bay, which survived the attacks of the Portuguese and the internal dissensions between Protestants and Catholics in the colony for twelve years.[29] Frenchmen at home had become increasingly interested in the possibilities of "Antarctic France," and Brazil narrowly escaped becoming a southern counterpart of Canada or "Arctic France." The decisive factors in determining the destiny of Brazil were the normal indifference of the French government to its great opportunity, and the ability of the Portuguese to rise to the occasion whenever there was a real threat to the colony. But in the end the French had left remarkably few marks on the body and the life of Brazil. Their great opportunity in Latin America was to come under the republics, and then not in the form of political or commercial advantage, but in cultural influences.

THE ENGLISH

As a maritime and trading power, with imperial ambitions of her own, it was inevitable that Tudor England should challenge the position of Spain in the Indies and on all the sea roads which led thither. Henry VIII's espousal of the Lutheran heresy further aggravated a natural rivalry which became personal and irreconcilable during the long reigns of Elizabeth and Philip II. Commenting on Drake's attempt on Cartagena, Richard Hakluyt, whose imperishable records tell the story of the English voyagers, calls "the Spanyard our greatest and most dangerous enemie." [30] The circumstance that Spain anticipated her in the discovery of the New World weighed heavily on the pride of England; and the exclusion policy of Spain that would close the doors of the Indies to all foreigners irritated her mightily. Said Hakluyt:

"Whosoever is conversant in reading the Portugall and Spanish writers of the East and West Indies, shall commonly finde that they account all other nations for pirats, rovers and theeves, which visite any heathen coast that they hav once sayled by or looked on." Lawrence Keymis, Raleigh's loyal lieutenant on his last voyage to Guiana, regrets Henry VII's refusal of Columbus's offer of "a new-found Utopia," and adds that "the penance of that incredulity lieth even now heavy on our shoulders." However, he probably expressed most of the Elizabethans' opinion of the Spaniards when he wrote: "Howbeit, the world hath reason to admire their constancie, and their great labours, and wee may well blush at our owne idle, despairefull, and loytering dispositions, that can finde abilitie in another barren and starved nation, to possesse so much of the worlde." For Spain, he continues, "without the Indies is but a purse without money, or a painted sheath without a dagger." [31]

In the last three quarters of the sixteenth century Englishmen were increasingly occupied against the Spanish establishments in the New World. Sonetimes, particularly in the earlier years, they operated quite openly as traders or plain smugglers, as John Hawkins did on his slaving voyages. More often they sailed as privateers or downright pirates, for the legalities of maritime enterprise were very vague in that age. Whenever a formal state of war existed between the two countries, the English were open and uninhibited in their hostilities against the Spaniards.

In 1526, Thomas Tison, about whom little else is known, was living somewhere in Latin America as the agent of English merchants who were apparently interested in the trading possibilities of the new Spanish colonies. Occasionally Englishmen went to the New World on French or even Spanish ships. A few accompanied Sebastian Cabot to the River Plate in 1526, and three were with Mendoza at the first founding of Buenos Aires in 1535. Because of their special skills, they later proved to be very useful additions to the struggling colony in Paraguay. They were Richard Lincoln of Plymouth, blacksmith; John Rute, or Root, of London, powdermaker; and Nicholas Coleman, of Hampton.

The first Englishman to sail his own ship to South America was William Hawkins, father of Sir John of Armada and other fame. In the words of Hakluyt, "Olde M. William Haukins, of

Plimouth, a man for his wisdome, valure, experience, and skill in sea causes much esteemed, and beloved of K. Henry the 8, and being one of the principall Sea-captaines in the West parts of England in his time, not contented with the short voyages then made onely to the knowne coasts of Europe, armed with a tall and goodly shippe of his owne of the burthen of 250 tunnes, called the Paule of Plimmouth, wherewith he made three long and famous voyages unto the coast of Brasil, a thing in those days very rare, especially to our Nation."[32] Hawkins made his first voyage to Brazil in 1530. About ten years later, Robert Reniger and several other "substantial and wealthie merchants of Southampton" entered the "commodious and gainefull" trade with Brazil. The Portuguese were traditionally friendly to the English, and the trading ships of Devon and Hampshire came and went at will along the Brazilian coasts until the Spanish conquest of Portugal in 1580. Even during the Spanish "captivity," whenever the Portuguese had a free hand they continued their good treatment of English merchants and mariners.

The experience of William Whithall at São Vicente illustrates the good relations which generally prevailed between the two peoples in Brazil during the half century that began with William Hawkins's first voyage.[33] Whithall, who married a local heiress, was a person of substance in the community about Santos. "I give my living Lord thankes," he wrote to a friend in England in 1578, "for placing me in such honour and plentifulnesse in all things." He had become a real Brazilian, and added with pride: "Nowe I am a free denizen of this countrey." As a result of Whithall's appeal, the company of "Adventurers for Brazil" was organized in London and in 1580 sent a shipload of merchandise to Santos to be exchanged for sugar and other produce of the country. "This voyage is as good as any Peru-voyage," he wrote, as he listed the goods which would have a good sale in Brazil. Among the items which he suggests for the cargo were several thousand yards of cloth—Manchester cottons, wool, linen, silk, and velvet; hardware—nails, scissors, knives, 6,000 fishhooks, locks, tin dishes, axes, hatchets, and pig iron; and a miscellany of other articles that included "gitterne (guitar) strings," "white sope," spices, wine, shirts, doublets, hats, two dozen "velvet girdles without hangers," "two dozen leather girdles," Venetian glassware, four

dozen reams of writing paper, and three dozen "frize gownes."
After specifying that he be addressed in any correspondence as
John Letoan (Leitão), the name by which he was known locally,[34]
he added that he would like to have for himself a dozen shirts,
and, with particular urgency, "sixe or eight pieces of sayes for
mantles for women, which is the most necessary thing that can be
sent." The reply, which was signed by five members of the company in London, is in the best tradition of England's commercial
history. "For our parts," they wrote, "we promise upon our credits
and fidelities to commit no outrage at the sea or land, nor suffer
any to be done in our company that we may let, but rather to protect all other such peacable merchants as we are, with their ships
and goods." And they ask that Whithall inform the Portuguese
that "the just cause of our comming is to trade as merchants peac-
ably, and not as Pirats to commit any offence to one or other."
When the ship *Minion of London,* three months out of Harwich,
arrived at the river of Santos there was much rejoicing and satisfaction among the local population. As a present for Whithall and
his wife, she brought a fine walnut bedstead, "with the canopy,
valens, curtaines, and gilt knops."

The undisciplined crews of Edward Fenton's ships, which had
been scared out of southern waters by the great fleet of Diego
Flores de Valdéz, threatened briefly to undo the good work of
Whithall and the London merchants. Then in 1594, James Lancaster in a "well-governed and prosperous voyage" sacked Pernambuco and raided the Portuguese shipping in the harbor, all
with the cooperation of Dutch and French ships that happened
to be lying in the roadstead.[35] As a final indignity, Lancaster
forced forty of his Portuguese prisoners to pull the carts laden
with loot to the water front, "which to us was a very great ease,
for the country is very hote and ill for our nation to take any
great travell [travail] in." Though Portugal was then a province
of Spain, the Portuguese in Brazil long remembered the violence
of Lancaster's attack, and after the restoration of Portuguese independence in 1640 it was some time before they welcomed English traders again. However, when William Dampier, the famous
navigator and reformed buccaneer put in at Bahia in 1699 on his
way to Australia he was well treated by the Portuguese.[36] "I
found much respect," he wrote, "not only from this Gentleman

[Master of the Port], but from all of that Nation both here and in other Places, who were ready to serve us on all Occasions." He found at Bahia "one Mr. Cock, an English Merchant, a very civil Gentleman and of good Repute, who had a Patent to be our English Consul." There were also in Bahia at the time a Dane and one or two French merchants. British merchants traded quite openly with Brazilian ports in the eighteenth century. For example, during fifteen months of 1793–94, thirty-seven foreign ships, most of them British, entered the port of Rio de Janeiro.[37]

A few English merchants made the beginnings of a promising trade with Spanish America, particularly with Mexico, during the middle 1500's. At that time, they were apparently accustomed to trade quite freely with Spain, where some of them resided in Seville and Cadiz. The accession of the half-Spanish and Catholic Mary to the English throne in 1553, and her marriage to Philip II the following year seemed to provide a favorable atmosphere for peaceful trading. However, the accession of Elizabeth in 1558 was gradually to undo these advantages, and during her reign the relationship between Spaniards and Englishmen was at best one of guarded suspicion, and at its worst one of all-out hostility. On one side was the rising antiforeignism of Spanish colonial policy and the persecution of Englishmen by the Inquisition; on the other side was the reversion of England to Protestantism and the growing readiness of English sea captains to use strong-arm methods against the Spaniards.

It was during the period before increasing tensions turned to open enmity that Englishmen traded in Mexico. Hakluyt recounts the experiences of four of these English merchants.[38] Robert Thomson went to Spain in 1553, where he met a fellow Englishman named John Field, who had lived in Seville for many years. "In whose house," says Hakluyt, "the said Thomson remained by the space of one whole year or thereabout, for two causes: The one to learn the Castilian tongue, the other to see the orders of the countrey, and the customes of the people." After two years in Spain, Thomson crossed to Mexico with Field and the latter's Spanish family. Shipwrecked off the Mexican coast, they were cared for and refitted by a rich Spaniard at Veracruz. After a year of activity in the country, Thomson was seized by the Inquisition and spent seven months as its prisoner before being remanded to Spain for further questioning. Eventually released, he married the daughter of a wealthy Spaniard who had made a fortune in Mexico.

After spending several years in Seville, where he married, Roger Bodenham took his own ship to New Spain in 1564 in company with the fleet of Pedro Menéndez de Aviles, the founder of St. Augustine, and returned after a year with a profitable cargo for his own account. John Chilton doubtless saw more of the New World than any Englishman of that age. With the valuable background of long residence in Spain, "being desirous to see the world," he went to Mexico. When he finally returned to London in 1586, he had been absent from England for twenty-five years. In the meantime, he had traveled from the northernmost province of New Spain, "toward the provinces of California," south by Cuba and Central America to Cuzco and Potosí in Peru, and trading everywhere without apparent hindrance. John Hawks, last of the four merchants to be interviewed by Hakluyt, returned in 1572 after five years in Mexico. Though silent about his own experiences, he wrote for the information of his contemporaries an excellent description of the viceroyalty of New Spain.

By this time Hawkins and Drake had clashed with the Spaniards at Veracruz, and the short-lived era of peaceful trading was over. Henceforth, for a quarter of a century English mariners harried the Spanish sea lanes and the coasts of Spanish America, and of Spain itself. When John Hawkins put in at Burburata on the second of his slaving voyages in 1565 with intent to trade peaceably with the Spaniards, "they made answere, that they were forbidden by the King to trafique with any forren nation." [39] Two years later, in the course of a similar venture with Francis Drake, after falling afoul of the Spaniards at Rio de la Hacha on the Venezuelan coast, he took refuge at Veracruz in Mexico, where he hoped to reprovision his ships. Instead, he was attacked by Spanish galleons in the harbor and by the fort of San Juan de Ulua and very badly handled. Leaving a large number of his men ashore in the hands of the Spaniards, he returned with Drake "from this sorrowfull voyage," not to come again to the scene of his trading operations for a quarter of a century.

In 1572, Drake made a profitable voyage to the Isthmus on

his own account. Then, after five years he sailed on his voyage of circumnavigation, in the course of which he raided the coasts and shipping of the west coast of Spanish America to the great advantage of himself and the queen. In 1585, with a large force he sacked the city of Santo Domingo and captured Cartagena and held it for ransom. Ten years later, another fleet under the joint command of Drake and Hawkins, both of whom died on the voyage, committed widespread depredations in the West Indies and along the Spanish Main. The Spaniards breathed easier in the Americas at the passing of "El Draque."

In the meantime, many captains of lesser fame went "aroving" to the New World. Among them were Richard, the son of John Hawkins, who was captured by the Spaniards; John Oxenham, the first Englishman to sail on the Pacific Ocean, who was executed by the Spaniards in Lima; the predatory Christopher Newport, who roamed the Antilles, burning towns and rifling the Spaniards of copper coins and church bells, chickens and goats and hogs, and sugar and tobacco; and the bold and ruthless Sir Thomas Cavendish, scourge of the Spanish shores of the Pacific, who was the third to sail a ship around the world.

Among them, too, was the courtly and romantic Sir Walter Raleigh, at heart an Italian of the cinquecento, but an incompetent leader of men on enterprises where daring and constancy were necessary above all other virtues.[40] By reason of his high position in England, he would disdain "the spoile & sackage of common persons" in which his fellow Elizabethans indulged with so much gusto. It did not become him, he wrote to Lord Howard and Sir Robert Cecil, "to run from Cape to Cape, and from place to place, for the pillage of ordinarie prizes." Instead, he would lay at the feet of the queen "that mighty, rich and beautiful Empier of Guiana, and of that great and golden Citie, which the Spaniards call El Dorado, and the naturals Manoa"—"a better Indies for her Majestie than the King of Spaine hath any." In his obsession he proved to be more gullible than the most quixotic Spaniard, and accepted as truth the fanciful yarns which Indians and Spaniards told him in order to be rid of him. The villain in the play that ended in tragedy in the headsman's ax in the Tower is a mysterious Spaniard named Antonio de Berreo, who always seemed to know more than he would tell. After sending out a ship the year before to make a reconnaissance of the region, Raleigh first went up the Orinoco from Trinidad in 1595. Interviewing Indian "Kings" along the way and showing them a portrait of Queen Elizabeth, he reached a point 400 miles from the sea before turning back. The Spaniards, to whom the Orinoco was a river of ill-omen, had a saying that, "He who goes to the Orinoco either dies or comes back mad (*loco*)." A subtle madness seems, in fact, to have come over the Englishman, and whatever sense of disillusionment there may have been deep within him, he persisted in his extravagant claims of the fabulous land that lay beyond the southern horizon. For several years after Raleigh's return to England, other men continued the exploration of the coasts and rivers of Guiana. Meanwhile, Raleigh's ill-fortune had increased and the queen who had once heaped favors on him was dead. A prisoner of James I, he was released on condition that he bring back the golden substance of El Dorado to a now incredulous England. It was twenty-two years since he had gone to the Orinoco, and probably only the Spaniards remembered much of his excursion to Venezuela. At least Gondomar, the Spanish Ambassador in London, remembered, and after Raleigh returned from the voyage which was foredoomed to disaster it was at his insistence that the last of the great Elizabethan adventurers was sent to the block.

Many Englishmen whose ships went down within swimming distance of the coast or went home without them became permanent residents of the Spanish Empire. If they avoided any savage Indians in the neighborhood and kept out of the way of the Inquisition until they could arrange their conversion to Catholicism, they had a good chance of survival. As in the particularly tolerant atmosphere of early Paraguay, the Spanish communities were generally disposed to admit a stray foreigner who was down on his luck, provided, or course, that he left any foreign attachments behind him, and entered wholeheartedly into the life of the colony.[41] In addition to the basic condition of acceptance of the Catholic faith, marriage to a woman of the country put—and still does in Latin America—the seal on a foreigner's integration with the community. For example, when the ship commanded by John Drake, a cousin of Sir Francis, was wrecked in the River Plate on Edward Fenton's expedition, he and a few more of his men settled among the Spaniards. Five years later, when Captains Withrington and Lister went up the river they heard that Drake was in Tucumán, and that Richard Faireweather, one of his companions, was married in one of the towns in the interior. John Drake is reported to have moved to Lima where he presumably married a *Limeña*.⁴²

The seventy-seven men whom John Hawkins put ashore on the Mexican coast in order to lighten the ships that had survived the Spanish attack at Veracruz fared badly at the hands of the royal officials and the Inquisition. The story of their long ordeal is told in the pages of Hakluyt by two of them, Miles Philips and Job Hortop. Twenty-three of them disappeared during their wanderings in the Pánuco country; the rest were seized and driven off to Mexico City. Here they were hospitalized for six months, while the townspeople showered them with food and attention. By this time the hostile government of the viceroyalty was well ayare of their presence and consigned them to a workhouse at Tezcoco in the valley of Mexico. Escaping from prison, they were farmed out to Spaniards for whatever services they could perform. Philips and several others were sent to the north as overseers in the silver mines, where they prospered. At this point in their fortunes, they were all seized by the newly-founded Inquisition, and for a year and half confined in the capital and questioned on their religious beliefs. At the end of their long interrogation they became the objects of an elaborate auto-da-fé, in which they were punished according to what the inquisitors considered the degree of their heresy. Three men, including one "Cornelius the Irishman," were burned at the stake. Several were sentenced to receive from one hundred to three hundred lashes, and from six to ten years as galley slaves in Spain. Philips was turned over to the Blackfriars for five years of penitence, while wearing the humiliating sanbenito of a convicted heretic. But he was well treated by the friars and spent the period of his sentence in supervising the Indian help about the monastery grounds, whom he called "a courteous and loving kind of people, ingenious and of a great understanding." When he was finally released and allowed to shift for himself, he learned the trade of silk weaving. Three of his fellow Englishmen married Negro women, one a mestizo, and another a Basque widow of means, and another was allowed to go to Spain, where he married a Spanish woman.

Philips was only concerned with keeping clear of the authorities and the Holy Office, and with finding a way to escape from Mexico. When at last he succeeded and reached England, he had been sixteen years out of the country. Yet in spite of his sufferings, the spell of the Indies must have been on him, for five years later John Saracoll, a merchant on Withrington and Lister's expedition in the River Plate wrote in his diary: "Wee took into our ship one Miles Philips, which was left in the West Indies by M. Hawkins." [43] As for Job Hortop, the Lincolnshire powdermaker, "replenished with many miseries," he spent a total of twenty-three years as a prisoner of the Spaniards, including five years in the dungeons of the Inquisition at Seville, twelve years at the oars of the royal galleys, and three years as an indentured "drudge" in the house of a Spaniard who had loaned him fifty ducats to buy a lightening of his sentence from the Inquisition. After that, Englishmen did not go to Mexico.

The seventeenth century was the era of the buccaneers. [44] The Stuart kings avoided open hostilities with Spain, though the Commonwealth interregnum of Cromwell waged a very active naval war with the Spaniards (1655-57). However, during the long periods of official peace the buccaneers carried on their own private war against Spain and all her works. The buccaneers probably began as adventurous smugglers, whose contraband operations were thwarted by the Spaniards. On occasion, whenever the Spaniards made their favored and normal vocation too hazardous, they become drovers and butchers of wild cattle on Santo Domingo, or even half-hearted planters or loggers of sorts. As co-operative companies of Englishmen, Frenchmen, and Dutchmen, they conducted an experiment in international living that was unique in its time. These mixed elements were held together by a common spirit of adventure and by their greed, but above all by their hatred of Spain. They made an organized, and generally profitable, even if highly speculative business of piracy. At first, the principal arena of their activities was the Caribbean, but they later broke into the Pacific and extended their operations from the west coast of Mexico south to Chile. Henry Morgan's pitiless pillage and destruction of the city of Panama in 1671 was a high point in their history, but the fifteen years that followed were the

culmination of buccaneer aggression and power, especially along
the coasts and shipping routes of the South Sea.

Always cruel and merciless with the Spaniards, the buccaneers tended in time to degenerate into seagoing hoodlums or
gangsters. Their inherent elements of disintegration proved too
strong for these freebooting fraternities to survive into a more
orderly age. The discipline of their leaders was too precariously
exercised over their ruffianly followers. The governments of England and the other countries of their origin became increasingly
impatient of their vagaries, and their brutality put them outside
the pale of tolerance, even in a not too squeamish age. Yet, directly or indirectly, they had been responsible for most of the
colonial acquisitions made at the expense of Spain in the area of
the Caribbean: Belize, Curaçao, Jamaica, and Santo Domingo.

Both England and Spain were inevitably drawn into the wars
of the eighteenth century, which were primarily concerned with
maintaining the balance of power in Europe. Just as inevitably,
these conflicts spread to the Spanish Indies. During the war of
the Spanish Succession, Admiral Wager captured or destroyed the
regular galleon fleet near Cartagena in 1708. The same year,
Captain Woodes Rogers went on the lucrative privateering voyage around South America which he later described with Gilbert
and Sullivan overtones. At the peace, England wrested from
Spain the *asiento* or monopoly for the supply of slaves to the
Spanish colonies, along with other commercial privileges.

The English derived little glory or profit from the similar
phase of the War of the Austrian Succession. The Hispanophobe
Admiral Vernon, whose agitation was largely responsible for
this ill-fated venture against Spain, received the plaudits of the
English public after capturing the decrepit Spanish fort at Porto
Bello on the Isthmus in 1739. But the next year he failed dis-
astrously in his efforts to take the great Spanish stronghold of
Cartagena, only to repeat the experience in 1741 before Santiago
de Cuba. The British Navy only redeemed some of its reputation
by the exploits of Commodore George Anson in his brilliant raid
into the Spanish waters of the Pacific.[45] Spain threw in her lot
with France late in the Seven Years' War, and in 1762 an English force took Havana only to return it to Spain by the treaty of
peace the following year. England's appetite for colonies was

whetted by her gains in North America and India during this war, and as she became aware of the defensive weakness of the Spanish Empire and the discontent of the colonies with the rule of Spain, she planned to compensate herself for the loss of her American colonies by conquests at the expense of Spain. The series of Napoleonic wars offered her the opportunity which she needed. In 1797 the English captured the valuable island of Trinidad off the Venezuelan coast. In 1806, a British force which had seized Cape Town at the tip of Africa crossed the south Atlantic and captured the city of Buenos Aires, only to be forced to surrender by a rising of the Argentine creoles. The next year a much larger expedition, after taking Montevideo on its way into the River Plate, attempted to recapture Buenos Aires, but met the same fate at the hands of the Argentines.

THE IRISH

As men without a country, the Irish presented no political problem to the authorities of Spain. Moreover, as confirmed Catholics and enemies of England they were peculiarly welcome in Spain and the colonies. During periods like the reign of Elizabeth, the Commonwealth, and the violations of the Treaty of Limerick under William III and Anne, many Irishmen went to Spain. There they served as volunteers in the Spanish armies in the European wars, became members of the regular orders of the clergy, or otherwise identified themselves with the life of the country of their adoption. Some of the more adventurous crossed the Atlantic to the colonies of Spain, where they are found in various occupations throughout the colonial period, and increasingly in positions of responsibility in the administrative service of Spain.[46] Many more entered Spanish America as "legionnaires" in the patriot forces of the Wars of Independence. Among the most famous of these volunteers were Colonel O'Leary, aide to Bolívar, General O'Brien, aide to San Martín, and Admiral William Brown, of the young Argentine Navy. A still larger number of Irish migrated to the republics, particularly to Argentina, during the great famine of 1846–47.

Several Irishmen or Spaniards of Irish ancestry attained to places of eminence in the colonial service during the later eighteenth and early nineteenth centuries. Carlos Morphi, or Charles

Murphy, an officer in the Spanish Army, was royal governor of the province of Paraguay between 1766 and 1772. Juan O'Donojú, former captain general of Andalusia, was the last viceroy of New Spain. General Leopoldo O'Donnell, Duke of Tetuan, and twice prime minister of Spain, was made governor general of Cuba in 1843.

The outstanding example of a rise in the colonial service or *Carrera de Indias* was that of Ambrosio, or Ambrose, O'Higgins.[47] Born in obscure circumstances at Vallenary, County Meath, in 1720, O'Higgins went to Spain, where his uncle, a Jesuit at Cadiz, took charge of his education. He was in Buenos Aires in 1757 and later acquainted himself with the provinces of Chile and Peru, the future scene of his extraordinary career. While in Lima he is said to have supported himself for a time as a hawker or street peddler. Returning to Spain, he became a Spanish citizen and in 1763 appears again in Chile as a surveyor in the royal service and with a cargo of goods to sell for his own account. Entering the army, he became a colonel by 1777 and took part in one of the perennial campaigns against the Araucanian Indians. By 1786, he was governor and intendant of the province of Concepción, and two years later he became captain general of Chile, president of the royal Audiencia and intendant of Santiago. Created a field marshal in the Spanish Army, and Baron of Vallenari and Marquis of Osorno in the Spanish peerage, the Irish immigrant was appointed in 1796 to the highest post in the colonial service of Spain, that of viceroy of Peru. His natural son, Bernardo, who was neglected by his ambitious father except in provision for his education and support, rose by his own talents and character to be a leader of the patriot forces in the war of independence and first president of the new republic of Chile.

One of the most interesting Irishmen who appear in the history of Latin America was the adventurer, William Lamport, known to the Spaniards as Guillén de Lamport, *alias* Guillén Lombardo de Guzman.[48] Even if one discounts some of the obvious cloak-and-dagger details of the autobiography, which he wrote in prison, the circumstantial and confirmed residue of his romantic story is sufficiently fabulous in itself to warrant a special place for him in the legends of the New World. He claimed that he was the son of Philip III by an Irishwoman who had been in

Spain. As told by himself, he escaped from London under threat of death from Charles I only to be captured by pirates on the way to France. Once in Spain, the Marquis of Mancera obtained a scholarship for him in a school in Galicia. While there his former piratical shipmates put in at a nearby port, whereupon Lamport and some Franciscan friars went on board and converted most of them to the Catholic faith, hauling off the more obdurate heretics to the local Inquisition. The king heard of this feat and invited him to court, where he was first introduced to the powerful Count-Duke of Olivares by the grandee, the Duke of Medinaceli. Having obtained the royal favor, he studied for a while at Salamanca and was then sent to Flanders on an official mission. On the way to the north in 1634 he is said to have set the tactical pattern of the Battle of Nordlingen, the last great victory of the Spanish *tercios,* for the Cardinal-Infante Don Ferdinand. After engaging in various other battles on sea and land, he was exiled to Mexico because of an affair with a woman of the court. The exile carried with it a pension of 10,000 pesos a year, so that he was able to continue his flamboyant style of living while posing as a teacher of Latin. He quickly recognized the military weakness of the viceroyalty and laid his plans to free it from the King of Spain, his alleged half-brother, whose title to the colonies he did not consider valid. By means of skillfully forged royal decrees naming him viceroy, he intended to oust the newly appointed Count of Salvatierra from the viceroyal palace and then to proclaim himself monarch of Mexico. It was at this point in his daring plot that he was seized by agents of the Inquisition, and the years from 1642 to 1659 he spent in the prison of the Holy Office, except for a brief escape in 1650. Though his guilt was clear, a great deal of mystery attaches to the reason for his long incarceration without trial, and to the solicitude of the royal court for his welfare in prison. Tried at last and declared guilty of a number of crimes, he was made the principal feature of an elaborate auto-da-fé. Thus, the brilliant and learned Don Juan of the Indies ended his restless career as a charred corpse in the Alameda of Mexico and a file in the archives of the Inquisition.

During the last century, Irishmen continued to play an important, and sometimes dramatic, part in the life of the republics. In Argentina, some of them, like the Duggans, became prosperous landowners. One of them, Edward Casey, came out in 1885 and founded the town of Venado Tuerto on the Pampas.[49] He was given a large land grant on condition that he colonize it with his fellow countrymen within a certain time. He brought out two shiploads of immigrants from Ireland, but when the time allotted for settling his grant was up he had not fulfilled all the terms of his contract. So when government inspectors came out from the capital to investgate, he got them drunk and showed them the same ranches three or four times. In Peru, one Carlos Fermín Fitzcarrald, son of an Irish adventurer named Fitzgerald and a Peruvian woman, carved out an empire for himself in the jungle wilderness to the east of the Andes.[50] By force of personality, an impressive physique, and great intelligence, he became the ruling power in the basin of the Ucayalí, and his domain extended thence across into the neighboring part of Brazil and into the valley of the Madre de Dios by way of the Manu. Thousands of Indians and a large force of white and mestizo rubber gatherers were subject to his will. An Irishman of a different type, was the cultivated and urbane Mr. Conroy, who created an extensive botanical garden on the banks of the Rimac in the outskirts of Lima, which became a favorite attraction of the Peruvian capital.[51] In Mexico, a group of Irishmen deserted the American army of invasion in 1848 in order to wage a holy war against the anticlerical faction in the country. Years afterwards, some of their descendants, known as the *Patricios,* or "Patricks," fought the famous Porfirio Diaz in the Tehuantepac country.[52]

THE GERMANS

One German went to Chile in the valiant company of Pedro de Valdivia. He was Bartholomeus Blumenthal, whose name was Hispanicized as Flores. Blumenthal—or Flores—was not only a good soldier, but a skilled builder who constructed the best houses in Santiago. In 1557, another German, whom the Spaniards knew as "Lisperguer," arrived with Governor García Hurtado de Mendoza. A century later, a descendant of both Germans, Doña Catalina de los Rios de Lisperguer, better known as "La Quintrala," daughter of Elvira de Talagante and Bartolomé, a cacique of the Mapochos, became the center of the most celebrated *crime célèbre* in the history of Latin America. A rich *en-*

comendera, she was accused of poisoning her Indian father, killing her lover, and making away in one fashion or another with more than a dozen other persons. Because of the influence of her powerful family connections and probably on account of other circumstances which do not appear in the court records of the time, this vampire of the valley of Chile escaped punishment and died in the odor of sancitity in 1665, to be buried in the Church of San Agustín in Santiago.[53] Though the technical services of Germans as gunners and artificers were very acceptable to the Spaniards, few of them made their way to the New World as individual volunteers in the armies of the Conquest. Many more went to the Americas as agents or employees of the great German banking and trading firms of the sixteenth century.[54]

The most famous of those concerns were the houses of Fugger and Welser. Founded by burghers of Augsburg, the ramifications of these powerful family organizations extended over western Europe. Those German bankers financed the rulers of the continent, who in default of a Bureau of Internal Revenue to wring money from their subjects, were perennially broke. In other words, the costs of government had outgrown the antiquated tax systems of the Middle Ages, and the German—and Italian—bankers filled the fiscal gap. They also operated mines and other industrial enterprises and traded in any commodities that afforded the prospect of large returns. Among the most important of the clients of the Fuggers were the members of the House of Hapsburg, who were notoriously improvident and impecunious. Their ties with the Emperor Maximilian gave them entree into the affairs of Spain when Philip of Burgundy married Juana, the light-witted daughter of Ferdinand and Isabella and mother of Charles of Ghent, heir to the Spanish throne. When the young Hapsburg prince became King of Spain as Charles I and aspired to the imperial crown, the Fuggers loaned him the money to bribe the electors who made him Emperor Charles V of the Holy Roman Empire. Once established as bankers of the new emperor, the profits and risks of whose account they shared with the lesser Welsers, the Fuggers became interested in the possibilities of sharing in the various overseas enterprises of Spain.

Several Germans sailed with Magellan and two or three of them were among the eighteen survivors who returned in the

Victoria of Sebastián Elcano. They told their fellow countrymen
of the marvels they had seen in the eastern Indies. So, when the
expeditions of Sebastian Cabot and Fray García Jofre de Loaysa
were outfitted in Spain to follow up the discoveries of Magellan
in the Orient, the bankers invested their funds in the ventures
and a number of Germans accompanied the fleets. Both voyages were failures; that of Loaysa ended in disaster in the wild
seas at the southern end of the continent, and Cabot allowed himself to be lured from his objective to follow the silvered mirage
of the White King into the dead end of the Argentine rivers. The
Fuggers wrote off their losses and planned and bided their time
while they intrigued with the emperor and influential men at
the Spanish court. When at last they were offered a concession
for the conquest and development of the west coast of South
America from the Straits north well into Peru, they became pan-
icky and refused it, for the factors of chance were too great for
sound and conservative bankers. After that, they were content to
gather the usufruct of the labors of bolder men while they sat
safely at their desks in Seville, and earmarked the bars of gold
and silver for shipment to Germany in payment of the debts of
the king-emperor.

The Welsers, less powerful and less cautious than the princely
Fuggers, received a grant for the government and exploration of
Venezuela as security for the funds which they advanced to the
ever-needy master of the wealth of the Indies. There followed the
strangest phase of the Conquest. For nearly twenty years, agents
of a German banking house were lords of the Spanish Main—
Herren Adelantados and *Gobernadores* and *Conquistadores*. Their
soldiers were Spaniards, who served under the Germans because
the king willed it so. A succession of men of guttural speech and
unpronounceable names came out to the little thatched village of
Coro on the windy Caribbean coast that was their capital. From
here all of them, save the *gemütlich* and sedentary bookkeeper,
Hans Seissenhofer, led expeditions into the endless wastes of the
Venezuelan hinterland in search of gold. For years each of them
wandered aimlessly through the back country, across the vast
plains of the Llanos, that were alternately flooded by the over-
flow of the rivers or parched by drought, through swamps and the
tropical rain forest, and among rugged mountains. They made no

permanent conquests, as the Spaniards did; the single town which
they founded—Maracaibo—was later abandoned by them; rapacious as they were, they found little gold for their greedy prin-
cipals in Germany, except from the Santa Marta country of
Colombia. Cruel and pitiless, their only policy toward the Indians
was one of enslavement or extermination, and wherever they
passed they left destruction and a heritage of hate in their wake.
In their long razzias into the wilderness, it was only the heroism
and skill of a few seasoned Spanish captains like Esteban Martín
and Pedro de Limpias, that enabled the raiding parties to hold
together against the hostility of nature and the natives.

Of the German leaders of those tremendous forays into the
sterile wastes of the backlands of South America, Ambrose Ehin-
ger died with an Indian arrow in his throat. George Hohermuth
survived the ordeal of his *entrada* across the Apure and the
Arauca and the Meta of evil memory, and under the eastern
flanks of the Andes, to waste away to death in Santo Domingo.
Philip von Hutten, a medieval *Ritter* at heart and the noblest of
the lot, returned from five years of wanderings in quest of El
Dorado to lay down his head on a chopping block at the behest
of a faithless Spanish official. With him died young Bartholomew
Welser, an adventurous scion of the banking family. Redheaded
Nicholas Federmann of Ulm, tough and durable, cunning and
stubborn, finally reached the goal of all their searchings on the
Colombian plateau with a band of scarecrows clad in the skins of
animals, only to find, by the final irony of fate, the Spanish company of Jiménez de Quesada already in possession of the coveted
riches of the Chibchas. When he retired from the scene to face a
reckoning with his employers in Europe, the House of Welser and
the Council of the Indies closed their books on the ill-fated venture of the Germans in the business of conquest.

When Pedro de Mendoza led his impressive expedition to the
River Plate in 1535, one of his fleet was a trading ship belonging
to Sebastian Neidhardt and Jacob Welser of Nuremberg. On
board were some eighty Germans and men from the Low Countries, most of whom returned to Germany with the proceeds of
their trading. One of those who stayed, to enter wholeheartedly
into the conquest of the region was Ulrich Schmidel, a Bavarian
harquebusier. He later went upriver with the remnants of **Men-**

doza's force and spent a total of twenty years between the unfortunate colony of Buenos Aires and the new settlements in Paraguay. A stout soldier, contentious and unimaginative, he had a great capacity for survival. He lived to return to his native town of Straubing with a flock of parrots, and his stolid head full of tangled memories, and there wrote the halting story of his long and adventurous and, at times, pleasant stay among the Guaranís.[55]

Hans Staden was a young Hessian from Homberg of the hats, who "proposed, if God willed, to see the Indies." Unlike the belligerent Schmidel, though for a time he was a gunner in the Portuguese service, he was essentially a man of peace. And unlike the Catholic Bavarian, he was a pious Lutheran, which made him suspect to the Portuguese in Brazil. Two other Germans, Hans von Bruchhausen and Heinrich Brandt of Bremen were on the ship that first carried him from Lisbon to São Vicente, where he found another compatriot, Helidorus Hassus, the manager of one of old Giuseppe della Doria's sugar mills. Hassus was later to lead a mixed band of Mamelucos and Indians to Rio to help Estacio de Sa fight the French. Staden spent a considerable part of two visits to Brazil as a prisoner of the Tupinambá's while being fattened for a cannibal feast that never came off. He escaped from his captors in 1554 and returned to Germany where, like Schmidel, he wrote a very entertaining book of his experiences among the aborigines.

Centuries later, toward the end of the colonial regime, a far greater German than any of these came to the New World. This was the Baron Alexander von Humboldt, naturalist and scientific explorer, the foremost intellectual figure of his time and the first citizen of Europe. In 1799, he landed at Cumaná in Venezuela in company with the French botanist Bonpland. This was the beginning of nearly five years of travel and observation in Spanish America, in the course of which he visited the valley of the Orinoco, Colombia, Ecuador, Peru, Cuba, and Mexico.

FLEMINGS AND DUTCH

During the reign of the Emperor Charles V, the Catholic Flemings among whom he grew up enjoyed special privileges in the Spanish Indies. Peter of Ghent, a Franciscan friar, founded a famous school in the city of Mexico shortly after the Conquest. In the years 1534-37 many Flemings from Brussels, Antwerp, Bruges and other cities in the Low Countries, including several from Lille in French Flanders, were licensed to go to the Spanish colonies. In 1528, García de Lerma, governor of the province of Santa Marta, took out a half dozen Flemings in his company, and about fourteen went out to the River Plate in 1535. One of them, known as "Leonard the Fleming," later worked as a tailor in the Spanish settlement at Asunción. Hans Staden found the agent of an Antwerp merchant established at São Vicente in southern Brazil in the middle of the same century, and the Portuguese seem generally to have placed few obstacles in the way of the Flemish traders. However, the privileged position of the Flemings in the Spanish colonies was short-lived, and after the abdication of the emperor few of them were admitted to the viceroyalties in the New World.

On the other hand, the Dutch, as Protestants and rebels, very early found the doors closed to the overseas dominions of Spain. After their successful struggle for independence the seven northern provinces of the Spanish Netherlands became bitter enemies of the Spaniards wherever they found them. As a matter of business, the Dutch West Indies Company preyed on Spanish shipping and carried on a lucrative smuggling trade along the coasts of Spanish America. In 1628, Admiral Piet Heyn, who had served in the Spanish galleys for four years, made one of the richest hauls in the history of the seas when he overhauled the treasure fleet off the north coast of Cuba.

Since at this time Portugal was under the domination of Spain, Brazil was also open to attacks from the Dutch. The West Indies Company made ambitious plans to obtain an extensive and permanent footing in Brazil. After the initial capture of Bahia in 1624, the city was retaken the next year, and six years later Olinda and its fort of Recife were taken. It was not until the arrival of Count Maurice of Nassau as governor in 1636 that the Dutch took serious steps to consolidate their position in northern Brazil. This member of the House of Orange gave the new colony an intelligent and efficient administration, but his ambition to found a great Dutch state in the New World did not meet with the approval of the profit-minded directors of the company. With

little help from Portugal, the Brazilians carried on a long and persistent war against his successors, until in 1654 the Dutch were
forced to abandon the country. The enterprise and the conciliatory policies of Maurice of Nassau left a permanent mark on the
history of northern Brazil. The land was enriched culturally by
the artists and builders whom he brought out from the Netherlands, while some of the Dutch colonists identified themselves so
thoroughly with the life of the region that they remained to found
families like those of Wanderley,[56] Rollenberg, and Lins, which
were to become prominent in the life of the north country.

THE PORTUGUESE IN THE SPANISH COLONIES

For purposes of the alien restriction laws, the Portuguese were
generally treated as Spaniards.[57] "There are some Portuguese
and foreigners in the city," wrote an anonymous Spaniard of
Quito in 1573.[58] In addition to the great Magellan, many served
without question of their nationality in Spanish voyages of
discovery or in the military forces of the Conquest, and Portuguese names appear frequently throughout the colonies as merchants and settlers, as well as soldiers.[59] A large contingent of
Portuguese horsemen distinguished themselves in De Soto's ill-
fated expedition on the mainland of North America.[60] In about
1526, Aleixo García, the first European to reach the Inca Empire,
crossed South America from the Brazilian coast to Peru by way
of Paraguay, where he gathered an army of two thousand Guaraní
warriors. During the early period of Spanish settlement in Paraguay, Portuguese from Brazil seem to have come and gone quite
freely between the two colonies.

For a long time after the papal Line of Demarcation was
drawn between the respective spheres of conquest of Spain and
Portugal and rearranged by the Treaty of Tordesillas there was
little opportunity for boundary disputes between the two powers
in the New World. Except for wandering parties in the interior,
like those which searched for El Dorado, the colonists of both
nations clung to the coasts or to the Spanish centers of population
in the Andes. Points of contact were eventually established on the
Amazon and on the River Plate, where the Portuguese located an
outpost at Colonia on the north bank of the river opposite Buenos
Aires. In the meantime, the Bandeirantes had pushed across the

hills of Brazil from the highlands of São Paulo and Minas into the valley of the Madeira, which the Spaniards approached from the west by the plains of El Beni. For the most part, the vast zone between was a no man's land left to the lonely Jesuit missionaries. The Spanish "captivity" of Portugal between 1580 and 1640 reduced such chances of friction as there were along the frontier by its subordination of the Portuguese colonies to the authority of Spain. Throughout most of the colonial period there was intermittent trade and travel by sea between the coast of Brazil and the River Plate. Thereby the Portuguese supplied, either illicitly or openly, Negro slaves and foodstuffs to the Spaniards at Buenos Aires, who were isolated from direct communication with Europe by the unintelligent policy of Spain and from the heart of the Peruvian viceroyalty by a long and hazardous overland route.

Men of other nationalities occasionally broke through the restrictive systems of Spain and Portugal to enter the colonies as soldiers or traders or settlers. One of Pizarro's original company in the conquest of Peru was the Greek, Pedro de Candia. The big Cretan later joined the side of Diego de Almagro in the civil wars and performed useful services as chief of the artillery, and in the forging of cannon and the manufacture of muskets. In this work he is said to have had the assistance of several other men from the lands about the Aegean. Another Greek, known to the Spaniards as "Master Francisco," posed as a surgeon among the Spanish armies in Peru and was several times threatened with hanging by the terrible Carbajal.[61] A Turkish miner, who called himself the Emir Sigala and was known to the Spaniards as "Captain Zapata," lived in the mining towns of the Andes during the seventeenth century.[62] As early as 1610, Vázquez de Espinosa found a Levantine living in Castrovirreina, and later in the century there were several well-to-do Syrian traders in Lima, who for a time threatened the ascendency of the Spanish merchants in the city. One married Doña Bernarda Morales Negrete, who endowed the Church of the Desamparados in Lima.[63] In 1698, a colony of Scotchmen was founded on the Isthmus of Darien, in defiance of the Spanish government and without support from the British government or its agents in the West Indies. A more unsuitable site could scarcely have been chosen, and the project which had been organized by the famous financial "wizard," William Patterson, was soon abandoned.[64]

Toward the end of the colonial regime the severity of the restrictive laws was considerably relaxed. Spanish policy was as intolerant of foreigners as ever and on occasion the higher officials of the viceroyalties might apply the old prohibitions with the early vigor. Yet the admission of foreign scientists, like La Condamine in the middle of the century and of Humboldt and Bonpland at the end of it is indicative of a weakening of the traditional xenophobia even in the high circles of the Bourbon monarchy. The spirit of the new age in Europe, where, for the first time since the Renaissance, an international community of the mind was cutting across national frontiers, found its way to the New World. It came in the books of the French philosophers that were read with such eagerness by the young intellectuals of the colonies; in the stories of the young American republic that were told by the New England ship masters who brought flour to Venezuela; in the conversation of the foreign merchants who began, very quietly at first, to settle in the port cities of South America; and stored in the fresh memory of the returning creoles like Bolívar, who visited Europe in increasing numbers. In such an atmosphere the old antiforeignism was outdated. Moreover, the newcomers profited from the growing resentment of the colonials against Spain, which presaged the *Independencia*. And when the great revolt came in the early nineteenth century, the active participation of many British and American volunteers in the revolutionary forces, and the open sympathy of their governments with the patriot cause, were to make their countrymen all the more welcome once independence was achieved.[65]

IMMIGRATION UNDER THE REPUBLICS

The early years of the republics were a time of good will toward foreigners, particularly toward Americans and British.[66] Many of them settled in the new nations as merchants or mine operators, as physicians or engineers or shipowners. They filled an economic gap which had been left by the disappearance of the Spanish element from the business life of the countries and gave a valuable impetus to the development of the republics. Many of them prospered and, marrying women of the country, identified themselves closely and permanently with the life of the community.

As the new governments established themselves more firmly and undertook a more ordered exploitation of the natural resources of their states, they became aware of the need for greater manpower and special skills to speed up their development. Much of their territory consisted of vast *despoblados* or wildernesses which if left a void, might be an invitation to aggression by foreign powers. The political philosopher, Alberdi, expressed this urge for more people than could be provided by the natural increase of local populations in his famous dictum, *"Poblar es gobernar."*

The result was official policies for the encouragement of European immigration. Governmental programs of systematic and organized colonization got under way before the middle of the century, but the movement did not reach its heaviest proportions until after 1890. Where only hundreds had come, in colonial times, now millions were to come. Sometimes the initiative came from individual promoters or colonization societies and sometimes from special interests like the coffeegrowers of São Paulo.

Migration to Latin America was favored by the same circumstances which accounted for the movement of European peoples into the United States during the same period: the opportunities offered by the New World for the improvement of the immigrant's lot; discontent with political conditions in Europe like the conservative reaction which followed the failure of the German revolution of 1848; freedom to try out social and religious experiments in a new and isolated environment, such as prompted the making of the Australian-American Socialist colony in Paraguay, and the Mennonite colony in the Gran Chaco of the same country; and plain venturesomeness and restlessness. Some of the colonies failed or disintegrated because of bad management; the quality of the immigrants or their inability to face pioneering conditions; the lack of funds to tide the colonists over the first critical year; or the selection of an unsuitable site, such as the Scotch found on the island of Chiloe, the Southerners in the lower Tapajoz in the Amazon Valley, the Californians in the Pachitea basin of Peru, and the Oklahomans in the upper Pilcomayo. Probably the most successful of the large-scale colonizing ventures were those of the Germans in southern Brazil and the mixed settlements in the *colonias* region of the rich Argentine province of Santa Fé. Immigrants were responsible for opening up new lands in many localities. Among these were the Germans in southern Chile and the Argentine Misiones, the Welsh in the remote Chubut valley in Patagonia, the Scotch and the Slavs in Tierra del Fuego, the Polish farmers in the Brazilian state of Paraná, and the settlers of various nationalities who cleared the forests of the Argentine Chaco and planted the area to cotton. The special skills of some groups gave an impetus to several industries, as the Cornishmen did to mining, the Manchester spinners to cotton textile manufacturing, the Italians to wine making in the Argentine province of Mendoza, the Swiss to dairying, the British to the improvement of cattle breeding, and, though a mixed benefit, the Chinese to truck gardening. American geologists did much to lay the foundations for the mineral industry of republican Brazil, and the corps of American school teachers whom President Sarmiento brought to Argentina performed an invaluable service to primary education in that country.

The largest single source of immigrants was Italy. Generally as individuals or in family units, great numbers of Italians settled in the states of São Paulo and Rio Grande do Sul, in Argentina, and in Uruguay. Many of them have risen to positions of great wealth and influence in those countries. Among South American presidents of Italian ancestry were Carlos Pellegrini of Argentina, and Arturo Alessandri of Chile. In Peru they occupy a place in the business community out of all proportion to their numbers. They are easily integrated with the life of the republics and even during the Fascist regime in Italy they presented relatively few problems to the Latin American governments.

Once the resentments of the wars of independence had died out with the generation which had fought them, and diplomatic relations established with Spain, many Spaniards migrated to the former colonies, as well as to Brazil, where they proved a very useful element in the population. The influx of Spaniards into Cuba after the Spanish-American War was sufficient to make them a major factor in the composition of the island population and in its economic and social life. Similarly, Brazil has been very hospitable to immigrants from the mother country, to the point of exempting the Portuguese from the quota limitations of her immigration law. Their plodding industry and steadiness of temper make them a very acceptable leaven in the social body of Brazil.

Until recently, the Latin American governments showed little concern with the integration of the various foreign elements into the political and social framework of the nations. Because of their cultural affinity with the Latin Americans, the peoples from southern Europe tended to adjust themselves quite easily to the conditions of their new environment and to forget their old loyalties. With the Germans and the Japanese it was otherwise. Isolated groups of agricultural colonists were left to their own devices, like the Japanese *nucleus* in the zone of the Sorocabana Railway in the state of São Paulo and the German settlements in Santa Catharina and Rio Grande do Sul and in the Chilean lake country. Here they set up institutionalized replicas of their homelands, with churches, schools, clubs, and newspapers. The atmosphere of large towns like Blumenau in Santa Catharina remained much more German than Brazilian. However, in spite of the persistence of old attachments, the German immigrants and their descendants might have accepted the facts of Brazilian nationality much more readily if they had not fitted so logically into the oversea designs of the imperial and Nazi regimes. Fanatical agents of the Berlin government labored to revive their dormant loyalties to the Fatherland, only to bring about a sentimental dichotomy within the Germanic communities. The Japanese, who were later comers, were most obdurate in their devotion to the mother country.[67] They generally lived in tight little Japans, embedded in the social body of Brazil, where their original patriotism was studiously cultivated by the Japanese government. In line with this policy, we have witnessed the officers and crews of a visiting squadron of Japanese warships stage an impressive ceremony before the hundreds of Japanese workers on a large coffee fazenda in the state of São Paulo. This perpetuation of early loyalties by both German and Japanese created serious security problems for the Brazilian authorities during the Second World War, and was to lead to the abandonment of its easygoing immigration policies.

Since the Second World War there has been a general tendency to be much more selective than formerly in the screening

of prospective immigrants. The principal criteria to be applied
are: (1) potential usefulness to the economic development of the
country, particularly to agriculture and manufacturing industry;
(2) probable ease of assimilation to the national population; and
(3) freedom from addiction to political or social doctrines inconsistent with the accepted ideologies or loyalties of the nation. The
new nationalism which is rampant in much of Latin America has
affected the official attitude toward foreigners and in some localities has even colored the former friendliness of the people
toward those outsiders who would live among them. This spirit
is reflected in laws and the provisions of the new constitutions,
some of them frankly hostile or discriminatory, and frequently in
the conduct of public servants, such as customs and immigration
inspectors and members of the national police. Economic competition, particularly where considerable numbers of foreigners
are employed within the country by American or European business organizations, is liable to foment this feeling against aliens,
which is played upon by labor leaders and radical agitators. The
presence of large mining and plantation enterprises of foreign
ownership may lead to charges of economic imperialism, particularly against the United States, and a new type of demagogic
politician is quick to make capital of this situation.

Although far from universal, for Mexicans are by nature a
friendly and warmhearted people, antiforeignism, usually with an
anti-American slant, is widespread in Mexico.[68] This sentiment is
the product of a number of circumstances, including the century-
old distrust of the United States, unfortunately revived by the
seizure of Veracruz in 1914, and the fruitless foray of General
Pershing into Chihuahua two years later; and not entirely allayed
by the subsequent restraint and consideration shown by the
United States in its dealings with Mexico. Argentina has a long
tradition of acceptance of the foreigner, but the perpetuation of a
belligerently nationalistic political regime might eventually affect
even the cosmopolitan public opinion of Buenos Aires. And while
xenophobia is completely alien to the hospitable atmosphere of
Brazil, there are indications that in some circles the foreigner is
no longer welcomed on his own individual merits as he once was.

The profound disturbance of international confidence incident
to the breakup of the Old World order during the past forty years

has had the effect of turning the Latin Americans' wider faith in humanity inward on themselves. While their own national egos have been fortified correspondingly, they have tended to narrow their national outlook and sympathies to a provincial body of attachments and interests. Following the model of the Hispanidad of Franco's Spain, there is a growing emphasis among the more nationalistic elements of the population on the narrower obligations, either regional or national in their scope, to the concepts of *Latinidad,* or *Argentinidad* or *Peruanidad.* Much of this sentiment is chauvinistic and isolationist—a form of international "escapism." To the extent that it is a revulsion against the turn of world affairs since 1914, it is understandable. As such, it represents a desire of the republics to live their lives according to a local pattern of their own making, unrelated to the stresses of the world outside. The presumption is that the foreigner has served whatever purpose may once have justified his admission into the national society and economy. In the minds of the extreme nationalists, he now embodies the disturbing forces in the world and by his home connections may be a potential threat to the national security and economic independence, if not to the cultural integrity, of the nation. In practice, the foreigner is liable to be put on the defensive and hedged about by restrictions. Under the circumstances, he must stand on his qualities as an individual, and his acceptance on that basis by the individuals who make up the nation where he is living. Thus, his status may become a personal one and his foreign origin and affiliations have little bearing on his successful adjustment to life in the country. It was so in colonial times and so it is today. The alternative is to relinquish his identity as a foreigner and by naturalization accept citizenship in the country. Some of the republics, notably Uruguay and Argentina, make the process of adoption very easy. In fact, the Uruguayan Constitution makes naturalization virtually automatic for responsible foreigners after from three to five years' residence in the country.[69] For those who have performed "notable services" or are of "outstanding merit," the period is even less. Even though they may have retained their original nationality, foreigners who have resided in the Oriental Republic [Uruguay] for fifteen years have the right of vote. In Argentina, according to the Constitution of 1950, foreigners who have resided for two years in the country may request Argentine citizenship. They acquire Argentine nationality automatically after five years of continuous residence, unless they declare their preference to the contrary.

Foreigners have played a much more important role in the life of Latin America under the republics than they did during the colonial period. There have been many more of them, both in actual numbers and relative to the population of the countries. Their influence has been particularly great in Argentina, Brazil, Chile, Paraguay, and Uruguay. It has been much less in Mexico, Colombia, and Venezuela. Present-day Argentina is much more the unfinished product of the various elements which have entered the country since independence than it is the heir of the colonial viceroyalty. If the genes in the composite body of the Argentine people could be counted, it would be found that the majority of them were of new European, rather than of old Spanish or Indian, origin. President Sarmiento who railed at the "barbarism" of the nation did not live to see the profound changes that were to be wrought in his people's ways by the influence of the foreigner. An examination of the telephone directories of cities like São Paulo and Porto Alegre in Brazil, Montevideo in Uruguay, Buenos Aires and Rosario in Argentina, and Concepción and Valdivia in Chile would reveal the extent of the "foreignization" of those countries. The impact of immigrants and their descendants in the civilization of Latin America is reflected, above all, in the economic life of the republics, but also in political and social habits, in the institutional forms of organized society, and in the cultural areas of education, journalism, architecture, music, language, food and drink, and the techniques of play and sport. The life of Latin America is much the richer for what they have brought to its original store of values and practices.

NOTES

1. *Leyes de Indias,* Book 8, Section 37, Law no. I.

2. On November 11, 1492, Columbus wrote to Ferdinand and Isabella, "Your Highnesses should not permit any foreigner to trade or set foot here unless they are Catholic Christians."

3. *Ibid.,* Law no. 31.

4. *Ibid.,* Law no. 7, also Book 3, Section 13, Law no. 18, first issued in 1556, and reissued in 1557, 1603, 1606, 1610.

THE FOREIGNER 235

5. *Ibid.*, Law no. 9.

6. *Ibid.*, Law no. 8. That the Spaniards sometimes had good reason to suspect foreigners is evidenced by the reports of the military weakness of the two vice-royalties in the seventeenth century made by Thomas Gage, the English friar, and an anonymous Portuguese Jew. Thomas Gage, *A New Survey of the West Indies, 1648* (New York, 1929), and José de la Riva Agüero, "Descripción anónima del Perú y de Lima á principios del siglo XVII compuesta por un judío portugués y dirigida á los estados de Holanda," in Congreso de Historia y Geografía Hispano-Americanas Celebrado en Sevilla en Abril de 1914, *Actas y Memorias* (Madrid, 1914).

7. *Ibid.*, Law no. 4.

8. *Ibid.*, Law no. 25.

9. *Ibid.*, Law no. 10.

10. *Ibid.*, Law no. 13.

11. *Ibid.*, Law no. 28.

12. "Foreigners enjoyed rights in Paraguay about as ample as those of the Spaniards themselves. Once they succeeded in entering the country, the laws of the peninsula, which were designed to restrict their activities, became a dead letter. From the beginning of the conquest, many foreigners take part in the events of the period. . . . The sentiment of hospitality and the absence of prejudices against foreigners constitute one of the outstanding characteristics of colonial society in Paraguay." J. Natalicio González, *Proceso y Formación de la Cultura Paraguaya* (Asunción, 1938), p. 233.

13. *Op. cit.*, Law no. 35.

14. Basil Hall, *Extracts from a Journal Written on the Coasts of Chili, Peru, and Mexico, in the Years 1820, 1821, 1822* (2 vols., Edinburgh, 1824), I, 272, 304, 306.

15. "The liberality with which the foreigner in Portuguese America was treated in the sixteenth century is evident to us. This is a liberality that goes far back, to the very roots of the Portuguese nation. It is not a matter of any virtue that has descended from the heavens upon the Portuguese; it is the quasi-chemical result of the cosmopolitan and heterogeneous background of this maritime nation." Gilberto Freyre, *The Masters and the Slaves* (tr. from the Portuguese, New York, 1946), p. 199. Commenting on the readiness of the Portuguese to admit foreigners into Brazil, Sergio Buarque de Holanda says: "Innumerable Spaniards, Italians, Flemings, Englishmen, Irishmen, and Germans came here to take advantage of this tolerance." *Raizes do Brasil* (2nd ed., São Paulo, 1948), p. 153. Foreign merchants could trade along the coast on condition of paying a ten per cent tax on their goods, and not trading directly with the Indians. See also Freyre, *op. cit.*, p. 40.

16. "In the first two centuries of the colony, the policy of the Kingdom in reference to the admission of foreigners into Brazil was very liberal. The Portuguese criterion in the selection of colonists was rather one of religion than of nationality, that is, the condition of being a Christian. However, only Catholics were considered as Christians." Caio Prado, *Formação do Brasil Contemporáneo* (São Paulo, 1942), p. 228.

17. Pietro Martire d'Anghiera, *De Orbe Novo* (tr. from the Latin, 2 vols., New York, 1912), p. 250. Peter Martyr said: "I, who have lived, not without credit, at

the Court of the Catholic King, have only been able by the greatest efforts to obtain authorization for one foreigner to sail (on the expedition of Pedrarias Dávila)." The work of Peter Martyr was originally published at Alcalá de Henares in 1516, and 1530.

18. He was the first quarantine officer in the port of Asunción. J. Natalicio González, *op. cit.*, p. 342.

19. Oviedo, *Historia general* (4 vols., Madrid, 1851–55), III, 12.

20. See Pigafetta, *Magellan's Voyage around the World* (tr. from the Italian, 2 vols., Cleveland, 1902), originally published at Venice in 1534 (or 1536), as *Il viaggio fatto dagli Spagnuoli atorno al mondo*.

21. Cristóbal Bermúdez Plata, ed., *Catálogo de Pasajeros á Indias* (2 vols., Sevilla, 1940, p. 42).

22. Antonio Vázquez de Espinosa, *Compendium and Description of the West Indies* (tr. from the Spanish, Washington, D. C., 1942), pp. 528, 652.

23. Agustín Edwards, *My Native Land* (London, 1928), p. 89. At that time, there were twenty-three other foreigners residing in Santiago, as follows: eight Frenchmen, six Portuguese, five Americans, one Austrian, one German, one Dane, and one Swede. Several British were then living in Valparaiso. Dr. George Edwards, the founder of the famous Chilean family, arrived from England in 1805. Edwards and other Englishmen began the development of the copper mining industry in northern Chile. Many foreigners settled in Lima about the same time, particularly after 1808, and were not interfered with by the Spanish authorities. W. B. Stevenson, *A Historical and Descriptive Narrative of Twenty Years' Residence in South America* (3 vols., London, 1825), I, 353.

24. Cristóbal Bermúdez Plata, *op. cit.* In his account of Robledo's expedition into New Granada, Cieza de León tells of a Frenchman in the Spanish force who was killed by the Indians. *The War of Chupas*, p. 17.

25. In 1729, a Frenchman named Domose settled in Chile and married Gerónima Caldera, an Araucanian chieftainess and owner of a large estate along the Maipu. Agustín Edwards, *My Native Land*, p. 119.

26. Acarette du Biscay, *Relación de un viaje al Rio de la Plata y de allí por tierra al Perú* (tr. from the French, Buenos Aires, n.d.).

27. Bernard Moses, *The Spanish Dependencies in South America* (2 vols., New York, 1914), II, 105-110.

28. See Afranio Peixoto, *Breviario da Bahia* (Rio de Janeiro, 1945), p. 20; also Gaffarel, *Histoire du Brésil français* (Paris, 1878); Bréard, *Les Marins honfleurais* (Paris, 1884); *Relation authentique du voyage du capitaine de Gonneville, publieé par M. d'Avezac, Extrait des Annales des Voyages* (Paris, 1869).

29. The German Hans Staden, who was an uneasy captive of man-eating Indians in the vicinity of Rio during this period, has much to say of the activities of the French. When a French trader appeared in the Indian village, Staden pleaded with him to take him away, but the Frenchman said to the Indians: "Kill him and eat him, the so-and-so, for he is a Portuguese, your enemy and mine." He also reported that a Dieppe ship took a Portuguese vessel in Rio Bay, and turned over one of the crew to "a king called Ita Wu who ate him." *The True Story of his Captivity* (New York, 1929), pp. 76, 101, 117. The book was originally published at Marburg in 1557.

30. Richard Hakluyt, *The Principal Navigations, Voyages, Traffiques and Discoveries of the English Nation* (3 vols., London, 1598–1600), VII, 99. References are to the Everyman Edition.

31. *Ibid.*, pp. 361, 388, 390.

32. *Ibid.*, VIII, 13.

33. *Ibid.*, pp. 15-24.

34. Henry Koster, another Englishman who lived in Brazil during the same period, was known to the Brazilians as "Henrique da Costa." Freyre, *op. cit.*, p. 197.

35. Hakluyt, *op. cit.*, VIII, 26.

36. *A Voyage to New-Holland, & c. in the Year 1699* (London, 1703, 1709), III, 33-37.

37. Caio Prado, *op. cit.*, p. 228.

38. Hakluyt, *op. cit.*, VI, 246-354.

39. *Ibid.*, VII, 25.

40. *Ibid.*, VII, 272-400.

41. Harris Gaylord Warren, *Paraguay: An Informal History* (Norman, Oklahoma, 1949), *passim*.

42. Though this should have been the surest way to end his travels, according to the records of the Inquisition at Cartagena, in 1650 one John Drake was admonished for straying from the strict path of Catholic orthodoxy. This was 68 years after the shipwreck in the River Plate, so that, if this was the original captain of Fenton's fleet, he must then have been of a very advanced age. Zelia Nuttall, *New Light on Drake* (Hakluyt Society Publications, London, 1916). In 1737, an English hatmaker was living in Lima, where he made fine hats of vicuña wool. He killed the market for hats from Europe, and when he returned to England after five years, he gave his secret to a mestizo who had worked for him and who continued to manufacture the hats in Lima. Jorge Juan and Antonio de Ulloa, *Noticiás Secretas*, II, 267.

43. Hakluyt, *op. cit.*, VIII, 139.

44. See Clarence H. Haring, *Buccaneers in the West Indies in the Seventeenth Century* (New York, 1910); John Esquemeling, *The Buccaneers of America* (tr. from the Dutch, London, n.d., originally published at Amsterdam, 1678); James Burney, *A Chronological History of the Discoveries in the South Sea or Pacific Ocean* (5 vols., London, 1803–1807).

45. See Richard Walter, *A Voyage Round the World in the Year 1740, 1,2,3,4, by George Anson, Esq.* (London, 1748, reprinted in the Everyman Library).

46. Writing of his attack on Guayaquil in 1709, Woodes Rogers said: "This day I heard 15 of 'em were kill'd and wounded, amongst them was the chief Gunner, an Irish-man, that fired the last gun at us, who had lived some Years amongst 'em." *A Cruising Voyage Round the World* (London, 1928), p. 130. Rogers's book was first published in 1712.

47. See Eugenio Orrego Vicuña, *O'Higgins: Vida y Tiempo* (Buenos Aires, 1946), pp. 34-43. The author dedicates his book to—among others—Juan MacKenna O'Reilly and Benjamín Vicuña Subercasseaux. Col. John MacKenna, of County Tyrone, was a captain in the Spanish Army when he went to Chile, where he gained the favor of Ambrose O'Higgins. He threw in his lot with the Chilean patriots in their war against Spain, and founded one of the principal families

of Chile. William H. Koebel, *British Exploits in South America* (New York, 1917), p. 193.

48. See Charles Henry Lea, *The Inquisition in the Spanish Dependencies* (New York, 1922), pp. 236-39; also, the fictionalized story of Lamport's life by Vicente Riva Palacio, *Memorias de Un Impostor: Don Guillén de Lamport, Rey de México* (2 vols., Mexico, D. F., 1946).

49. Francis W. Herron, *Letters from the Argentine* (New York, 1943), p. 81.

50. Report of S. James Taylor, United States Rubber Development Commission, June 30, 1945.

51. E. George Squier, Peru: *Incidents of Travel and Exploration in the Land of the Incas* (New York, 1877), p. 51.

52. Miguel Covarrubias, *Mexico South: The Isthmus of Tehuantepec* (New York, 1946), p. 225.

53. See Luís Galdames, *A History of Chile* (tr. from the Spanish, Chapel Hill, North Carolina, 1941) p. 115; and Agustín Edwards, *My Native Land* (London, 1928), p. 62.

54. Germán Arciniegas, *Germans in the Conquest of America* (tr. from the Spanish, New York, 1943). See also by the same author, *The Knight of El Dorado* (tr. from the Spanish, New York, 1942), p. 161; and Adolph F. Bandelier, *The Gilded Man and Other Pictures of the Spanish Occupancy of America* (New York, 1893), pp. 16-17.

55. Ulrich Schmidel, *Viaje al Rio de la Plata* (tr. from the German, Buenos Aires, 1942).

56. The Dutch founder of this family was Gaspar van der Lei, who became a Catholic and married a daughter of the rich Mello family in Pernambuco. Freyre, *op. cit.*, p. 197.

57. *Leyes de Indias, op. cit.*, law no. 5. Cieza de León mentions "a Spaniard of the Portuguese nation, named Magallanes," who was a soldier in the conquest of Peru. *The War of Las Salinas* (Hakluyt Society Publications, London, 1923), p. 61.

58. Eliécer Enríquez B., ed., *Quito a Través de los Siglos* (Quito, 1938), p. 52.

59. "In 1536 it was ordered that any married Portuguese accompanied by his wife be let to go freely to the Indies." Irene A. Wright, *The Early History of Cuba 1492-1586* (New York, 1916), p. 194.

60. Garcilaso de la Vega, *The Florida of the Inca* (tr. from the Spanish, Austin, Texas, 1951), p. 378. See also *The Gentleman of Elvas, Relacão Verdadeira* (Evora, 1557; translated from the Portuguese, 2 vols., New Haven, 1932).

61. Garcilaso de la Vega, *Historia General del Perú* (reprinted, 3 vols., Buenos Aires, 1946), II, 271.

62. Carlos Pereyra, *Las Huellas de los Conquistadores* (Madrid, n.d.), p. 270.

63. Juan Bromley and José Barbagelata, *Evolución Urbana de la Ciudad de Lima* (Lima, 1945), p. 16.

64. Frank Cundall, *The Darien Venture* (New York, 1926).

65. On the subject of American and British volunteers in the armies and navies of the Independencia, see Charles Lyon Chandler, *Inter-American Acquaintances* (Sewanee, Tennessee, 1917); William H. Koebel, *British Exploits in South America*

(New York, 1917); Alfred Hasbrouck, *Foreign Legionaries in the Liberation of Spanish South America* (New York, 1928); and Basil Hall, *op. cit.*, I, 62.

66. "Thirty years ago, the Chilenos welcomed all foreigners with overflowing hospitality, and with a primitive warmth and simplicity that was delightful. Such welcome is now seldom shown, except in remote places in the country." Mrs. C. B. Merwin, *Three Years in Chile* (New York, 1863), p. 72 quoted in Tom B. Jones, *South America Rediscovered* (Minneapolis, 1949), p. 84. Mrs. Merwin's husband was United States Consul at Valparaiso in 1853.

67. See João Frederico Normano, *The Japanese in South America* (New York, 1943).

68. "Mexico . . . has done everything to prevent foreigners from establishing themselves there. And those who do live in Mexico and whose heritage is neither Mexican nor Spanish always remain foreigners in the eyes of the Mexicans." Herbert Cerwin, *These are the Mexicans* (New York, 1947), p. 339.

69. See Russell H. Fitzgibbon, ed., *The Constitutions of the Americas* (Chicago, 1948), p. 721.

Chapter VII

THE CHURCH

IN INTERNATIONAL parlance and protocol, the Spanish
monarch was "the Most Catholic King," as his French counterpart was "the Christian King." The title was, in fact, a tribute
to the firm orthodoxy of the Spanish nation. The Catholicism of
the Spains was an embattled faith, belligerent and fanatical. It
was a soldier's religion, and the Spanish cross was a shining
Toledo sword hammered out on the anvil of the secular war
against the infidel. *Santiaguismo,* or the cult of St. James, the
Spanish Mars, was the natural expression of this militant fervor
among the soldiery. It was to be expected that the military orders
should flourish in such an atmosphere, and when Ferdinand took
over the grand masterships of the four orders of Alcántara, Almansa, Calatrava, and Santiago, several thousand knights were
enrolled under their banners.

At least, things were so among the great mass of Spaniards, and more particularly at the precise moment when the New World was discovered. Some of the things that had gone on during the Middle Ages between Christian and Moslem were another matter.[1] It was significant that when Columbus interviewed the queen before his first voyage, the meeting took place at the armed camp at Santa Fé, outside Granada. The reconquest of the Moorish kingdom in that year placed the final seal on a process of political and spiritual unification that had been centuries in the making. It was the zeal of Isabella that brought to a head the ferment of uncompromising orthodoxy which became the mark of Spain in the sixteenth century. Here was, indeed, the stuff of a great Crusade, and the wandering Italian with a far vision in his head was to furnish the scene for it.

The Spanish Church was like no other in Europe, nor is it now.[2] The basic Judaic elements were strong in Spanish Christianity, perhaps as a result of the deep Semitic tinge to the race. Though there was a pronounced neo-Scholastic movement in Spain, represented by such illustrious figures as Francisco Suárez, Luís Molina, and Vitoria, it was often more concerned with human conduct, as became a Spanish creed, than with metaphysics. For Spaniards were little given to theology as it was unrelated to the practical problems of men. The popular faith was sustained by some inner fire and did not have to be fortified by any ratiocination. It was an emotional religion of a single-minded people, and there was nothing lukewarm or indifferent about it. The average Spaniard accepted the official version of the faith and asked no questions, nor did the Church encourage curiosity about holy things. If he did not comprehend the doctrine of the Trinity, he shrugged his shoulders and stowed it away with the other mysteries in his brain. Above all, he was preoccupied with his own individual salvation, for Spanish religion was obsessed with the concept of future punishment. And as the punitive ideas of the Spanish clergy were particularly forbidding, there was a strong incentive for the communicant to follow the prescribed formula of deliverance.

The road to salvation had little to do with morality. Beyond the admonition and example of some saintly cleric, so common in Spain, a Spaniard usually depended on his strong sense of right and wrong which had its roots deep in the racial ethos. It had been developed pragmatically—and somewhat opportunistically—out of their long experience of living together. In it there was probably as much of stoic philosophy and of folk wisdom, like Sancho's "Honesty is the best policy," as there was of Christianity. In Spain, ethics probably bore much the same relation to religion as equity did to the formal law. Foreign observers have frequently commented on the rituaristic emphasis in Spanish religion as satisfying the form to the neglect of the spirit.[3] In worship there was much stress on the externals of the cult—the drama of the mass and the sacraments, the sensuous appeal of the pomp and pageantry, of the mighty music and solemn processions, and the glory of the cathedrals, like those of Sevilla and Toledo, that were so worthy to be the house of God.

The Crucifixion made a specially strong appeal to the religious imagination of Spaniards, even sometimes to the macabre and morbid. To Spaniards in such an ecstasy of devotion, the adoration of the agonizing Christ on the Cross might be a spiritual self-flagellation. It is the sterner aspect of Christianity that is sometimes reflected in the paintings of Rivera and Zurbarán, just as the madonnas of Murillo represented the growing popular addiction to mariolatry.

So much for the religious faith of the great majority of the Spanish people. Among the intellectual or spiritual elite of Spain, variations from the generally accepted norm of religious doctrine and practice were very common. In fact, the body of heterodoxy was so considerable, and so important to an understanding of the cultural history of the nation, that Sr. Menéndez y Pelayo has written a veritable library on the subject.[4] It would have been strange, indeed, if a people so independent had not chosen its own personal religious faith according to the convictions of its mind and the promptings of its spirit. There were many sensitive ones who were discouraged when they looked for the warm soul of the Christian faith among all the impressive and ponderous mechanics of the Church—the ceremonial and ritual that obscured the divine presence for whose comforting hand and guidance they were groping. There were many who objected to the formal intervention of the priesthood in their relationshp with deity. As Spaniards, they wished to have their own private approach to the Lord Almighty.

Spanish Mysticism

It was the wide prevalence of this urge for the personal expression and communication of religious fervor that accounted for the extraordinary growth of mysticism in Spain.[5] In no other European country did mystics play so important a role in the religious life of the nation. Their number included such distinguished names as Ramón Lull, the Catalan missionary and philosopher of the thirteenth century; Santa Teresa de Avila, busy founder and abbess of many convents and prolific writer of lucid prose, patroness of Spain, and certainly one of its two greatest women; her friend, the Carmelite friar, Juan de la Cruz, one of the finest poets of his time; Ignacio de Loyola, founder of the Jesuit order; and Fray Luís de León. Because of their unconventional mentality, they were always suspect to the unimaginative ecclesiastical authorities and were sometimes persecuted as potential, if not actual, heretics. Yet, by their enthusiasm and freshness of view, and by their manifold good works, they did much to vitalize the national religion.

In their behavior and personality, the mystics were generally quite normal and very practical people. However, around the fringes of the world of mysticism there lived a lesser breed of "inspired" men and women. Some of them followed the inner spirit into dark and dangerous corners, where in time, to their great sorrow and discomfort, they were to run afoul of the Inquisition. Some were known as *Alumbrados* or *Iluminados,* or the "lighted" and "illuminated ones." Except for persons who were only unusually endowed with intuition or prescience, and therefore suspect of sorcery or witchcraft, these border cases ran the gamut of mental aberration from plain cranks, through visionaries of varying degrees of sanity or clarity, to the hysterics and neurotics, and the downright hallucinated and possessed. In these morbid precincts of the Spanish psyche the Inquisition was to find many of its victims.

Of other unorthodox forms of religious thought, Erasmianism made a particularly strong appeal to Spaniards of superior mind. Among these in high and influential places who were openly or secretly partisans of the great Dutch humanist were no less than the Emperor Charles himself and Archbishop Carranza, primate of the kingdom. In the New World its influences reached the famous Vasco de Quiroga, Bishop of Michoacán, through the medium of Sir Thomas More's writings.

Erasmianism was not a philosophical system or a definite body of doctrine, but only represented the eminently civilized views of the foremost thinker in Europe. He was the spokesman for reason in an atmosphere that was increasingly embittered by the schism in western Christendom. His wisdom and moderation and lofty humanity offered the only alternative to the wars of religion, as the Continent was eventually to find to its infinite sorrow. Meanwhile, Charles V, champion of the unity of Graeco-Christian civilization, and other political and moral leaders grasped eagerly at the dicta of Erasmus as a solution of their deep anxieties. Though he steadfastly refused to throw his vast intellectual and moral prestige onto the side of the religious revolution that was launched by Luther and Calvin, he boldly criticized the abuses and wrongs of the Church which others, too, condemned in their hearts but lacked the courage openly to denounce. In other words, through him they disapproved vicariously of many religious customs and conditions of the time. Perhaps he represented the longings of superior men everywhere for the golden age which the Renaissance, with its revival of classical learning, and a return to the purer Christianity of the Church Fathers appeared to promise. To Spaniards, in particular, his ideas offered some relief from the incubus of medievalism which the Church would present for its own greater security and some glimpse of the Renaissance whose liberalization of thought it feared. Men, afraid to speak of their visions in a world where dreams were anathema, yet desired to belong to his select spiritual company as some silent and exalted confirmation of their own unproclaimed ideals. To Spain, the very awareness of his presence in Europe and of his moral power must have tempered somewhat the rising intolerance of the counterreformation.

STATE AND CHURCH IN SPAIN

An understanding of the Spanish Church is incomplete without a recognition of its peculiar position as an appanage of the State.

When Ferdinand and Isabella set out to build a strong centralized monarchy, one of the major obstacles to the attainment of
their objective was the independence and power of the higher
clergy. For all secular purposes the bishops and abbots conducted
themselves much as the lay lords of the land, even to leading their
retainers to battle. When, along with the *grandeza,* they were ultimately reduced to obedience to the crown, the central authority
of the monachy systematically brought the ecclesiastical organization within the apparatus of the State. The process that was
begun under the Catholic Kings was continued under Charles V
and carried to its completion under Philip II. While Philip was
personally among the most pious of Spanish kings, the Church
dared take no liberties with the royal prerogative of omnipotence
during his long reign. By this time the exercise of the *real petro-
nato* gave the crown a strong leverage for its control of the
Church. This was the privilege of "patronage," grudgingly granted
to the Spanish crown by the pope in 1484, whereby all appoint-
ments to the hierarchy of the Spanish Church had to be approved
by the monarch. The power was also extended to the selection of
the higher clergy for positions in the colonies, where it was eventually inherited by the governments of the republics, further to
bedevil the relations between Church and State.

The monarchs were not concerned with points of theological
dogma as such—that was what bishops and inquisitors were for—
but with the internal unity of the nation. The Church was expected not only to refrain from opposing the will or the interests
of the crown, as it had once done so lightly, but to see that all
Spaniards thought alike on religious matters. As it was, there
were enough sources of friction and dissent among the Spanish
peoples to plague the central authority indefinitely. But for the
most part they were old and familiar grievances with which the
new imperium could deal in its own time and way.

HERESY AND THE INQUISITION

What the rulers of Spain feared above all else was the spread of
religious heresy in the kingdom. Since faith still retained much of
its fervor from the Middle Ages, religion preoccupied the minds
of men much more than it does today, when there are so many
other things to differ about, and any mass departure from ortho-

doxy had explosive possibilities for society and the State. The concern of the sixteenth-century State about the menace of heresy was comparable to that which today exists in the United States about the danger from communism. Any divergences from traditional belief were correspondingly serious, especially if espoused by a considerable number of nonconformists. At no time did there exist in Spain such a large body of dissenters of any one dispensation as the Calvinists represented in France. If there was much heresy or nonconformity of sorts it never offered a unified front to government, but was scattered among many sects or creeds or shades of thought, so that it was easier to deal with piecemeal, according to its relative gravity or urgency. Besides some outright Protestants, which included that arch antitrinitarian, double heretic, and Calvinist martyr, Miguel Serveto, the principal problem was represented by late converts from Islam or Judaism. These were the so-called "new Christians," and there was a widespread, and probably well-founded, suspicion that a good many of these eleventh-hour conversions were not authentic, since the alternative was expulsion from the country. The religious purge of these suspected elements, which began in 1492, and continued for many years, constituted the main task of the Inquisition. Without the challenge presented by these various heterodox or free-thinking groups, the capricious and unpredictable nature of the Spanish temper would by itself have appeared to offer ample justification for setting up machinery for the discouragement and control of independent thought. For in Spain, as its rulers, lay and clerical, were aware, conformity with anything could never long be taken for granted.

The Inquisition was the machine. The Spanish Inquisition was very different from the papal Inquisition of the Middle Ages, which put down the Albigensian heresy in southern France and other divergencies from accepted dogma.[6] It was much more professional in its efficiency. In its prime, it was the most efficient organization in Spain, and one of the most effectual in carrying out its purpose of any in Europe. It was the handiwork of Tomás Torquemada, a Dominican friar, who used his position as confessor to Ferdinand and Isabella to further his great and terrifying design. When it was established in 1480, it was what Torquemada wished it to be.

The Spanish Inquisition began its existence with the enormous advantage of the backing of the crown. In fact, it was primarily an instrument of the royal authority and not of the papacy. It was frequently at odds with the popes and ignored the protests and pleas of Rome as if they served entirely different faiths. There was no higher authority to which its victims might appeal for relief from its cold and relentless power. As inquisitor-general, the implacable friar administered the Holy Office with fire and fury during the years of its inception, and after him his successors continued his policies and methods until Spain was well purged of heresy. It long outlived its usefulness and, for all practical purposes, was finally snuffed out by Napoleon more than three centuries after its birth.[7]

In the beginning it served the ends of the State by suppressing heresy, which was a threat to national security; it assured to the established Church a virtual monopoly in the field of religion; and its festivals provided the Spanish rabble with entertainment and with food for its sadistic appetites. In terms of current American institutionalism, its functions were a combination of those of the FBI, of congressional committees for the investigation of subversion, of the "watch-and-ward" societies, and of a federal penitentiary. Its procedural devices included the browbeating and intimidation of witnesses; the systematic defamation of character; the use of the *agent provocateur* to incriminate suspects; resort to physical torture to extract confession or delation; the public humiliation of the suspected or guilty; the confiscation of property of heretics—itself an inducement to findings of guilt; the seizure and destruction of obnoxious books; and the burning of contumacious heretics.

In time the Spaniards took their Inquisition to the New World, as they took all the other paraphernalia of Spanish life, and set it up in Cartagena, Lima, and Mexico City.[8] That was about 1570, previous to which the bishops had dealt with heretical matters. It was established with the royal blessing and much fanfare, and the colonials were ordered to greet the inquisitors with salvos of artillery and other "extraordinary demonstrations."[9]

At first, there was some concern for saving the Indians from the error of their theological ways, but by one of those quixotic quirks peculiar to the Spanish mind, the aborigines were early and mercifully exempted from the jurisdiction of the Inquisition.[10] As the Indians were not considered to be *gente de razón*, or "reasonable people," they were held to be incapable of the mental processes necessary for the commission of heresy. If the Indians were not proper provender for the Hispanic Moloch, it satisfied its voracity with other fare. Besides the usual crop of small-fry eccentrics and psychopaths, its favorite diet consisted of Portuguese Jews, "new Christians," like the famous Carvajal family in Mexico,[11] priests who were too inquiring or who violated the sanctity of the confessional, bigamists, and occasional English or Dutch sailors who were too slow in getting back to their ships.

In 1548, before the installation of the royal Inquisition, Gerónimo de Loayza, the Bishop of Lima, had a Fleming burned as a heretic.[12] At an auto-da-fé staged in Lima in 1621, a stoical Englishman, who had been condemned to death for Lutheranism, calmly seated himself on the pile of firewood and remained immobile and expressionless as the pyre was lighted and the flames enveloped him. Sometimes heretical foreigners escaped from the clutches of the Inquisitors by espousing Catholicism as an alternative to the stake or prolonged imprisonment. All the possibilities of punishment were illustrated by the various fates of the English sailors whom John Hawkins abandoned at Veracruz in 1567.[13]

The Inquisition was much more benign in the New World than in the mother country. There was much less intellectual activity and such as there was inclined to be orthodox. As the Frenchman, Frézier, said of the Peruvian branch of the Holy Office, "as for Hereticks, I am sure none fall into their Hands. They there study so little that they are not subject to run astray through too much Curiosity." [14] In the three centuries of Spanish rule in Mexico, only forty-three persons were sentenced to death by the Inquisition. During the same period in Peru, of about 3,000 persons who were brought before the Inquisition only thirty were executed.[15] Of these relatively few obdurate heretics, half were burned alive. Of the remainder, many were released. Suspects might be detained for months pending trial, only to be turned loose with a reprimand and warning after a perfunctory hearing by the local *Suprema*. Even if cleared of the charges made against them, the psychological ordeal of an appearance be-

fore the sinister tribunal was generally enough to deter the too
unconventional or unorthodox from backsliding. Others were
fined or sentenced to various penalties, which ranged from the
public humiliation of wearing the sanbenito at an auto-da-fé to
the rare sentence of perpetual incarceration in the inquisitorial
dungeons. This record compares very favorably with the holo-
causts in Spain, where in the time of Torquemada alone more
than two thousand persons are said to have been burned.

The attitude of the local population toward the Inquisition
changed greatly in time. Father Vázquez de Espinosa, who was
in Peru in the early seventeenth century, says it was then highly
"esteemed and reverenced" in that country.[16] Secure in the support of the crown, the Holy Office long behaved as a separate—
and often superior—arm of government in the New World. Everybody in Lima, including the viceroy and his wife, all the royal officials, and the authorities of the university, was ordered out to
attend an especially impressive auto-da-fé in Lima in 1592, fea-
turing four English pirates and about forty assorted performers
of lower category as lesser, if reluctant, attractions. During this
stage of its history in the colonies,[17] the Inquisition was probably
at the peak of its popularity. The auto-da-fé made a wide appeal
to a variety of popular instincts. It strengthened the religious zeal
or fanaticism of the populace, and discouraged any temptation to
indulge in doctrinal speculation which might be lurking in its
mind. It provided satisfaction for the latent sadism that at various periods of history has found an outlet in the contemplation
of gladiatorial combats, exhibitions of mass persecution, or the
morbid spectacle of public hangings. As entertainment, its pageantry also offered all the spectacular attraction of a modern circus day plus the lure of an old-fashioned "revival" meeting. If
there were foreigners among the victims, it provided an occasion
to indulge the xenophobia which was particularly common among
Spaniards during this period.

The everlasting snooping and meddling and prying into private lives, the persecution of men of good repute in the community, the scandalous conduct of inquisitors who yielded to the
temptations and immunity of power, the forbidding and sinister
atmosphere within which the Inquisition worked—all these finally
turned the original good will of the populace into deep contempt

and repugnance. As universal censor and official busybody, it poked its long nose into too many books and boudoirs.[18] In the "enlightened" and skeptical eighteenth century, it became an anachronism. It had long outlived any usefulness it may ever have had and now had only a nuisance value. It was a bogy without substance and a butt of irreverent jokes. When the support of the royal authority on which it leaned was finally removed during the wars of independence, the people turned on it with all their fury, as they did in Lima. William Stevenson, who witnessed the spectacle, describes the joy with which the Limeños sacked the quarters of the Inquisition and destroyed its instruments of torture.[19] Captain Basil Hall, who was in Peru during this period, wrote: "Everything connected with the recently abolished Inquisition is viewed at Lima with a degree of scorn and hatred, very remarkable in a city so crowded with clerical establishments, and where the observances of the church form so great a part of the business of the people. But whatever is the cause of this unmeasured detestation, nothing can be more determined than it is." [20]

The Church in the New World

The religious conquest of the New World was contemporaneous with the military, and, for all practical purposes, was as thorough. Not since the pagan peoples of northern Europe were brought to the Christian faith in the early Middle Ages has there been a missionary enterprise so vast in its scope and, at least in its numerical results, so successful. Whatever its weaknesses, it was a true crusade, conducted with fervor and devotion, courage and self-sacrifice. If its agents were intolerant of the cults that were to be supplanted, the sixteenth century was nowhere a time for tolerance, and, after all, intolerance is of the very essence of any crusade. The faiths that fell before the onslaught of the Cross ranged from the crudest fetishism to elaborate systems of religion, and even to the monotheism of the Incas.[21] In the wave of iconoclasm, roadside shrines were overturned and temples which had the sanctity of St. Sophia's or the Kaaba, like holy Pachacamac on the Peruvian coast or the Aztec Teocalli, were razed, so that there would be no visible reminders of the old religions. Where there was an influential priestly class, as in Nahuatl

Mexico, it was liquidated. There was thus created a spiritual and emotional vacuum which Christianity was to fill with the drama and color of its ritualistic pageantry, the charm of its biblical lore, the majesty of its places of worship, and the moral precepts and consolations of its faith.

To the Indians, it seemed that their own gods had failed them in the great crisis of their race, so in a mood of mixed resignation and opportunism, they were more receptive to the appeals of the missionaries. The actual work of conversion was soon over except around the margins of the conquered lands, where it went on for centuries. Often there were mass "conversions," to which the people were ordered by their caciques, when thousands might be baptized in a single ceremony. Under the circumstances, there was naturally no time for a thorough indoctrination in the articles of Christian faith. The Spanish missionaries very wisely recognized the intellectual limitations of their converts and early abandoned any discussion of theological dogma as beyond the mental depth of their parishioners. It was generally a very simple and uncomplicated religion which was offered to the Indians and accepted by them.[22] And the priests sometimes winked at harmless vestiges of their original faith which the Indians persisted in incorporating into the Christian worship, particularly if they could be explained by biblical parallels.[23] If it had not been something very satisfying and substantial which the Church gave to the native peoples of the New World, they would not have remained so persistently loyal to it to this day.

To carry out its manifold purposes—religious ministration, education, charity, and care of the sick—the Church created a vast institutional mechanism in the New World. It duplicated the organization of the metropolitan hierarchy and added to that basic pattern a comprehensive and far-flung missionary system under the direction of the regular orders. The ecclesiastical organization was more elaborate than that of the lay government, and its agents and ministers were probably more numerous. Among the heads of the colonial episcopate were many famous bishops, men of strong and domineering personalities, who waged bitter battles with viceroys and captain-generals over questions of precedence and principle. The eternal rivalry between Church and State was complicated by the custom of having bishops serve, on occasion, as interim viceroys, thus giving them a foothold in the rule of the colonies.[24]

The regular orders—Dominicans, Franciscans, Augustinians, and the rest—entered the missionary field very early during the period of the Conquest. Later, the powerful Society of Jesus was to bring to the colonial scene a very special element of superior learning, an international personnel, administrative skill, and strong and bold policy. As each of the orders appeared in the New World, it was assigned definite areas as its "provinces." There were sharp rivalries between the orders for territory that was more lucrative both in terms of souls to be won and more material gains to be made. Sometimes in the cities there were unseemly street brawls between friars and monks of the rival orders. In the frontier zones the missionaries were often the only representatives of Spanish authority and civilization, as Humboldt was to find in the later years of the colonial regime, when he went from Caracas deep into the Venezuelan hinterland.[25]

THE INSTITUTIONAL MACHINERY

By 1600, the larger colonial cities had an elaborate network of churches and conventual establishments. The orders vied in the size and sumptuousness of their buildings, and much of the wealth derived from the mines and from agriculture went into their construction and adornment. The old Augustinian convent of Acolmán near Mexico City is typical of these impressive structures, and one who has observed the dead splendor of Antigua in Guatemala is vividly reminded of the power and riches of the Church in that distant time. There were churchly cities that have retained a certain religious and conservative tone to the present. They included places like Puebla in Mexico, Córdoba in Argentina, Sucre in Bolivia, Arequipa in Peru,[26] Bahia in Brazil, and Cuenca in Ecuador. Cuenca, a town with some 500 Spanish residents, had four friaries and a nunnery, a hospital, and several parish churches and shrines. So many of the local population went into the service of the Church that because of its extreme ecclesiolatry it became known as Cuenca de los Clérigos. At the same time, Quito, the capital of the province, had a cathedral and seven parish churches, and eight convents of friars and three of nuns, including one of 200 nuns, for a population of 3,000 Spaniards and mestizos. Among smaller towns noted for their ecclesiastical atmosphere were Olinda in northern Brazil, and Cholula in Mexico, once a religious center of the Toltecs.

In his encyclopedic *Compendium*, the nomadic Carmelite friar, Antonio Vázquez de Espinosa, has described with pride and gusto the convents and monasteries of the various cities that were so many stops on his endless travels. Of Lima, then the capital of South America, he said: "This famous city has remarkable Dominican, Franciscan, Augustinian, Mercedarian, and Jesuit convents." [27] At that time—the second decade of the seventeenth century—Lima had about 25,000 inhabitants. There were then six convents and five monasteries in the city, besides a number of Recollect houses of the various congregations, whose members were largely devoted to religious contemplation and to social welfare activities among the poor who lived on the outskirts of the city. In the central convents of their orders, the Dominicans housed over 250 friars, the Franciscans over 200, the Jesuits about the same number, and the Augustinians more than 150. Each order had its own church, some of which, like La Merced, are still the favorite places of worship of the Limeños. Each, also, had its college, which was largely devoted to instruction in the conventional curriculum of the time, which included Latin, philosophy, theology, and canon law. The best of the clerical colleges were San Martín, which was founded by the Viceroy Enríquez and later administered by the Jesuits; and Santo Toribio, established by the famous Archbishop Mogrovejo, for the training of priests. The Jesuits also conducted a royal school in the outskirts of Lima for the education of the sons of Indian caciques and other leaders of the native population. "They educate them," says Father Vázquez, "and teach them good manners, Christian doctrine, reading, writing, and music; this is a very important medium adopted to succeed in rooting out idolatry among this nation, and to give them greater knowledge of, and affection for, the tenets of our Holy Faith." The Royal and Pontifical University of San Marcos, which stood in the same general relation to the *colegios mayores* of the orders as the basilica did to their churches, offered a much more comprehensive course of study, including medicine and the civil law.

At that time, there were six nunneries in Lima. The largest

was La Encarnación, in which there resided over 700 persons, including nuns, and their personal maids and servants. It was a very aristocratic house, and nuns who entered it were required to bring a dowry of 2,000 gold pesos. It was founded by Doña Mencia de Almaraz y Sosa, widow of the famous rebel, Francisco Hernández Girón, and its endowment was greatly increased by later bequests of the pious. Much attention was devoted to music and to the many religious festivals, especially the three-day fiesta celebrating the Ascension of the Virgin, at which time the nuns changed their ordinary white-veiled vestments for "new and ornate regalia." According to Father Vázquez, "each nun seems beyond praise in the perfection of her adornment and the fragrance of sweet perfume."

Only second to La Encarnación was La Concepción, which had a population of some 500 nuns and service personnel. It belonged to the female branch of the Franciscan order. Its founder was Doña Inés Muñóz de Ribera, one of the most famous women in the early history of Peru. After the assassination of her first husband, Francisco Martín de Alcántara, half-brother of Francisco Pizarro, she married Antonio de Ribera, one of the founders of Lima and a man of great wealth. Much more modest than these magnificent establishments was the convent of the Santísima Trinidad of the Order of St. Bernard, whose founder, Doña Lucrecia de Sansoles, Father Vázquez describes as "a woman of great force and discipline of character, but severe and somewhat overzealous." The other three nunneries—Santa Clara, the Franciscan convent of Barefoot Nuns of San José, and Santa Catalina de Sana, of the female wing of the Order of St. Dominic—were also of lesser category. In the middle of the eighteenth century, Juan and Ulloa listed further convents of nuns in Lima, including nine Recollect houses.[28] In their time there were also four other convents in which some of the sisters were not recluses bound by the usual vows. One of these was a retreat for wives who wished to get away from their husbands.

In addition to the schools which were sometimes attached to the convents of friars, the regular orders maintained a number of welfare institutions which ministered to the needs of the population of Lima. No city in Europe had then a more elaborate hospital system. Perhaps the most important of these charitable organizations was the Confraternity of La Caridad, of the Carmelite nuns. In an outburst of pride, Father Vázquez called it "unique in the world." This famous sisterhood operated a hospital for sick women of the lower classes of Lima, and "a refuge and seminary beyond compare for impecunious young ladies and girls." Some of the inmates elected to take the veil of the order; to those who left, La Caridad provided marriage dowries. The Confraternity also distributed food and alms to the homes of the poor, and visited and cared for the bedridden who could not be moved. It shared with the Confraternity of the Prisons, or that of San Pedro y San Pablo, the task of removing the bodies of executed criminals from the gibbets along the highways and giving them decent burial. The purpose of this powerful organization was "to give aid without limitation of amount to all the poor Spaniards, Indians, Negroes, and Mulattoes in both prisons of this city and capital, with very ample rations." "And," adds Father Antonio, "that is not the least, for they inquire into their cases and possible release, and cure those sick in body and soul." On its staff the Confraternity of the Prisons maintained a doctor, a surgeon, and an apothecary for the benefit of prisoners who needed medical care, and two lawyers to defend the accused in the courts. Father Vázquez concludes his account with the remark: "and so the nobility of this city warmly support this Confraternity."

Another confraternity or brotherhood of similar purpose administered the Royal Hospital of San Andrés, which was established by Hurtado de Mendoza, Marqués de Cañete, one of the early viceroys. For a time it was managed by agents of the viceregal government, but this early experiment in "state medicine" was evidently unsuccessful, for, says Father Vázquez, "it was observed that the administrators appointed by the government did not exercise the care and devotion which the hospital required." Then, on the initiative of a Jesuit priest, a group of prominent and wealthy persons took over the administration of the hospital as a board of directors. They elected a full-time salaried superintendent and named eight deputies from among the citizenry to serve in pairs on a rotating basis for a week at a time. Thenceforth, the hospital was run with ever-increasing efficiency, as each superintendent aimed to surpass the record of his predecessor. By 1615, it had over 500 beds, distributed in several wards over a large area of ground. It accepted patients who were "ill with any disease," and in addition to its facilities for medical treatment, maintained an insane asylum.

The Hospital of Santa Ana, founded by the first Archbishop of Lima, followed the same general plan as that of San Andrés, but was larger, and also had a woman's ward. Of the various infirmaries within the hospital compound, Father Vázquez wrote: "the beds are neat and clean and the wardrobe so extensive that it can furnish what is needful for 1,000 beds; and as the Indians are used to their meals of Indian corn and herbs, seasoned with (chili pepper), they prepare them for them after their fashion; . . . they care for each one with great solicitude and attention; the deputies are present at their treatment, their dinners and suppers; they look after both the food that is provided for them and the preparation of the remedies prescribed for them."

Espíritu Santo was a sailor's hospital. It was well supported by the income derived from a special tax levied on shipping and cargo at the port of Callao. The Hospital of San Diego was dedicated to the care of convalescent invalids and the aged. It was operated by the humble friars of San Juan de Diós. Father Vázquez could not remember the names of its founders, but added that "they are written in the Book of Life."

Though its people did not have the Limeños' reputation for devoutness, Mexico City was even better supplied with the institutional apparatus of religion. Also, as a rule the churches in the provincial towns of New Spain were architecturally superior to those of Peru. "There are in Mexico City," says Father Vázquez, "splendid and famous convents with sumptuous temples, richly and perfectly appointed, with large incomes and charitable contributions which support them. All of them contain schools of Arts and Theology; the chief one, Santo Domingo is one of the best and richest to be found in the Indies, and I doubt whether there be its equal in Spain. It has over 200 friars, many of whom are highly educated and great preachers. . . . The Church has become a glowing coal of gold, with great majesty of chapels along its sides." [29] In all, he lists twenty convents of friars, one Benedictine monastery (Monserrate), and sixteen nunneries. Several of these dated from the Conquest, like the Franciscan con-

vent-school of Santiago de Tlaltelolco, which was founded by the
famous lay friar, Pedro de Gante, illegitimate son of the Emperor
Charles, for the catechizing and instruction of Indian boys. In
the early seventeenth century, it was ministering to the spiritual
and educational needs of over 30,000 Indians. Father Vázquez
waxes particularly eloquent about the convent of his own order
that was located at the place in the pine-clad mountains above
Mexico City known as El Desierto. It is "a spot which seems
like Paradise," he wrote of it. Of La Encarnación, one of the
convents of nuns, Mme. Calderón de la Barca wrote in the middle
of the last century: "This convent is in fact a palace." She describes the fruit trees and flower gardens and fountains of its
courtyards, and its spotlessly clean kitchen. Each nun had one
or two personal servants at her command, "for," she adds, "this
is not one of the strictest orders. . . . The convent is rich; each
novice at her entrance pays 5,000 dollars into the common stock.
There are about 30 nuns and 10 novices." [30]

In the early seventeenth century there were nine hospitals in
Mexico City. The General Hospital for the Indians was a secular
institution. It was established by the Viceroy Monterrey, who,
among other benefactions in its favor, assigned to it the income
from a comedy theater which he founded. Los Desamparados, a
"rich and sumptuous" hospital for "the destitute" of the city, was
operated by the Order of San Juan de Diós. It was particularly
noted for the revolving door in which mothers placed their babies,
for whom homes and foster parents were found by the friars. La
Concepción was founded by the Conqueror, Hernán Cortés, for
the care of the sick among the poor of the city, and was richly
endowed by him from the income of his large estates. San Hipó-
lito was a combination hospital and insane asylum. It had a
special interest in providing for the needs of the passengers who
arrived at Veracruz on the annual fleet of galleons from Spain.
For this purpose, it sent down several mule trains loaded with
food and other necessities. Amor de Diós was devoted exclusively
to the treatment of syphilis among the poor, and San Lázaro to
the care of persons afflicted with incurable diseases such as
leprosy, while Jesús María de Indios ministered only to sick
Indians.

A similar pattern of ecclesiasticism prevailed in most other colonial cities, the only limitation being one of means rather than of zeal. Thus, Buenos Aires, a poor city until the last century, had no splendid churches or convents.[31] In spite of all the good works of the friars and nuns, the lush growth of the conventual system in the New World was an unhealthy development.[32] There was too much parasitism with the piety, too many drones with the workers. The energies and talents which vegetated in the tranquil eddies of the cloister were needed for the work of the colonial world, cultural as well as economic. Sometimes it must have seemed as though the Spanish Empire were one vast dependency of the Church. Convent life was physically relaxing, mentally soothing, and aesthetically satisfying. It offered "security" in a world where there were no pensions, social insurance, or veterans' benefits. It provided an opportunity for premature retirement for the softer generation who followed the Conquest. Perhaps the scarcity of openings in other fields, determined by the younger generation's aversion to certain occupations as well as by the restrictive regime of Spain, favored the claustrophilia of the times. It is worth noting that in the eighteenth century, when the Spanish government relaxed the monopolistic rigors of its political and economic controls, relatively fewer men in the colonies chose a cloistered life.

Women, too, were lured into the convents by the siren song of security as well as led by religious zeal. For those who took the final step beyond the novitiate, there were many compensations for the irrevocable vows, besides the consolations of the faith. Under the rule of a tolerant abbess, the discipline could be lax. There were music and good food and congenial company, and if their clothes seemed monotonous, so, for the Brazilian nuns at least, was likely to be the casual covering of the women in the haremlike confinement of the "big houses." There were the happy fetes of the Virgin Mother and of the patron saints. When the priest came around each day to conduct the service of the mass in the convent chapel, it was a mild reminder that they were not so many caged amazons in a manless world. If they came from the country, they had at least the satisfaction of relief from the hazards and uncertainties, the isolation and loneliness, of frontier life. In northern Brazil, so many daughters of the planter aristocracy chose the safe and pleasant life of a nun that often there was actually a dearth of available brides for the young scions of the ruling families. In fact, the incidental neutering of so many persons, and particularly of so superior a segment of society, through the celibacy of the regular clergy, male and female, was certainly an important contributory factor in the slow growth of population among the European element in the colonies.

THE CLERGY

Success of the Church in the accomplishment of its basic purposes largely depended on the quality of the clergy. Except among the Spanish minority, there was no hard core of deep faith to fall back upon. And even among Spaniards and Creoles, religion finally tended to become a matter of habit that was accepted and observed without question. It was very good for the womenfolk of the family, and its pompous fiestas relieved the routine of daily life. But, save in a crisis in one's affairs, it was not something to become too aroused about. A man had other things on his mind, and, anyway, it was too cold in Potosí or Bogotá to do much hard thinking and too hot in Belem or Piura. This all meant that the priests had to keep the fire of the faith from flickering, especially in the isolated towns and villages where the admonitory finger of the bishop or the provincial did not reach so easily. It was not easy to do, for the flesh was weak and the devil was all about in seductive guises, both animate and inanimate.

Most of the early missionaries who came to the New World were holy men, exemplars of all the apostolic virtues—unfaltering faith in their mission, courage and abnegation, humility of spirit and goodness of heart. They were true and saintly men of God. They went among the aborigines without hesitation or fear, regardless of whether their flocks were to be of sheep or wolves, Tainos or Caribs. They lived under the most primitive conditions and many were martyred. Of such were Motolinia and Las Casas, Francisco Solano and Pedro Claver, "apostle of the Negroes," and hundreds of others.[33]

As time went on and the initial task of converting the Indians to Christianity was largely completed, the compulsions and pressures—and inspirations—of the heroic age of the Church were relaxed. The Church, and even the mendicant orders along with it, became wealthy from the benefactions of the pious, the largess of the state, the income from its rents, the returns on its investments in mortgages and mines, and the sale of the crops and herds from its lands. The Church had become too rich for its own good, and by 1800 it was the biggest business in the colonies. Individuals died and even families came to an end through sterility or accident. But the Church had the gift of perpetuity, and what fell into its hands remained, by the misleading term of mortmain, its inalienable possession. Such an atmosphere was not congenial to the growth of spiritual fervor.

Yet, whenever there was a call to a new missionary enterprise, the regular orders rose to the challenge, as the great *entrada* of the Franciscans into upper California late in the eighteenth century was to demonstrate. There were always mission fields on the frontiers of settlement—or beyond them—in northern Mexico, and Arauco in Chile, in the Maynas region of Amazonia and the back country of Venezuela, where life was both a spiritual and physical adventure. And there were always bold and devoted men like Eusebio Kino and Junípero Serra, who were ready to open them up for Spain and the Church.

The greatest temptation to the individual cleric was probably the opportunity for making money that often lay all about him. In Fernández de Lizardi's picaresque satire, *The Itching Parrot,* the advice of one of the characters is: "Study to be a priest as I do, for it's the best career of all and you may shut your eyes and stop worrying. . . . A priest is well received everywhere; everyone venerates and respects him, even though he is a fool, and they overlook his defects; no one dares to censure him or contradict him in anything; he has a place at the best ball, at the best game, and even in the ladies' parlor he's not to be ignored; lastly, he never lacks for a peso, if he has to get it for a Mass badly said at top speed." [34] If the Church sought affluence, so did many of its priesthood. Some of them shared in the profits of the Conquest, either from the loot of the Indian treasure, as in Peru, or from the provisioning of the military. Father Luque, the silent partner of Pizarro and Almagro in the conquest of Peru, very obviously did not acquire the working capital for that lucrative venture as the parish schoolmaster at Panama! Oviedo, the chronicler, called Father Valverde, who was the chaplain of Pizarro's expedition, "an uneasy, turbulent and dishonest priest." [35] It is doubtful if so unsavory a cleric would have refused a share of the Inca's ransom at Cajamarca. Oviedo tells of another priest, Juan de Sosa, who financed and led an expedition to settle the Veragua country on the Isthmus, on orders from the widow of Diego Colón, whose father-in-law had discovered that land.[36] The old chronicler had known him many years before as a poor priest in the Tierra Firme, when he himself had gone a-conquering in that neighborhood. He later made eight or 10,000 gold pesos in the conquest of Peru, a sizeable nest egg for anybody in those times. Incidentally, Oviedo, who was no heretic, remarks on one occasion: "I do not wish to give or to deny credit to Erasmus or his discourses; but in these Indies things have happened among the clergy that it is better to keep quiet than to stir up the question." [37] Bernal Díaz tells of an avaricious Franciscan, Fray Pedro Melgarejo de Urrea, who arrived in Mexico during the siege of the Aztec capital. "The reverend father," he says, "made a fortune in a few months, and returned to Castile." [38]

Unscrupulous and worldly-minded clerics found many profitable ways to evade their vows of poverty. Sometimes they exploited their Indian charges as shamelessly as did the corregidors, the king's men in the cities. One of the most severe indictments of priestly morals was made by the Spanish naval officers, Jorge Juan and Antonio de Ulloa, who spent several years in the New World during the 1740's.[39] Though the harvest continued throughout the year, saints' days seem to have provided a particularly lucrative occasion for exacting tribute from their parishioners in one form or another. A village priest of the province of Quito told Juan and Ulloa that each year he received over 200 sheep, 6,000 chickens, 4,000 guinea pigs, and 50,000 eggs from his flock. On Sundays, each Indian woman brought the padre an egg, or if the hens were not laying, its equivalent in value; each man contributed a bundle of firewood, and the children brought bundles of fodder for his animals. The priest sold this produce in the city, and, on a salary of 700 or 800 pesos, could make from 5,000 to 6,000 pesos a year. The Spanish observers also heard that the curate's concubine forced the Indian women of the locality to make cotton and woolen cloth for the profit of her priestly paramour, thus "making the whole town a textile mill." This abuse had been the object of a law issued in 1631.

The central government in Spain must have been deeply concerned about the irregular behavior of some of the clergy, for there is a considerable body of legislation on the subject.[40] No cleric was to be alcalde or mayor of a town, or exercise the profession of lawyer or notary. They were prohibited from trading in any form, and from operating a mine. If they employed the Indians for any work, they were to pay them. Some of these decrees were aimed at other forms of clerical misconduct. One ordered the prelates to stop gambling among the priests in their dioceses. In the pulpit, the preachers were to stick to "doctrine and example," and not to stir up passions and confusion among their congregations by haranguing them with "scandalous words." The bishops were commanded to expel from the land all priests who were "troublemakers and men of evil life." An early law (1541) directed that friars who took to vagabondage should be brought back to their convents.

Another problem involved what was known among the more ascetic and aging members of the Spanish clergy as carnality. Of the seven capital sins, the term included lust and gluttony. As Spaniards were by necessity a frugal and underfed people, they tended to hold overeating a very venial peccadillo, if a form of depravity at all. As for the other sin of the flesh, its indulgence came to be very widespread among the Churchmen in the New World. The opportunity for erring was ubiquitous, and, unlike the hill people in Kipling's *The Man Who Would Be King*, there was little public sentiment against it. Concubinage became not only common, but was probably the rule in some communities. The practice of lechery among the priesthood must have begun very early in the Conquest. Bernal Díaz tells of an escapade of Father Benito Martínez, who had been chaplain to Velázquez, the governor of Cuba.[41] When he came to Mexico, he was imprisoned by the bishop for having carried away from Spain a woman named María Rodríguez. Oviedo recounts the story of the particularly scandalous conduct of a priest who was in the force of Gonzalo de Badajoz in the conquest of the Isthmus.[42]

Captain Woodes Rogers, the British privateer, who was a character out of "The Pirates of Penzance," writes gaily of an incident which occurred "in Tecames Road" on the west coast of South America in 1709. "We put our young Padre ashore, and gave him, as he desir'd, the prettiest young Female Negro we had in the Prize, with some Bays, Linnen, and other Things, for his good Services in helping to promote our Trade for Provisions here. We sent also a Male Negro and Piece of Bays to the *Tecames* Padre, in acknowledgement of his Kindness. The young Padre parted with us extremely pleas'd, and leering under his Hood upon his black Female Angel, we doubt he will crack a Commandment with her, and wipe off the Sin with the Church's Indulgence." [43]

Juan and Ulloa paint a dark picture of clerical license in the southern viceroyalty in their time.[44] "Both the regular and secular clergy live licentiously, scandalously, and as they please," they wrote in their confidential report to the king. They said that most priests resided outside the convents in their private homes, so that they could live with their mistresses without interruption. Some even kept their *barraganas* in their cells in the convent. According to the Spanish travelers, the convents in the smaller places were liable to be "public brothels." The priests were given to riotous living, and frequently organized *fandangos*, or dances and drinking parties, that turned into veritable orgies. All this, they said "is accepted as custom." It was to the credit of the priests that they had the reputation of recognizing their children and providing well for them. Frézier, the French engineer, who was on the coasts of Peru and Chile in the early eighteenth century, wrote that "The Religious Men (friars), excepting the Jesuits, are still more unlicensed than the Clergy (parish priests), and much addicted to Libertinism, which the too great Veneration the People have for their Habit, very much facilitates." [45] The Portuguese in Brazil appear to have been particularly tolerant of the notorious unchastity of their priests, and there has long been a responsible body of lay and clerical opinion in Brazil which favors the marriage of the clergy as the proper recognition of an accomplished fact.[46]

Foreign observers have left us many—and often sympathetic —pictures of the Latin American clergy during the nineteenth century. Some of the priests whom they met were epicures and sybarites; some were lazy, some were ignorant, a few were bad, but most were good of heart. One of those who knew and liked them best was John Lloyd Stephens, lawyer and globe-trotter, self-made archaeologist, promoter, and roving United States Consul to the "Government" of Central America.[47] Since his official duties were negligible, he traveled extensively through the area of his jurisdiction and up into the southern states of Mexico. At Palenque in Chiapas he shared an excursion with four festive padres of the neighboring villages.[48] While three of them played monte, the fourth played his violin for their entertainment. Of the local priest, Stephens wrote: "We rode over to his house, and waited while he secured carefully on the back of a tall horse a little boy, who looked so wonderfully like him, that, out of respect to his obligation of celibacy, people felt delicate in asking whose son he was. This done, he tied an extra pair of shoes behind his own saddle, and we set off with the adiós of the whole village." When Stephens visited the Maya ruins with them, they brought along a large train of Indian carriers loaded with bedding, provisions, "and multifarious articles; besides which," he adds, "more favored than we, they had four or five women." Of his delightful companions, Stephens wrote: "They were all intelligent and good men, who would rather do benefits than an injury; in matters connected with religion they were most reverential, laboured diligently in their vocations, and were without reproach among their people." At Utatlán in Nicaragua, Stephens found a village priest, who laughed uproariously at everything except his religion. "On further acquaintance," adds Stephens, "we found in him such a vein of strong sense and knowledge, and, retired as he lived, he was so intimately acquainted with the country and all the public men, as a mere looker his views were so correct and his satire so keen, though without malice, that we improved his title by calling him the laughing philosopher."[49] At Quetzaltenango in Guatemala, an attractive curate played an air from Rossini for Stephens and Catherwood, his companion, while 3,000 Indians went about their worship in the Church.[50] Of another priest whom he encountered, he wrote: "I had an opportunity of seeing what I afterward observed throughout all Central America: the life of labour and responsibility passed by the cura of an Indian village, who devotes himself to the people under his charge. Besides officiating in all the services of the church, visiting the sick, and burying the dead, my worthy host was looked up to by every Indian in the village as a counsellor, friend and father. The door of the convent was always open, and Indians were constantly resorting to him." [51] Captain Basil Hall found earlier a similar priest in Chile. "He had been for upwards of 50 years," he wrote, "the pastor of a remote Indian village, where he had acquired, by his talents and virtues, an important and extensive influence over the natives; whose conditions he had greatly improved, by converting them to Christianity, and introducing education, together with the arts of civil life." [52]

CHURCH AND STATE UNDER THE REPUBLICS

Independence radically disrupted the life of the Church in Latin America. The colonial Church had remained very Spanish and the top layers of the hierarchy were predominately of Spanish origin. It had always leaned heavily on the favor and support of the crown, and, now that the authority of Spain was gone, there were serious readjustments to make. As the Church was an inflexible institution and had had no organized opposition during the three centuries of its existence in the New World, change did not come easily to it. It had never had to make concessions to anybody, least of all to the secular power.

Under the republics, it was faced with a new situation, many of whose elements were not favorable to it, particularly to its more mundane appurtenances. For its wealth was a temptation to the new rulers, who were hard put to it for money to run the new states, and who may have sacrificed their personal fortunes in the wars against Spain. Grudges and bitter memories appeared to plague the Church. For, whereas a large part of the parish clergy had sided with the patriot cause, and two curates, Hidalgo and Morelos, had given their lives as leaders of the revolt, too many of the bishops had made no secret of their sympathy for the royalists.[53] Thus, the Church started anew under the handicap of its identification with Spain. The hierarchy did not accept the new order gracefully and thereby laid up much trouble for itself.

The Church became a major and disturbing issue in politics. What was to become the classic party division between Conservatives and Liberals was responsible for the bitter struggle between Church and State which has bedeviled the national life of several of the republics, above all in Mexico.[54] The Liberals usually espoused a policy of anticlericalism, while the Conservatives championed the Church and its time-honored prerogatives. The issue usually took concrete form on the question of lay or clerical influence on public education, the matter of disestablishment of the Church, and the problem of civil marriage. The controversy was frequently personified by certain dictators. In the confused beginnings of the Central American Union, the principal protagonists were Francisco Morazán on the Liberal side and Rafael Carrera on that of the Conservatives. In Ecuador, where the perennial contest between Conservatives and Liberals was carried on with particular bitterness, Gabriel García Moreno all but turned the country into a theocracy in his zeal for the Church. In Venezuela, Antonio Guzmán Blanco went almost as far in the other direction in his war on the clergy.[55] In Colombia, the controversy has persisted into recent years. In Uruguay, José Batlle y Ordóñez, the famous social reformer, who was twice president, went to the extreme of forbidding his newspaper to spell *God* with a capital *g*.

Religious peace came to certain countries earlier than to others. In Peru, the Church managed to hold most of its original power in the nation. Sometimes, feelings on either side never reached the point of violence. In such an atmosphere a reasonable settlement was possible, as happened in Chile, where an especially moderate archbishop worked out with a conciliatory government a sound basis for a modus vivendi.

The struggle between Church and State reached its most virulent form in Mexico. The wealth of the Church offered too strong a temptation for the Liberal leaders to ignore. Opinion was inflamed in true Mexican fashion, and from the beginning it was an uncompromising battle on both sides. The first stage of the contest culminated in the so-called "War of the Reform," in the course of which Benito Juárez and the Lerdos managed to strip the Church of much of its property. During the long regime of Porfirio Díaz, the Church substantially recovered its earlier position in the country, so that when Díaz left Mexico in 1911, the stage was set for a resumption of the old struggle. One of the prime objectives of the Mexican Revolution was to break the power and influence of the Church once and for all. To that end, all its properties were secularized. Many churches and convents were

turned over to lay uses. The public celebration of religious services was prohibited, and the members of the clergy were not
allowed to wear the traditional garments of their profession.
Everything possible was done to humiliate the priesthood. Instruction in the new public schools was given a strongly anticlerical and "socialistic" slant which further antagonized not only
the Church, but its conservative supporters, both among the
former ruling class and the Guadalupe-worshiping peasantry. For
a while armed revolts of the Indians seriously interfered with
normal life in some of the states of the republic.

The violent anticlericalism of the Revolution was embodied
in the famous Constitution of 1917. In scornful language this
highly emotional document refers to "religious associations called
Churches." "Freedom of belief," it says, "shall be maintained by
complete freedom from any religious doctrine, and, based on the
results of scientific progress, shall struggle against ignorance and
its effects, servitudes, fanaticisms, and prejudices." [56]

The ordeal of the Mexican Church came to a head during the
administrations of Calles and Cárdenas, but under the presidency
of Avila Camacho the persecution was relaxed and concessions
were made to a widespread public demand for the reopening of
the churches to public worship. While a badly battered Church
still leads a very restricted life by the suffrance of the State,
there is at last a measure of religious peace in the turbulent land.

Two of the most understanding and sympathetic of American
writers on Mexico have calmly summed up the account between
the Church and the Indian in Mexico. One of them, Charles
Macomb Flandrau, who wrote before the Revolution, says: "I
cannot linger in Mexican churches day after day, as I have done,
watching the Indians glide in, remove the leather bands from
their foreheads, let their chitas slip gently to the pavement, and
then, with straight backs and crossed hands, kneel in reverent
ecstasy before their favorite images, without rejoicing that a profound human want can be so filled to overflowing. And I cannot
but doubt that it could by any other way we know be filled at
all." And again he writes: "So one's attitude toward the Church
in Mexico becomes at the last curiously ill-defined. The Church
is corrupt, grasping, resentful; but it unquestionably gives millions of people something without which they would be far more

unhappy than they are, something that no other church could give them." [57] The other, Frank Tannenbaum, writes: "Whatever his future, the Mexican Indian, looking back upon the history of his race, must count it a good fortune that the Catholic Church came with the Spanish Conqueror. . . . That the Indian has a future in Mexico is in no small measure due to the saving influence of the Catholic Church and the Catholic religion. . . . It saved the Indian's status as a human being in the eyes of his conquerors. . . . It saved the Indian's sense of the meaning of life, and as much as anything else, preserved him from complete moral degradation, from spiritual annihilation." [58]

The Latin American Church is passing through a period of transition, a time of soul-searching.[59] Much of what has happened in Latin America and in the world outside has passed it by and its more open-minded leaders feel the need to adapt it to the new conditions. The Papacy has shown an increasing interest in the fortunes of the Church in Latin America, and has recognized its importance in the Catholic world by the appointment of a number of Latin American cardinals. For many years, the only cardinal in Latin America was the Archbishop of Rio de Janeiro. Now there are ten cardinals, three of whom are Brazilian. For the Brazilian Church—placid and decorous, moderate and wise in the ways of men and governments—is the favored daughter of Rome. The Mexican Church, which is none of these, but has suffered much for the faith, has never been honored with a cardinal's hat.

To find the place which properly belongs to it, the Church must first solve many problems. One of these is the steady encroachment of the State on its spiritual and beneficent areas of action. The sphere of public education which it controls is gradually being reduced and circumscribed. The growing welfare activities of the State impinge widely on a traditional province of the Church. The use of the mass media of the press and radio as instruments of official propaganda is capturing ever more of the popular mind that once looked to the Church for guidance. The new hyperpatriotism which is identified with the extreme nationalism of many of the republics is drawing so heavily on the citizen's emotional reserves that little capacity for loyalty is liable to be left for other impersonal attachments.

No uniform pattern governs the relations between Church

and State in the New World. While complete uniformity in this respect may not be desirable, there is an air of the provisional about some of the existing arrangements between the lay and religious powers that makes for needless tensions in their relationship. The Peruvian Church is a branch of the national government, and like any other employees of the state, the clergy, from the cardinal-archbishop of Lima down to the lowest hedge priest in the sierra, draw their salaries from the treasury. In Mexico, the Church lives as a virtual prisoner of the state, a trusty, it is true, but a prisoner none the less. In Brazil and Uruguay, the Church is completely free and disestablished, and enjoys the unrestricted usufruct of its properties. The success of the settlement in these two countries demonstrates that the Church flourishes best where it is separated from the State and is not dependent on the national budget for its support.

The Catholic Church no longer has a monopoly of religion in Latin America. At one time or another, the door has been opened to the evangelical sects by Liberal regimes in the republics, and the principle of religious tolerance has been written into most of the constitutions. Though the competition of other faiths is resented by the Catholic hierarchy as so much poaching on its preserves, the rivalry for souls can be a strong incentive to the Church to put its own house in better order. Protestant organizations have done good work in distributing the Bible in the vernacular, and some of the evangelical churches have been responsible for the establishment of excellent schools, as well as hospitals and agricultural experiment centers.[60] The ministers of the older and more responsible Protestant sects have long since learned to conduct their affairs with dignity and decorum, so as to avoid friction with any latent hostility which may exist in the country to foreign missionary enterprise. It is unlikely that Protestantism will ever be the faith of more than a minority of the population in any Latin American country.[61] It not only labors under the disadvantage of a late start in the field, but of the circumstance that it is a "foreign" religion, largely identified with the Germanic peoples of northern Europe and their overseas derivatives. It is therefore considered to lack a natural affinity for the Latin temperament, the Huguenot experience in France notwithstanding. Largely for different reasons, Protestantism has made considerable progress in Brazil and Mexico, a phenomenon entirely unrelated to the fact that the first Protestant service held in the New World was celebrated in Rio Bay.[62] In matters of religion, the Brazilians are Laodiceans and given to experimentation in faith, as in more profane areas of culture. Their eclecticism accounts, *inter alia*, for the peculiar position of Positivism, the philosophy of Auguste Comte, among a select minority, the popularity of Spiritualism at another social level, and the subtle attraction of Hindu cults for so many Brazilians. In Mexico, the evangelical sects have helped to fill a religious void made by disaffection from the old Church during the Revolution.

The Church needs to raise the standards of its clergy. This involves reforms in the administration and curriculum of the seminaries, and the attraction to the priesthood of young men of ability and character, who now turn to the other professions for a career. Though a leaven of foreign priests is always desirable, in order to keep the national churches from falling into the errors of provincialism, it is to the interest of the Church to strengthen the local element in the clergy and to prepare it for leadership and greater responsibility. The introduction of a considerable company of Maryknoll Fathers from the United States has been a strong force for improving the quality of religious ministration, particularly in more remote areas that are sometimes neglected by the hierarchy and generally shunned by the superior priests.

The religious indifference of most of the male population presents a serious problem to the Church. This is particularly true of what may be called the middle and upper classes of society, that is, the natural leaders of the community. Part of it may be due to the counterappeal of materialism and its sterile attractions or to a self-conscious pose of skepticism and cynicism. Much of it is plain inertia, an absence of interest in spiritual things. In some quarters, the notion may prevail that the Church is only for women and serves to keep them from getting out of hand. The Church must be flexible enough in its appeal to take care of the religious needs of all levels of the population—the students, who may consider themselves above the need of religion; the laborers, who are subject to the antireligious counterpropaganda of Leftist organizations; and the Indians, who have never really been Christianized and live in a half-world of faith and fancy.

There is an impressive body of lay opinion that is acutely aware of this problem and is working from the outside to revitalize the Church. Meanwhile, there exists an immense spiritual void, which only an awakened Church can fill.

NOTES

1. During much of the Middle Ages, the Spaniards were a singularly tolerant people, and for long periods between fighting, lived in harmony with the Moslem in the peninsula. During the reign of Alfonso IX of Castile, Christians, Mohammedans, and Jews used the same church in Toledo for the celebration of their rites. According to Roger Merriman, "Intolerance was emphatically not an indigenous natural trait." He said that the Catholic Kings, especially the Queen, urged intolerance in the nation. *The Rise of the Spanish Empire in the Old World and in the New* (4 vols., New York, 1918–34), I, 87-88; II, 86, 90; III, 402-3.

2. "Spain was the nation which created a Christianity that was most its own." Angel T. de Ganivet, *Idearium Español* (Madrid, 1905), p. 13.

3. For example: "The Spaniards . . . are always attentive to the exterior Duties of Religion." Amédée François Frézier, *Relation du Voyage de la Mer du Sud aux Côtes du Chili, de Pérou, et du Brésil* (2 vols., Paris, 1716; Eng. tr., London, 1717), p. 209; "Les Espagnols mettent toute leur religion dans la pratique du culte extérieur." Giacomo Casanova de Seingalt, *Mémoires* (8 vols., Paris, 1910), VII, 368.

4. Marcelino Menéndez y Pelayo, *Historia de los Heterodoxos Españoles* (8 vols., Madrid, 1880–86).

5. See Joaquim P. Oliveira Martins, *Historia de la Civilización Ibérica* (tr. from the Portuguese, Madrid, n.d.), pp. 267-74.

6. The best-known authority on the Inquisition was Charles Henry Lea. His leading works are: *History of the Inquisition in the Middle Ages* (3 vols., New York and London, 1888); *History of the Inquisition of Spain* (4 vols., New York, 1906-7); *The Inquisition in the Spanish Dependencies* (New York, 1908). The Chilean historian, José Toribio Medina, has also written a number of scholarly studies of the Inquisition in various parts of the New World.

7. Edgar Allen Poe's short story, "The Pit and the Pendulum," deals with the last moments of the Spanish Inquisition.

8. Of the Portuguese Inquisition in Brazil, Kidder wrote: "Though the Portuguese are far more tolerant than the Spaniards, yet the Government of Portugal held on to that cursed engine of Roman intolerance until 1821." James C. Fletcher and D. P. Kidder, *Brazil and the Brazilians Portrayed in Historical and Descriptive Sketches* (Boston, 1857), p. 52.

9. *Leyes de Indias, libro 1, tomo 19, ley 5.* Also laws nos. 1 and 2 of the same series.

10. Fernando de los Rios, "The Action of Spain in America," in Charles Griffin, ed., *Concerning Latin American Culture* (New York, 1940), p. 75.

11. See Lesley Byrd Simpson, *Many Mexicos* (New York, 1941), p. 168.

12. Bernard Moses, *The Spanish Dependencies in South America* (2 vols., New York and London, 1914), I, 330.

13. See above, p. 316.

14. Frézier, *Voyage, op. cit.,* p. 105.

15. Salvador de Madariaga, *Cuadro Histórico de las Indias* (Buenos Aires, 1945), p. 220.

16. Antonio Vázquez de Espinosa, *Compendium and Description of the West Indies* (tr. from the Spanish, Washington, D. C., 1942), p. 447.

17. Bernard Moses, *op. cit.,* I, 369.

18. On the censorship of books by the Inquisition, see Irving A. Leonard, *Books of the Brave* (Cambridge, Mass., 1949), *passim.*

19. W. B. Stevenson, *A Historical and Descriptive Narrative of Twenty Years' Residence in South America* (3 vols., London, 1825), I, 267-74.

20. Basil Hall, *Extracts from a Journal Written on the Coasts of Chili, Peru, and Mexico, in the Years 1820, 1821, 1822* (2 vols., Edinburgh, 1824), I, 107.

21. On the ultimate attainment of the aboriginal religions, see the account of King Nezahualcoyotl's worship of "The Almighty God, Creator of all things, hidden and unknown," as told by the Hispanicized Aztec, Fernando de Alva Ixtilxochitl, in Harriet de Onis, ed., *The Golden Land: An Anthology of Latin American Folklore in Literature* (New York, 1948), pp. 54-59. Of Inca monotheism, Garcilaso wrote: "The Incas, Kings of Peru, with the natural light which God gave them, reached the concept of a Maker of all things, whom they called Pachacamac, which means the creator and sustainer of the universe." Garcilaso Inca de la Vega, *Comentarios Reales de los Incas,* II, 67. Also, Atahualpa's reply to Padre Valverde's harangue regarding the Trinity, at Cajamarca: "The first is the god three and one, which makes four, which you call the creator of the universe; by chance, it is the same whom we call Pachacamac-Viracocha . . . We worship only Pachacamac as Supreme God and the Sun as a lesser divinity, and the Moon as his sister and wife." Garcilaso, *Historia General del Peru,* I, 71. See also Philip Ainsworth Means, in *The Maya and their Neighbors,* p. 439.

22. Juan and Ulloa said that the Indians only went to church from fear of punishment. They declared that they never learned "the most essential points of religion." However, they recognized some exceptions: "There are many who, in the culture of their minds, sanctity of manners, and delicacy of conscience, equal the most wise and circumspect." Jorge Juan y Santacilla and Antonio de Ulloa, *Noticias Secretas de América* (2 vols., Madrid, 1918), I, 410. "The Indians never really assimilated the spirit and beauty of the Christian religion." Herbert Ingram Priestley, *The Coming of the White Man 1492-1848* (New York, 1929), p. 106. The Peruvian scholar, Luís Valcarcel, says: "The Indian, though baptized and accordingly incorporated formally into the Church, was never a true Catholic; he never understood the mysteries of the faith, nor could he ever go beyond the limits of the pure externals of worship." *Ruta Cultural del Perú* (Mexico, D. F., 1945), p. 101. See the remarks of George Kubler on the process of Christianizing the Quechua race, in *Handbook of South American Indians* (5 vols., Washington, D. C., 1946 seq.), II, 400-3.

23. "The Indians had an infinite number of other ceremonies and customs which resembled to the ancient law of Moses, and some to those which the Moores

use, and some approached more to the law of the Gospel." José de Acosta, *The Natural and Moral History of the Indies* (2 vols., tr. from the Spanish, London, 1880; originally published in 1590), II, 369. Among such parallel customs and ceremonies were the sacrifice of animals, the burning of incense, confession, washing to cleanse the person of sin, marriage by a priest, convents of nuns.

24. See Bernard Moses, *op. cit.*, II, 206-32 (Ch. XII, "The Church in relation to the civil government").

25. Alexander von Humboldt, *Personal Narrative of Travels to the Equinoctial Regions of the New Continent, during the Years 1799–1804* (7 vols., London, 1814–29). Humboldt admired the Aragonese Capuchins of the Apure missions and their treatment of the Indians. *Ibid.*, II, 28, 61, 72, 75.

26. James Bryce wrote of Arequipa: "There are scores of other churches and convents, far more than sufficient for a city of 35,000 people. Their bells clang all day, and clerical costumes are everywhere in the streets. What is still more remarkable, the men, as well as the women, are practicing Catholics, and attend church regularly, a rare thing in most parts of South America. The city was an ecclesiastical stronghold. . . . Two centuries ago . . . probably one-third of the whole population consisted of priests, monks, and nuns, and the Church ruled unquestioned." *South America: Observations and Impressions* (New York, 1916), pp. 67-68.

27. Vázquez de Espinosa, *op. cit.*, pp. 434-47.

28. Jorge Juan y Santacilla and Antonio de Ulloa, *A Voyage to South America* (tr. from the Spanish, 2 vols., London, 1806), II, 37.

29. Vázquez de Espinosa, *op. cit.*, p. 157.

30. Frances Erskine Inglis (de) Calderón de la Barca, *Life in Mexico during a Residence of Two Years in that Country* (London, 1843). Reference is to the Everyman Edition, p. 143.

31. H. M. Breckenridge, *Voyage to South America,* in A. Curtis Wilgus, *Readings in Latin American Civilization* (New York, 1946), p. 101.

32. See Bernard Moses, *op. cit.*, II, 204.

33. Of Father Motolinia, Bernal Díaz said: "All that he got in charity he distributed in the same manner, and was frequently without a morsel to eat. He also always went barefooted, and wore a tattered habit, and constantly preaching to the natives, was very popular among them." *The True History of the Conquest of Mexico,* p. 430. Reference is made to the 1927 edition of the Keating translation, published by McBride and Company. On the missionary friars, see Fernando de los Rios, *op. cit.*, p. 57.

34. José Joaquín Fernández de Lizardi, *The Itching Parrot (El Periquillo Sarniento),* (New York, 1942), p. 37.

35. Quoted by Frederick A. Kirkpatrick, *The Spanish Conquistadores* (London, 1934), p. 167.

36. Gonzalo Fernández de Oviedo y Valdés, *Historia general y natural de las Indias, islas y tierra firme del mar oceano* (4 vols., Madrid, 1851–55), II, 480.

37. *Ibid.*, II, 239.

38. Bernal Díaz del Castillo, *The True History of the Conquest of Mexico.* Reference is to the 1927 translation, published by Robert M. McBride & Company, p. 306. The parish priest of the town of Teococuilco in Mexico died in

1631 after 35 years service, leaving a fortune of 200,000 pesos. Simpson, *Many Mexicos, op. cit.*, p. 153.

39. Jorge Juan y Santacilla and Antonio de Ulloa, *Noticias Secretas de América* (2 vols., Madrid, 1918), II, 11-18.

40. *Leyes de Indias, libro* I, *tomo* 12, *passim.*

41. Bernal Díaz, *op. cit.*, p. 111.

42. An Indian chief and his "young and gentle wife" traveled with the Spanish company. One night the priest "hiço echar de baxo de su hamaca el principal, é tomó en la hamaca á su muger é durmió con ella, ó mejor diciendo no la dexo dormir ni estar sin entender en su adulterio." Oviedo, *op. cit.*, III, 48.

43. Woodes Rogers, *A Cruising Voyage Round the World* (London, 1928), p. 187. First published in 1712.

44. Juan and Ulloa, *Noticias Secretas, op. cit.*, II, 169-178.

45. Amédée François Frézier, *op. cit.*, p. 56.

46. Richard Burton, the famous Orientalist, who was for a time a British consular officer in Brazil, wrote: "Many of the highly educated, if not the vulgar, advocate the marriage of the clergy. . . . The parishioners have little objection to a Vigario who takes a wife and makes an honest man of himself. The climate is not favorable to chastity." *The Highlands of the Brazil* (2 vols., London, 1869), I, 406. See also Fletcher and Kidder, *op. cit.*, p. 381. Of a village priest whom he met in a village in the Peruvian Andes, William Stevenson wrote: "The cura complained bitterly of a want of society in his place of exile . . . and jocosely said, that if the Pope himself were cura of Ocros, he would wish to have a wife to keep him in good humour." *Op. cit.*, II, 27.

47. *Incidents of Travel in Central America, Chiapas, and Yucatan* (2 vols., New York, 1849). This delightful work has recently been reprinted. Stephens went to Central America in 1839.

48. *Ibid.*, II, 329-334.

49. *Ibid.*, II, 180.

50. *Ibid.*, II, 209.

51. *Ibid.*, I, 170. See also I, 174, and II, 255.

52. Basil Hall, *op. cit.*, I, 36. See also William Lewis Herndon and Lardner Gibbon, *Exploration of the Valley of the Amazon, Made Under the Direction of the Navy Department* (2 vols., Washington, D. C., 1854), I, 88 and 174. Originally issued as a government document, this reconnaisance report by two officers of the United States Navy, has recently been reprinted for trade distribution.

53. Another factor in the new situation which faced the Church is brought out by Luís Alberto Sanchez: "Our liberators were free thinkers, liberals, and many of them heterodox. Neither Bolívar nor San Martín nor O'Higgins were fervent Catholics, rather they were Masons, like Miranda, the precursor." *The Presence of Tradition,* a pamphlet published by the Pan-American Union.

54. On this general subject, see J. Lloyd Mecham, *Church and State in Latin America: a History of Politico-Ecclesiastical Relations* (Chapel Hill, N. C., 1934).

55. See Francisco García Calderón, *Latin America: its Rise and Progress* (tr. from the French, London, 1915), 109.

56. Russell H. Fitzgibbon, ed., *The Constitutions of the Americas* (Chicago, 1948), pp. 498, 507, 550.

57. Charles Macomb Flandrau, *Viva Mexico!* (New York, 1909, reprinted 1951), pp. 275, 277.

58. Frank Tannenbaum, *Mexico: The Struggle for Peace and Bread* (New York, 1950), pp. 36, 38, 39.

59. On contemporary religious conditions and problems in the South American republics, see Philip Guedalla and others, *The Republics of South America* (a report by the Royal Institute of International Affairs, London, New York, and Toronto, 1937), pp. 244-264. For a Catholic layman's impressions of the needs of the Church in Latin America, see Joseph F. Priviterra, *The Latin American Front* (Milwaukee, 1945), pp. 33 ff.

60. Among the Protestant missionary schools in Brazil are Bennett College in Rio de Janeiro (a well-known school for girls), Colegio Americano in Porto Alegre, Colegio Isabel Hendrix in Belo Horizonte, the famous Mackenzie technical college in São Paulo, and Colegio Granberry in Juiz da Fora.

61. See the brilliant and unimpassioned statement of the Protestant case in Latin America, by John A. Mackay, *The Other Spanish Christ* (New York, 1933).

62. "Rio de Janeiro will ever be remembered as the first spot in the Western Hemisphere where the banner of the Reformed religion was unfurled." Fletcher and Kidder, *op. cit.,* p. 59. Agassiz, the famous scientist, who visited Brazil in the 1860's, remarked that: "As a general thing, Protestantism does not attract the Southern natives, and it may be doubtful whether its advocates will have a very wide-spread success." Though he had a low opinion of the Brazilian Church in general, Agassiz considered the priests patriotic, tolerant, and liberal. Of the Brazilians, he said: "Oppression in matters of faith is contrary to the spirit of their institutions." Louis and Mrs. Agassiz, *A Journey in Brazil* (Boston, 1869), p. 496.

Chapter VIII
THE WOMAN

B UT FOR her ghost, wandering some tropic strand in the
Caribees, no one knows who was the first European woman
to come to the New World. Not even Sr. Bermúdez Plata knows.[1]
She was probably an Andaluza, and apparently she came with
the supply fleet of Antonio de Flores in 1494, two years after
the Admiral reached the islands.[2] Perhaps she was not considered
important enough for the chroniclers to take notice of her. Maybe
Spaniards expected as much of their women and did not believe
the arrival of this *Fulana de Tal* in the Indies was news worth
recording for posterity. At any rate, Isabela, the settlement where
she came out of the foul caravel into the freshness of a "rosy-
fingered dawn" on Hispaniola had been named for a very important woman. Whoever she was and whatever her state, she
was a very noteworthy and gallant woman, who deserved better
of Spain and history than has been her lot.

THE INDIAN WOMAN

Before she came to the New World, there were many other women here, millions of them. They were all Indians—Maya, Carib, Guaraní, Quechua, and so on through the gamut of the bronze peoples. They were virgins and matrons, mothers and wives, prostitutes and nuns, slaves and chieftainesses and empresses, all the roles that women have ever played anywhere. Perhaps some of them were the Amazons of whom Orellana's men told and whose belligerent independence would have delighted the existentialist soul of Mlle. Simone de Beauvoir.[3] They were gentle or fierce, merciful or cruel, humble or proud, loving or hateful— like any woman or all women. There was a great variety in their appearance and habits, in their position in the aboriginal community, and in their relations to the men of their race. In fact, there was much less uniformity among them than there was among the women of Spain.

Sometimes they were little better than domestic animals— beasts of burden brutalized by endless labor and the claims of a precarious existence in a society forever threatened by starvation or war. Then all the woman could hope for was somehow to keep the family alive and together. If she had sensibilities at all, she must have sensed a sort of elemental kinship of a common maternity with the female beasts about her in the jungle. Sometimes a tribe had a margin of food and peace; then she shared in the surplus and her lot was better than that of her downtrodden sisters. There were peoples whose women apparently found much more in life than struggle and misery, like those whom Herrera says the conquerors met in Colombia.[4] They are "fair of feature," he says, "not too dark complexioned, and with more grace than the other women of the New World. . . . They wear garlands of roses in their hair, and artificial flowers made of cotton, which they dye various colors." But the Spaniard observes that "they are a dissolute people, because they sing and dance and lie, like everybody else in the Indies." The Anonymous Conqueror wrote of the Aztecs, "there are no people in the world who hold women in less esteem, for they never tell them what they do, even though they should know that by doing so they would be benefitted."[5] Yet, in Colombia there was said to be a tribe whose women spoke a language of their own and which they kept secret from their men. These were tribes in which the traditional roles of the sexes, except for the biological, were reversed. Women were important persons in their own right, more important sometimes than their men, who did the hard work of the tribe. There were true matriarchies, in which the women were the bosses and the men were underdogs, as around Lake Nicaragua, where husbands were cowed and often beaten by their wives.[6]

As the vision of El Dorado grew out of the rich substance of the Conquest, the legend of the Amazons had its origins in the female warriors who fought the Spaniards, sometimes alongside their men, at other times perhaps alone.[7] Before ever Orellana went down the Marañón and fell in with some very waspish women who fired arrows at his men, the Spaniards had already encountered their like among the Caribs and other peoples about the Carib sea. Some of them were as resolute and as skilled with the bow as any of the men. Herrera recounts the story of the Carib girl in the vicinity of Cartagena who killed eight Spaniards of a landing party before she was overcome,[8] and another battle in New Granada where a young Indian woman came out of a hut and wounded four Spaniards with arrows.[9] Of the Indians of the Urabá region, Oviedo wrote that "the women go to battle with their men, and also when they are mistresses of the land and command and captain their people." It was these proud ladies who supported their breasts, "which they value highly and of which they have beautiful ones," observes Oviedo, with a golden bar decorated with birds and other figures in relief.[10] He also said that the Punta de las Mujeres (Point of Women) and the Isla de las Amazonas, off the Yucatan coast were so named by the early discoverers "because they observed that the women of those islands were all archers and fought with bows, like the men." [11] Oviedo talks of a young Indian chieftainess whom he captured with twenty other women and a man near Santa Marta.[12] She died a prisoner, and "in my opinion," he says, "from anger at being captured, though she was very well treated." This *cacica* was handsome, and she was so light of color that she actually seemed a woman of Castile. "Seeing her naked, without a smile or any sign of levity, but only with a severe expression on her face, she was to be admired for her manner and dignity of bearing." Of the women who went virtually naked, Oviedo remarked: "the true adornment of a woman is modesty and not clothing . . . . I have seen many naked Indian women who looked more modest than some fully-clothed European women."

The Indian peoples of the New World differed greatly in their standards of sexual morality. As was natural, the Spaniards viewed the habits of the Indians in terms of their own practices and of Christian dogma, as when Balboa, normally a humane individual, executed some Indian sodomists in Panama.[13] Some tribes were very austere and puritanical in their customs; others were quite loose and promiscuous. For example, the people of Cumaná in the Tierra Firme were reported to "esteem virginity very little." [14] Adultery, for example, might be a capital offense against society, or only an occasion for medieval jokes in cuckoldry. In one part of Mexico, according to Herrera, adulteresses were served up and eaten.[15] In Oaxaca and the Mixteca, the death penalty was sometimes commuted to loss of the ears or nose.[16] Some nations were monogamous in principle; in others, the play of polygamous instincts was limited only by economic and other nonethical considerations, like age, inertia, the law of supply and demand, and love. For example, in one part of Tierra Firme, according to Oviedo, an Indian had as many wives as he wished, and they all lived together in the same house without bickering or jealousy![17] It was customary to give a visiting friend the choice of his women and to provide a house apart for them during his stay. If she wished to leave with the visitor, it was not in order for her hospitable lord to protest. Among the Urabá Indians, it was the custom to swap wives, sometimes with special inducements. Oviedo says that the one who drew the older woman in the trade was considered to have the better of the bargain, "since she has more sense and will serve him better and also because there will be less jealousy all around." [18]

The individual Indian woman differed greatly in attractiveness within each tribe and from one people to another. The range of appeal was liable to be especially wide in the Inca and Nahuatl lands. In both there was a female aristocracy, whose members were superior in beauty and bearing to the ordinary run of women in the country. In Peru, membership was based partly on birth into the Inca's household and partly in selection from among the population of the Tahuintinsuyo. The *coyas,* or women of the Incaic elite, the Spaniards called "princesses." By right of superior breeding and manners, they were "ladies," and once baptized, they became a *doña,* like any *hidalga* of Castile, and were accepted as such. By a process of natural selection over a long period of time, there was developed a class whom the Spaniards recognized as taller in stature, lighter in complexion, and altogether more beautiful and desirable than the generality of Quechua women.

Pedro Pizarro, who was secretary—but no relation—to the conqueror, said of the women of the Incas: "These daughters of the Sovereigns of this land, whom they called Coyas, which means beloved Ladies, were much courted. They were carried on the shoulders [of men], some in litters, others in hammocks. . . . These women were very well served and much feared, as well as delicate. They were well provided with all that they wished and needed. . . . Among the Ladies were some tall ones, not among the daughters of the Kings, but amongst those of the Orejones, their kinsmen. . . . These ladies are very clean and dainty, and they wear their black hair long upon their shoulders. They were considered beautiful, and almost all the daughters of these Lords and Orejones were so. The Indian women of the Guancas and Chachapoyas and Cañarís were the common women, most of them being pretty; the rest of the womanhood of this kingdom were thick, neither beautiful nor ugly, but of medium good looks. The people of this kingdom of Peru were swarthy in color, and among them the Lords and Ladies were whiter than Spaniards." [19]

In default of women of their own race the Spaniards did not hesitate to mate with the *coyas,* either as wives or in a more informal, and less binding, though sometimes as enduring, tie. In either event, they found in these gentlewomen consorts who had been trained in the domestic virtues and were otherwise gifted by circumstances of birth or education. The Church frowned on the practice of unsanctified cohabitation, and encouraged and facilitated the marriage of Spaniard and Indian according to its rites. In time the coyas disappeared as a separate caste and more women arrived from Spain. As a result, marriages between Spaniards and Indian women became rarer, though widespread interracial concubinage persisted throughout the colonial period.

Among some of the aboriginal peoples, there was a clearly defined class of prostitute. Of the Indians of Nicaragua, Oviedo wrote that there were "public women" who "yield themselves for ten cocoa beans," the common currency of middle America.[20] Some of them had pimps to live with them, "not to share their gains, but for their pleasure and to go about with them, and to watch the house while they went to the market to sell themselves, and to serve as a general handyman." The Nicaraguans also had a yearly saturnalia or *putería bacanal,* when any woman might give herself to any man without fear of reproach or reprisal.[21]

Father Sahagún, who wrote of the various types of the native population of New Spain, has described in language of the Old Testament the Aztec harlot and her ways in bawdry.[22] She takes so much pains in adorning herself, he says, that when she is all made up she seems like a rose. She even bathes herself frequently, an idiosyncracy which Spaniards could never understand and associated with the Moslem as a heathenish practice.[23] She apparently makes lavish use of the native cosmetics, including *axi* or chile pepper, with which she anoints her face to make it shine; red cochineal dye to color her teeth; *tzictli* or chicle, which she chews so vigorously her teeth "click like castanets"; and the local paints and pigments for brightening the general scenic and sensory effects of the ensemble. She either lets her hair flow loose down her back or braids it around her head, so that the ends stick out like horns from the top of her crown. So bedecked and bedizened with all her finery, she struts along "the path of the beasts," winking and waving, and laughing and leering, at the men whom she marks for her prey. Thus was the gaudy face of sin in old Mexico.

At the other extreme of women's sphere in Mexico, Sahagún recounts the exhortation of noble Aztec parents to their daughter on her reaching "the years of discretion." [24] Each in turn admonishes her with "tender and affectionate words" and points out to her what she may expect of the world and what it expects from one of her lineage and position, and of the obligations which she owes to her ancestors and her family. It is no rosy picture that her father and mother draw of the world into which she is

to be initiated. "This world," says her father, "is evil and griev-
ous. . . . In it there is no true pleasure or rest, but there are hardships and afflictions and weariness to exhaustion. There is weep-
ing and sadness and unhappiness . . . the road of life is not a
little hard, it is frightfully hard." Like any woman of the people,
she must learn how to spin and weave, but she must also learn
the art of painting on cloth. Her mother tells her that she should
have the bearing and manners, the carriage and speech, and the
serenity of demeanor that become a patrician lady. In her dress
she should show good taste and modesty, her clothing should be
neither "fantastic" nor plain, but becoming to one of her station.
She should neither rouge her lips nor paint her face, for these are
the marks of "evil women." And, above all, she should observe
the rule of chastity, and of fidelity to her husband.

In their dignity and nobility of spirit, there is something of
the old Roman about these admonitions of an anxious father and
mother to their "beloved first-born daughter." They are an expression of the soul of a people who had traveled far along the
way to what their European conquerors would have called "civilization." They also express the violent pressures that exist in a
militarized society which still lives by war and knows no peace.
So there is a deep melancholy and pessimism about them. The
chronicler Herrera said: "The Ladies gave many counsels to their
daughters, reminding them that they had borne them and reared
them, that they should serve the gods well, that they should be
clean and diligent, that they should manage their affairs with
care and good order, and other admirable things that were not
of barbarians." [25]

THE SPANISH WOMAN IN THE CONQUEST

The women of Spain were very fit to be mothers and wives of
conquerors. Among the "distinguished qualities" which, according to Havelock Ellis, they have always had, are courage, strength
of character, emotional stability.[26] They are neither the tem-
pestuous Carmens nor the downtrodden "clinging vines" they
are usually represented abroad. They are not temperamental or
flighty. On the contrary, they impress one by their calm self-
possession and serenity of manner, their repose of facial expression and lack of waste motion, the external restraint which con-

ceals the intense and ardent emotions deep within them. If she sometimes seemed to live in haremlike seclusion, it was not so much because of the Moorish jealousy of her husband, as because of the long turbulence of Spanish history which made it unsafe to be outside the fortresslike homes. In the Middle Ages, she was seldom softened by being sheltered against the extramural hazards of the times, for her usual fiber was too tough, but the custom outlived its usefulness, particularly for the women of the middle class. However, the great masses of Spanish women always lived without the walls and developed the boldness and independence and self-reliance that have characterized them since the days of Rome.[27]

Havelock Ellis considers the modern Spanish women superior to the men, because war and the migration to the New World removed the most virile part of the male population.[28] "Castile makes men and wastes them," ran an old saying. But events did not take the toll of her numbers and strength, as they did of the men of Spain. So when the wars were over she was much better prepared for her responsibilities than were the men who were left. In fact, she carried some of their burdens. She was probably at her best in the period of the Conquest, for never before or since has she played her role as well and on so heroic a stage as then. As mate and companion of a generation of supermen, she rose to the lofty challenge of the time.

Never the facile or fickle inamorata, she has excelled rather as mother and matron than as lover. With her, love is too demanding, too all-consuming, to be merely a romantic or biological adventure, with only sentimental or cutaneous sensations as its own reward. She has not been easily won, but only after long wooing. She is not "swept off her feet" by any impetuous suitor, but remains the mistress of any amatory situation. Casanova, with an international background of philandering as a basis of comparison, probably spent more time wooing Doña Ignacia, the devout *Madrileña*, than any of his conquests.[29]

The Spanish woman takes her love very seriously, and woe to the man who would accept it too lightly or frivolously! Though during courtship it is she who holds the upper hand, it is not as a preliminary to lifelong domination of her partner. According to the very Spanish dictum of Salvador de Madariaga: "The two sexes keep to their original and natural roles. . . . However will-ful, capable and energetic—and Spanish women often are all three—women accept as a matter of course, nay, as a matter of nature, the supremacy of the male. There is in all this nothing but instinctive fidelity to natural laws." [30] Nor does she wish to spend her life doing the things that have always been accepted as a man's work. In a "career" disassociated from a man—the *hombre querido*—she is out of her element and unhappy.[31] In the rich store of Spanish proverbs, there are many old saws that ex-press in earthy terms the traditional division of man's and woman's responsibility in the life of Spain.[32]

Spanish women came over in considerable numbers long be-fore the Conquest was completed. Some came with their husbands or to join them; some came to find a husband or a lover among the womenless men; others came for the adventure of it as the men had come. Whatever their purpose, or the circumstances of their coming, they were very courageous women, for the hazards they faced were great and there were many privations to endure.

Sometimes they had little to say about it, for their husbands packed them off to the Indies willy-nilly because they had to. Prompted by the Church, which had the most powerful lobby in Spain, the Spanish state was strong for marriage. It was seriously concerned about the goings-on of Spaniards with local women in the New World. For example, when Governor Obando took over the young colony in Santo Domingo, he found that 300 men whom Columbus had left were living quite openly with Taino girls. The custom spread with the Conquest and was well estab-lished before the wheels of the imperial bureaucracy got around to grinding out the necessary laws for its control.

The Spanish Crown, in other words, the Council of the Indies, believed that the presence of Peninsular wives in the New World would be a restraining influence on the wild and anarchic pas-sions of the conquerors. Also, they suspected the loyalty of the mestizos who would be born of Spaniard and Indian, and pre-ferred to have as many all-Spanish children born as possible. After the reign of Queen Isabella, herself a model of the domestic virtues, who may have had good reason to distrust her husband's fidelity, and so, by mental association, the constancy of all men, the morality of indiscriminate miscegenation was agitated only by the churchmen. In 1539 a law was promulgated under the title: "Single women are not to pass (to the Indies) without license of the King, and married women are to accompany their husbands." [33] There must have been much evasion of the law, for it was repeated thirty-six years later. If a husband in the colonies sent for his wife, she needed only a simple permit from the *Casa de Contratación,* or India House; if he returned to Spain to take her back with him, he had to obtain a royal license.[34] Viceroys and other officials were required to carry their wives with them when they first went out to their posts.[35] Some of the conquerors who appeared to be in no hurry to have their wives join them were sternly admonished by the agents of the crown. Under the circumstances, separations were frequently very long. Thus, Francisco de Aguirre, a fire-eating conqueror of Chile, was re-united with his wife and some grown children after a lapse of twenty-three years. In the meantime he had sired, and acknowledged his responsibility for, at least fifty mestizo children.[36] When his superior officer, Valdivia, visited Peru during the civil wars, Pedro de la Gasca, who was the king's man in that country, ordered him to terminate his liaison with Inés Suárez and to have his wife rejoin him in Chile. Valdivia carried out his part of the arrangement, but he was killed by the Araucanians in the ambush at Tucapel as his wife was on her way out from Spain.

Inés Suárez, like so many of the conquerors, was an Estremeña. In 1537, she went out to the Tierra Firme, the north coast of South America, to find her husband.[37] She travelled with a young niece, who disappears from history at this point. From Venezuela, Inés went on to Peru, in itself a considerable feat for a lone woman in those times. In Peru she learned that her husband had died, but instead of returning to Spain she settled down on a piece of land near Cuzco to wait for developments. They came in the form of Pedro de Valdivia, who had recently taken a prominent part in the Pizarros' victory over the Almagro faction. More important, he was to be the conqueror of Chile. He had a wife in Spain, but Spain was far away, and once in Chile it seemed still farther. So Valdivia moved in with the young widow from Estremadura while he planned his long foray into Arauco. And when he left Cuzco for the Valley of Chile with his little band Inés Suárez rode by his side. She rode through high mountains and over long stretches of desert country with the 150 immortals until they reached the hill where Santiago was to be. For ten years she was the companion of Valdivia. She shared in all the hardships of the beleaguered colony, and in the wars with the fierce Araucanians she cared for the wounded and cheered the hard-pressed soldiery. There were times when she took a man's place in the fighting. "A woman of great energy and loyalty," a Chilean historian has written of her, "discreet, wise and kind, she enjoyed the esteem of all the conquerors." [38] When the news of Gasca's order arrived from Lima ahead of Valdivia, she determined not to take advantage of the six months of grace allowed before the separation, knowing that the final break would only be more difficult. So she went to a priest who had been her friend and he advised her to marry one of the other conquerors in the town. When Valdivia returned from Peru he found her already married to Rodrigo de Quiroga, a good man, who was later to be a governor of the colony.

The Spanish government early put into effect a system for licensing all persons who wished to go to the Americas and could pass a security test that was largely a matter of meeting certain religious and moral criteria. The necessary administrative machinery was set up in the *Casa de Contratación,* or India House, in Seville, which was authorized to grant permits for travel. Some classes of travelers were removed from the jurisdiction of the *Casa* and were required to obtain the permission of the crown to leave the country. In actual practice, it is likely that such cases were handled directly by the Council of the Indies or its secretariat. The publication of a catalogue of "passengers to the Indies" has been undertaken by the head of the Archive of the Indies, which is located in the former building of the *Casa.*[39] As a result, it is now possible to follow the migration of Spanish women to the New World from the time the register was first opened.

The first entry in the passenger book was made in 1509, when one Diego Ternero *and his wife* were given permits to go to the islands. The same year, Isabel Rodríguez, wife of Pedro López Marruquín, of Baeza in the Province of Jaén, received a license to cross the Atlantic. By the next year, two wives went out with their children to join their husbands, probably in Santo Domingo.

One of them, Teresa Sánchez, wife of Pedro Garrido, took out three young daughters. Catalina Hernández, of Mérida in Estremadura, had permission to go to the Indies for five months to collect certain debts (*maravedís*) owed to her, perhaps a small estate left to her by a dead husband. For the first time, the name of a single woman—Isabel Galinda, of Villalba—appeared in the register of passengers.

After 1510 the number of women and children who crossed the ocean increased year by year. More and more women were traveling alone, as did Ana Díaz, widow of Diego Sánchez, a cooper, and Beátriz Alvarez, wife of a Portuguese barber, in 1511. Fifteen other wives and widows crossed the same year, four of them with children. One of them is Antonia García, *"la Pavona"* ("the Peacock"), wife of Diego de Denia. Also, the better-to-do travelers were often accompanied by servants. In 1512, Isabel de Cárdenas goes to the Indies with her husband and with Spanish, Negro and Indian servants. In the same year, Maria Hernández takes ship with her husband, Pedro de León, and their five children, Guiomar, Hernando, Diego, Belita, and little Francisquito.

The five years, 1513–17, were remarkable for the large numbers of single women who received licenses to go to the Indies. They were mostly Sevillanas or hailed from the towns in the neighborhood, like Alcalá. They landed in the islands in the quiet period that followed the first rush of Spaniards into the Antilles and that preceded the conquest of Mexico. The new settlement in Cuba must have been greatly enlivened by the arrival of these festive young Andaluces, and those who were of a mind for marriage could have found no more promising field for their endeavors. Some of them were later to follow their new husbands to Mexico long before the fighting was over and to share with them the multiple hazards of that mighty adventure. They were women of the people, the Catalinas and Leonors from the *barrios* of the Macarena and Triana, without any claims to category, like Inés Ruíz, whose father was a barber of Seville, and Maria Gutiérrez, a fisherman's daughter, but a great many men in the new lands were the happier for their coming.

The chroniclers Cervantes Salazar and Herrera tell of the heroic wives who replied to Cortés when he tried to have them stay in Tlascala during the siege of Tenochtitlan that "it was not right that women of Castile should leave their husbands when they went to war, and that where they were to die, their wives, too, should die with them." [40] Among them were Beátriz de Palacios, María de Estrada, Juana Martín, Isabel Rodríguez, and the wife of Alonso Valiente. Isabel Rodríguez was a veritable Florence Nightingale of the sixteenth century. "The skirmishes, single combats, and pitched battles continued, with much shedding of blood," wrote Herrera; "as the wounded Spaniards had few (medical) supplies, and every day there were at least a hundred wounded among them and the Indian allies, God provided a Castilian woman, named Isabel Rodríguez, to tie up their wounds and to make the sign of the cross over them." So many recovered from their wounds and went back to the fighting that "it was a strong argument for the fact that God was on the side of the Castilians, since he returned so many to health by the hands of that woman." Sometimes men who were mortally wounded, as was Magallanes, the brave Portuguese soldier, staggered to her side to die in her arms and to be comforted by her as by a mother in their last minutes of life. Beátriz de Palacios was the mulatto wife of Pedro de Escobar. She foraged for food for him and his friends and prepared a meal for them when the day's fighting was over. When the pressure from the Aztecs was hardest, she joined her husband in the ranks. When one of them was wounded, she tended his wounds, and she saddled the horses for the men and "did other things like any soldier."

Bernal Díaz devoted much more space to the horses of his companions than he did to their wives.[41] It is worth noting that of the small company who conquered Mexico, two were wife killers. Of these guilty of uxoricide, the elder Suárez hit his wife over the head with a handmill, with fatal consequences to her. Another who murdered his wife was Juan Pérez. Also, one Escobar, a "brave man but very turbulent," was hanged for the double crime of mutiny and raping a married woman, a confusion of justice which could probably have occurred only among Spaniards. Bernal Díaz mentions three soldiers who married Indian women: Alonso de Grado, who took to wife one of the many daughters of Montezuma; Juan de Cuellar, who married Doña Ana, "the beautiful daughter of the Lord of Tezcuco"; and

Alonzo Pérez, "a brave soldier, married to a handsome Indian of the Islands." He also tells of Juana de Mansilla, the Penelope of the Conquest, whom the royal commissioner in Mexico City tried to force into marriage with another man though she believed her husband was still alive with Cortés in Honduras.[42] When she refused, she was beaten as a witch, and when the soldiers came back from Honduras they paraded her through the streets of Mexico City on horseback, "like a Roman matron" as a tribute to her constancy.

During the same fateful years, Juan Guillén took a train of eleven females to the New World, consisting of his wife, María de Malaver, their eight daughters, and two unidentified women. When Rodrigo Zambrano went out to the islands, he was accompanied by his wife, Inés, and their four daughters and a son. The family, the basic institution of Spain, was being transplanted bodily in the New World because there were Spaniards there who needed their women and children about them, and their women joined them because they, too, were Spanish and the family was theirs to tend and keep. In November, 1533, Francisco Pizarro entered Cuzco, the capital of the Inca Empire. The next year, these entries appear in the register of the India House at Seville: "Lorenza Sánchez, with her husband, Gaspar Pérez, to Peru," and "Mencia del Campo, with her husband, Diego de Zamora, and three sons; Luís, 10; Hernando, 4; and Diego, at his mother's breast, to Peru."

This is probably the Doña Mencia, who, widowed in the wars, was to marry Francisco Hernández Girón, last of the rebels against the royal authority in Peru. According to Garcilaso, she was "young, noble, beautiful, and virtuous." She accompanied her husband from Lima to Cuzco, where he organized his rebellion. He later summoned her to join him in the campaign in the sierra, where she shared all the hardships and privations of the soldiers. When Hernández Girón re-entered Cuzco after his initial victory, she was hailed by his partisans as "Queen of Peru." [43] Again she followed him into the low country, where he was defeated by the royal forces at Pucara. Here he abandoned her to the mercy of the victors and fled into the mountains, only to be captured and beheaded.[44] Doña Mencia was held in such esteem by everyone in Peru, that after her husband's defeat and flight she was conducted back to Cuzco by a special bodyguard of high royalist officers. Shortly afterward she entered a convent in Lima and closed the door on a life of adventure and tragedy.

On the opposite side in the same rebellion, another Spanish woman displayed the same fortitude and nobility of character. This was Doña Francisca de Zúñiga, wife of Pedro López de Cazalla.[45] She, too, went into the Andes and "to serve, not his Majesty, but her husband. And although she was a delicate woman and ailing," says Garcilaso, "she forced herself to ride in a chair atop a saddled mule, and she rode over the rough places and bad passes in these roads as easily and successfully as any of the company. In the evening she would regale them all with a supper and again with lunch at midday, for which she begged supplies from the Indians and then showed the Indian women how to prepare the meal."

Other Spanish women whose names do not appear in the books of the *Casa* came to Peru during the terrible years when Spaniards had turned from the conquest of the Indians to warring with each other. One of them was Doña Catalina Leytón, or Leitão, the Portuguese wife of Francisco de Carbajal, the indomitable old warrior who was Gonzalo Pizarro's principal lieutenant in his war with the royalist party. Known for his ferocity as "the Demon of the Andes," nearly everyone in Peru but his wife made way for him. She, and their adopted daughter, Juana, were the only persons in the land who dared face him down and whom he would heed. Garcilaso tells of a big banquet which Carbajal gave in his house in Cuzco to celebrate his victory over Diego Centeno.[46] As the evening wore on there was much drunkenness and loose talk about the new kingdom that Gonzalo was to set up with Carbajal's help. When tongues were thickest and noisiest, Doña Catalina entered the room and jeering (*"haziendo escarnio"*) the drunken figures around the table and on the floor, said: "You're a fine lot who would rule Peru!" To which her husband answered: "Shut up, old girl; if you give them two hours sleep, any one of them could rule half a world."

To return to the passenger lists of the India House: large ready-made families continued to migrate to the more settled lands like New Spain which, except for the Chichimec country, was pacified long before Peru. In 1535, the year of the founding of Lima, Juan de Muzientas, a shoemaker, moved to Mexico with his wife, Marina de Prado, and nine children, including five daughters. The next year, Doña Juana de Sosa, who must have been a matron of distinction, led out a company of seven women, eight men, and a page to the same destination. In 1537, Bartolomé Valdés, his wife Elvira, four sons and as many daughters, plus Alonso, a manservant, shipped from Seville to Veracruz. The following year, one Dr. Robles, who was doubtless a royal official, moved to the Tierra Firme with a veritable clan, that included his wife, Juana Jofre de Guevara; his mother, María de Herrera; two daughters, María and Juana; three sisters, Catalina, Francisca, and María; and twelve nieces and nephews.

It was in this year, 1538, that Don Pedro de Alvarado, second only to Cortés in the conquest of Mexico, conqueror, and now Captain General of Guatemala, and one of the magnificos of the Indies, brought his second wife out to his new capital.[47] She was Doña Beátriz de la Cueva, niece of the Duke of Albuquerque, and a great lady in her own right. Eleven years before he had married her sister, Doña Francisca, who had died of fever off the Mexican coast before reaching Guatemala. His new bride was eventually to die in the governor's palace in a night of terror, as a cataclysm of nature released the water stored in the crater of a volcano above the city. But now she came in much splendor, as befitted a scion of the *grandeza,* and spouse of the lord of the new kingdom of the Maya-Quiche. With the governor and his wife came a fine company of retainers and dependents, of substantial men with wives and children, including one Hernán Alvarez, a widower, with nine children to find places for in the New World. In the governor's retinue were three maids of the household and a dozen other servants, male and female.

And there were Doña Ana Fadrique and eight other young ladies of good family and marriageable age.[48] The return of Alvarado and his train to Guatemala was celebrated with a round of festivities that lasted for several days. At one of these affairs, the local contingent of ex-conquistadors was present en masse. Sitting in stiff-backed chairs along the walls of the *sala* of the governor's palace, as millions of other Spanish-Americans have sat since then, the veterans must have been ill-at-ease in the presence of all the new finery from Spain. They were gnarled and battle-scarred, and their party manners had never been very good anyhow. Stout Bernal Díaz, chronicler of the Conquest, who had settled in Guatemala, was probably one of the guests; but it was some anonymous spectator who served as society reporter of that afternoon's function.

While the aging veterans were herded into the big hall, the damsels who had come from Spain watched them through a door at one end of the room. One of them spoke up and remarked to the other: "They say we are to marry these conquistadors!" Another added: "Do they mean that we are to marry these broken-down old men? The rest of you can do what you like, but I do not intend to marry any of them. To the devil with them! They must have escaped from hell, they look so crippled. Some of them are lame and others are one-armed. Some have lost an ear and others an eye. Some of them have only half a face and the best of them have long scars across their faces." Then the first answered: "We are not marrying them for their elegance, but for their Indians. Since they are old and worn out they will soon be dead. Then we can have the young husbands that we want. It will be like changing a broken old bottle for a strong new one."

One of the old conquerors who was sitting close to the door overheard the conversation and, turning on the young ladies, poured out all his scorn on them. Then he told his companions what he had heard and said to them: "Marry these dames and you will see how they repay the favor you do them!" "At this," says Garcilaso, "he went to his house and called a priest, and was married to a noble Indian woman, by whom he already had two natural children.[49] He wished to legitimize them, so that they could inherit his Indians, and not some *señora*, who would enjoy what he had earned by his labors, and who would treat his children as servants and slaves."

In spite of the profusion of offerings and of exceptional orgies of lubricity in certain localities, there was no universal carnival of the flesh in the early years of the Conquest. Sometimes the Aztec and Inca princesses may have satisfied the conquerors' yearning for all that women could give them, for the aristocratic ladies met a cosmopolitan standard of feminine refinement that would have made them at home in Madrid, or Paris, or Rome—

and sometimes did. Even Catarina Paraguassú, the daughter of a Tupi chief, who married Alvares Caramurú, the patriarchal Portuguese pioneer of northern Brazil, seems to have charmed the higher social orders of Western Europe. Anacaona, the tragic Cleopatra of the Tainos, was unfortunate only because the Spaniards who came her way in the Antilles were the men of Roldán's company, who were the brutal scum on the first wave of conquerors and who saw in her only a highly desirable female animal.[50] But to many Spaniards the *India* had the fame of being frigid, and sometimes their ugliness cooled the ardor of the newcomers.[51] As Spanish wives or mistresses appeared in the New World, the lure of the Indian women declined proportionately. Oviedo, who went a-conquering on the Spanish Main before he settled down in Santo Domingo to write the saga of the early period of the Conquest, could not have been unique in his deep affection for his wife. When she died in the Indies, he wrote of her: "[She] had built our house in Darien according to her tastes. It had fine quarters above and below, and there was a pretty garden with many orange trees and other plants, on the banks of a pleasant stream that flowed by the town. When I saw her dead, I almost lost my senses, not only because she was so dear a companion to me, but I always wished to live in a married state, like a Christian. I was not accustomed to the mistresses that my neighbors had, and sometimes two of them." [52]

When the first Spanish women arrived in the Indies, they immediately gave an air of permanence to the new society, even though their menfolk were still fighting Indians all around them. This process began very early, when Diego Columbus, son of the Admiral and first Viceroy of the Indies, brought out his wife Doña María de Toledo, of the illustrious house of Alva, and niece of the Catholic Kings, to Hispaniola. With her came their ladies, and the viceregal court that was set up at Santo Domingo added a familiar touch of Spain in the tropical wilderness, and a refining influence that extended throughout the Caribbean. "With the Vicereine," says Oviedo, "there came a number of ladies and damsels of good family, and all of those who were young were married in this city and in the island to rich and important men who lived there, since at that time there was a great lack of women of Castile. . . . So, with these Spanish women who came then, this city was much ennobled, and today there are many children and grandchildren of those marriages, who comprise the principal wealth of this city." [53]

Another Spanish matron who had a part in transplanting some of the values of Spanish civilization to the young colonies was Doña Isabel de Bobadilla. She came of the high nobility of Castile and was the wife of Pedrárias Dávila, governor of the isthmus country. [54] The terrible old tyrant must have inspired some deep attachment in his wife, for when he insisted on her remaining in Spain because of the risks of life in Darien, she wrote this tender letter to him: "My dear husband, we have been united from our youth, as I think, for the purpose of living together and never being separated. Wherever destiny may lead you . . . I should be your companion. There is nothing I would fear more, nor any kind of death that might threaten me, which would not be more supportable than for me to live without you and separated by such an immense distance. I would rather die and even be eaten by cannibals, than to consume myself in perpetual mourning and in unceasing sorrow, awaiting, not my husband, but his letters. My determination is not sudden or unconsidered; nor is it a woman's caprice that moves me to a well-weighed and merited decision. The children God has given us will not stop me for one moment. We will leave them their heritage and their marriage portions, sufficient to enable them to live in conformity with their rank; and, besides these, I have no other preoccupation." One of their children, Doña María, married Hernando de Soto, governor of Cuba and explorer of the southern part of the United States. During the absence that was never to end, she served as his regent in the island. "A woman of a fine presence and a good heart and of superior judgment," Oviedo, who knew her, said of her. [55] Another daughter was to marry Vasco Núñez de Balboa, whom her father came out to Panama to supplant and whose death he planned and consummated. Though the betrothals were made, the prospective bride remained in a convent in Spain, while the conqueror lived quite contentedly with his Indian paramour and the marriage had not yet taken place when Vasco Núñez was beheaded in the January twilight at Acla. [56]

Oviedo, who had the reputation of being an able and conscientious royal official, knew all the major participants in the unsavory events that followed the execution of Balboa. He explains his reasons for leaving the accursed atmosphere of the Isthmus for the peace of Santo Domingo in these words: "After I had made my arrangements with Pedrarias, and to *remake my conscience* and put an end to the contentions, and because I wished to come to this city to rest with my wife and children, being aware of the little justice there was in the Tierra Firme." [57]

One who did not wish to leave the Isthmus was the wife of Pedro de los Rios who was a governor in Castilla del Oro during the period when the current of conquest was moving across the Darien country on its way southward into Peru. Though he was a "caballero of good breeding" according to Oviedo, "he was not suited to governing a land so newly settled. For he was greedy, and his wife, through whom he governed, was insatiable in her avarice." [58] When he went to Spain to retire in his home city of Córdoba, his wife refused to join him. "Because of Peru," adds Oviedo "there was much gold in Panama, and with her cattle and other assets which she had, she did very well for herself, because she was fond of receiving money."

Pizarro landed at Tumbes in 1532. Two years later, the *Casa de Contratación* was already issuing permits to Spanish women to go out to Peru. Others whose names do not appear on the books of the India House, like Inés Muñoz, the mistress, and later to be the wife, of Pedro Martínez de Alcántara, half-brother of the Conqueror, came very early. Though Peru was no fit place for a lady for many years, they came anyway, and, lady or no lady, they accepted the risks and privations along with the satisfaction of being near some man they cherished. The first sizeable contingent of Spanish women of category reached Peru in 1544 with the ill-fated Viceroy Blasco Núñez Vela.[59] The party included thirty-six married women and eighty-seven girls who traveled with their parents. And though there was no real peace in the torn land for another ten years, it was these women and their daughters who laid the foundations of Spanish society in colonial Peru.

One Spanish woman who found no rest in Peru was Inés de Atienza.[60] The widow of Pedro de Arcos, she was too young and fair for her own good and unable to take care of herself among the wild and unsettled soldiery who had been her husband's companions. She was caught up in the maelstrom of violent passions and swept along with them as the mistress of Pedro de Ursua, who had been chosen by the viceroy to lead the dangerous veterans of the civil wars on a wild-goose chase into the Amazon Valley in search of El Dorado. When Ursua was murdered by the monstrous Lope de Aguirre, Inés transferred her attachment to Lorenzo de Salduendo, Aguirre's lieutenant and partner in crime. When Salduendo, too, was put out of the way, Inés was stabbed to death one night in the wilderness by the great river by two of Aguirre's bravos. Doña Inés had not remarried and violated one of the rules of this turbulent age, so that she was no longer any one man's woman.

In the New World, widowhood usually ended in early remarriage, with only a decent interval of mourning. There were never enough women to go around, and marriage was accepted as the normal life of a woman. And, even if a widow prepared to relapse into celibacy, an alternative seldom favored by women of Spanish temperament of whatever age, all the pressures of society operated to make her take another husband. The only respectable alternative was retirement to a nunnery. Otherwise there was no safe place for a lone woman in this rough-and-tumble age. Those widows were liable to be "well-heeled," and progressively more so with each husband, so that for the indigent Conquistador one of them offered, with the other advantages of marriage, the added attraction of a retirement pension. In the warm autumnal affection of these buxom widows many a conqueror found an enduring refuge from years of war and violence, and a richer reward than Inca gold or high office.

The story of Doña Antonia Hernández was probably repeated in substance many times.[61] She first married Miguel de Güemes, one of the original conquerors of Mexico. As one husband after another succumbed to the hazards of the Conquest, she married in succession, Baltásar Rodríguez, Bartolomé de Perlaes, and Juan de Moscoso. Marriage, frequently repeated, atoned for the more irregular man-and-woman relationships that were common in a world torn loose from its conventional moorings. So, Inés Muñoz, who, as we have seen, came out to Peru as the paramour of Francisco Martínez de Alcántara, half-brother of Pizarro, and later married him.[62] After his assassination, she married Antonio de Rivera, a member of the most illustrious family of early Lima.

In 1573, she founded the Convent of La Concepción with a large endowment. Other titles to fame were the fact that she brought the first cat to Peru and that she and her husband grew in their gardens by the Rimac the first olives in South America.

Similarly for Doña Catalina de Alconchel, who was lover of the Inquisitor Alonso Gutiérrez de Ulloa, and had two children by him. She married later Pablo de Montemayor, and on his death Jusepe de Rivera y Dávalos, a distinguished Alcalde, or Mayor, of Lima and son of Nicolás de Rivera the Elder.

The first Spanish women to arrive in the Bogotá country came with Governor Luís de Lugo, one of the more antipathetic figures of the Conquest.[63] There seem to have been four wives and two other single females in the party. Each of the early governors of New Granada brought out in his train a number of his countrymen, and in the large retinue of Dr. Miguel Díez de Armendáriz there were three wives with their husbands, and two widows in search of husbands, each with a daughter. Dr. Miguel apparently exhausted the limited possibilities for philandering in local Spanish circles, for, according to Germán Arciniegas, "they said he carried on love affairs with Doña Ana, the wife of Sebastián de Heredia, and with La Pimentala, and with Lucia de Alvarez, and with La Sotomayor de Alcocer, who belonged not only to Alcocer but at times to Pedro de Orsua." [64]

Meanwhile, there occurred in another part of Colombia one of those tragedies that so often stalked these inseparable Spanish couples. In 1545, there arrived in Santo Domingo from Spain Jorge de Robledo and his wife, Doña María Carvajal.[65] They shepherded out to the island with them, fifteen or sixteen "well-disposed" young ladies, some of whom were relatives of Doña María herself, while others belonged to the family of the Marshal Jiménez de Quesada, the conqueror of Colombia. Robledo, a singularly attractive person, left his wife in the safety of Hispaniola while he went on to the Tierra Firme to take part in the conquest of the lower Cauca country in New Granada. Later he asked her to join him at Cartagena but shortly afterward he left the coast with an expedition into the interior, from which he never returned. For in the back country he fell afoul of Sebastián Benalcázar, who had come up into the Cundinamarca highlands from Peru by way of the Quito country, and became a victim of the old conqueror's jealousy. Heartbroken and bitter, Robledo's wife hounded Benalcázar implacably until the crown yielded to her petitions and summoned him to be tried for murder. When he died at Cartagena in 1551 while awaiting a ship for Spain, Doña María wrote off the account of her vengeance as paid in full.

Pedro de Esquivel was not a major conquistador. He was one of the Sevillanos who accompanied Pedro de Mendoza on his ill-fated expedition to the River Plate in 1535. With him went his wife, Isabel de Guevara, who after twenty-one years wrote a letter to the Princess Juana as one Spanish woman to another.[66] But many things had meanwhile happened in Spain that Doña Isabel had not heard of. The Princess Juana had been Queen of Castile, had become mad, been widowed, and was already dead. Other women came out with Isabel de Guevara: Marí Sánchez, of Coria, the wife of Juan Salmeron; Ana Muñoz, who may not yet have had a man of her own; and others who left no names in the books of the Casa de Contratación.

Things went ill with the colony of Buenos Aires from the beginning. The Indians of the pampa were implacable and gradually drew tight the lines of death around the settlement by the riverbank. Inside the beleaguered town, people went hungry and died of starvation. In the records there are dark hints of cannibalism, and Doña Isabel wrote long afterward: "If it were not for the honor of the men, there is much more that I could write your Highness truthfully." The men were so enfeebled by their privations that the small band of women had to take over much of their work, even to firing the guns at the stockades when the Indians attacked. "Had it not been for the care and solicitude that we had for them, they would all have died," said the wife of Esquivel.

After most of the colonists had perished, the rest abandoned the place and started upriver into the Guaraní country in two brigantines. In the long journey, the women not only took care of the men who were sick and comforted them and cooked the endless fish that were their food; they cheered them on when they seemed too weary to go any further and handled the heavy boats when the men collapsed at the oars. "For the men's lives were in their hands," and "only love impelled them" to do all they did for them. When at last the survivors reached the site of Asunción,

there was at least a promise of plenty in the rich soil, though it
was the women who tilled the new fields until the distant colony
got on its feet and the men recovered from the alternate torpor
and violence of their ways. In her letter to the Queen, Juana la
Loca, Isabel de Guevara asks for herself a perpetual *repartimiento* or grant of land and Indians, and for her husband, whose
services to the Crown had caused hers "to be forgotten," she
besought "some employment—according to his quality, for on his
part he merits it." As a significant comment on the turbulence of
life in the young colony by the Paraguay, she adds, "Three times
I have saved his life with the knife at his throat." If Argentina
would erect statues to its benefactors, it is to these devoted and
heroic women that they should be dedicated.

THE CONQUEROR AND THE INDIAN WOMAN

When Spaniards and Portuguese encountered Indian women, the
customary pattern of their relationship was generally very simple.
It was uncomplicated by any efforts at moralizing or rationalizing
on either side. On the one side, the elements in the situation were
men who had left behind them in Europe their womenfolk and
whatever rules had guided their mutual association; on the other
were women of another race, their strong bodies on perpetual
display in the hot lands, their impulses uninhibited by custom or
religion, and, as Gilberto Freyre suggests, probably stimulated by
priapic considerations.[67] They were liable to be flattered by the
attentions of their conquerors and impressed in proportion to the
Spaniard's rank. However, among the civilized nations of Mexico
and Peru, there was a tendency for men and women to seek their
social level in their opposites. A Spanish common soldier who took
an *India* of his own class as a long-time partner was likely to give
her more affection and consideration than if he were a caballero
and she were of lower station. In the prevailing atmosphere of
compliance and co-operation, it is unlikely that there was often
need to resort to force. The best proof of this genetic pudding is
in the continental scope of the miscegenation which resulted from
the existence of such favorable circumstances. For a new mestizo
world was created for Spain, and, in Brazil, for Portugal.

Qualifying factors in the process were the fastidiousness of
the conquerors and the seriousness of their intentions. Some who

had travelled widely rated the women of the various tribes within their ken and experience. Two expert commentators in the matter were Pedro de Cieza de León [68] and Ulrich Schmidel.[69] Both were young soldiers who got about a great deal in the Indies and must have met many of the local girls wherever they went, the one from the Spanish Main south into Peru; the other, in the River Plate country. Of the Indians in the Urabá region of Darien, where he began his long wanderings, Cieza de León said: "Their women are the prettiest and most lovable of any that I have seen in the Indies. They are clean in their eating and have none of the dirty habits of other nations." He was very young and impressionable then, for years later he said as much of the Chachapoyas, who lived in the Peruvian montaña. Of the latter, he added: "Their women are so beautiful that many of them are worthy to be the wives of the Incas, or inmates of the Temple of the Sun. To this day the Indian women of this race are exceedingly beautiful, for they are fair (of complexion) and well formed." Of the Arma district in Colombia he wrote that "The women of these Indians are the ugliest and dirtiest that I have seen in all these parts." He thought better of the women in the Carrapa region of Colombia, whom he called "well disposed, and of good countenance, and very amorous." So, in his opinion, were the women of Latacunga in Ecuador, and of Cajamarca in Peru. Of the famous Cañarís of the same Quito country, he remembered: "The women are very pretty, amorous, and friendly to the Spaniards. They are great laborers, for it is they who dig the land, sow the crops, and reap the harvests, while their husbands remain in the houses, sewing and weaving, adorning their clothes, and performing other feminine offices. When any Spanish army passed through their province, the Indians at that time being obliged to supply people to carry the baggage of the Spaniards on their backs, many of the Cañarís sent their wives and daughters and remained at home themselves." Yet it was the warriors of this tribe who comprised the imperial guard of the Incas!

Ulrich Schmidel catalogues in even more specific terms the women of the various tribes along the Paraná and the Paraguay. Of the Timbús, he said: "The women are horrible, and both young and old tattoo their faces with a blue dye." The Corondás also had the same blue spider pattern tattooed on their "ugly" faces. Whereas their women "cover their shame with a cotton rag," the Chanas "expose it to the air, and everybody goes as naked as when Almighty God put them in the world." Both men and women of the Agaces were "handsome and tall," and the women painted their faces. Among the Carios, who also went naked, the father sold his daughter, the husband his wife if she did not please him, and brother sold sister. A woman could be bought for a shirt, a knife, a hatchet, or any other trade goods. The same Indians presented six girls and seven deer to Juan de Ayolas, the Spanish commander. At the same time they gave two girls to each soldier, "to take care of us," says Schmidel, "cook and wash for us, and to attend to anything else that we needed done." As though the two apiece were not enough, the soldiers captured many more of these women, "which was a big help to us." He said that the Surucursis lived a good family life with their handsome wives and their children. The German admired the manner in which the women of the Jerús painted their bodies with blue paint. "This painting," he commented, "is very beautiful and a painter in Europe would have to work hard to equal it. The women are good-looking after their fashion, and they sin when they have a chance. However, I do not wish to speak more about this just now." To this picture he adds that the women are "great lovers, affectionate and ardent; at least *I* think so." Of the Mbayas, he says that the women are handsome, and then appends as a fashion note that "they cover their shame from the navel to the knees. These women stay at home and don't work in the fields, since it is the man who looks for food. The women spin and weave cotton, do the cooking and give pleasure to their husbands and to any of their friends who ask for it. For the time being I will not say any more about this. If somebody doesn't believe this, or would like to see it, let him make the trip."

It was the chief of this tribe who bestowed "three handsome young women" on the captain of Schmidel's company. To the hilarious amusement of the camp, "about midnight, when everything was quiet, our captain lost his three girls. Perhaps he wasn't equal to the three of them, because he was in his sixties and was aging, but if he had parceled the girls out among the soldiers, I am sure they would not have gotten away."

Of the Corocotoquís, the gossipy German remarks that their

women "wear a *tipoy,* which is a big cotton shirt without sleeves."
This, incidentally, is the Mother Hubbard which was to become
the distinctive dress of the Paraguayan country woman. These
women, he added, stayed home and "sewed things for the house,"
while the men worked in the fields and brought in the food.

There was the Pocahontas of the Pascas, who saved the life
of Lázaro Fonte, one of Jiménez de Quesada's officers in the conquest of Colombia.[70] Fonte was accused of trying to cheat the
king out of the royal "fifth" of a batch of emeralds that was part
of the loot of the Chibchas. When he was sentenced to be hanged,
his companions protested, and the penalty was commuted to exile
among the savage Pascas. He was led off and tied to a tree where
the Indians would find him and make sure of his speedy death.
But an Indian girl who had taken a fancy to him followed him,
and when the braves arrived at the tree in the morning, they
found the girl sitting by him in a protective attitude. Then she
told them their Spanish enemies had sent him away because he
opposed their plan to burn the village. So the Spaniard gained
his life, the girl a lover, and the tribe a valuable member.

Hernán Cortés, who was a prodigious man of war, was also a
prodigy of amorousness. His career as a Don Juan began when
he was a student at Salamanca and continued during his stay in
the islands. It was of this period of his life that Bernal Díaz
wrote: "I have heard that when he was a lad in Hispaniola he
was very wild about women." [71] While he was in Mexico, what
one of his biographers has called his "primitive polygamous temperament" never seemed to slacken its ardor. In Cuba, not exactly a prudish community, there was a series of escapades that
appeared to shock most everyone in the colony except the several
women concerned. Particularly scandalized was the fat governor,
Diego Velásquez, himself no "lady's man," who reproved the
future conquistador for disturbing the domestic peace of the
island. Here he married his first wife, Catalina Xuárez, under
circumstances that suggested some form of duress from a third
party. Later, when he was the mighty lord of New Spain, he was
very dilatory in sending for Doña Catalina to join him, and her
death shortly after her arrival from Cuba led to much wagging
of malicious tongues.

The most important woman in the life of the Conqueror was

the famous Doña Marina, known to the Indians of Anahuac as Malinche. She was given to Cortés along with nineteen other women by a local chief when he stopped on the Tehuantepec coast on his way to Mexico. Of the aboriginal gentry of Campeche, by her superior intelligence, breeding, dignity of bearing and beauty, she would evidently have stood out among women of whatever race. She became the devoted and loyal companion of Cortés, and she bore him the ablest of his sons. When he wrote to the Emperor Charles about her, he called her his "interpreter," whom he had found in Putunchan.[72] She was that and much more to him, and as important in her way to the success of the Conquest as was Alvarado or Sandoval. She was fluent in Maya, Aztec, and the language of her lord. She sensed intuitively the attitude of the natives wherever the Spaniards went and was invaluable as a go-between in dealing with them. Later, she married Juan Jaramillo, "an officer of merit" as Bernal Díaz says, and encomendero of Xochimilco. It was a "good marriage" and it was as wife of a Spanish captain that she went along on the terrible expedition into Honduras. She had become a great lady in her own right, the first in modern Mexico. And as the kings of Spain sometimes gave their most valiant cities the title of "Ever Heroic" so was Doña Marina *la siempre heroica*. "The excellent Doña Marina," Bernal Díaz called her, "she had by her birth an universal influence and consequence through these countries; she was of a fine figure, frank manners, prompt genius, and intrepid spirit; an excellent linguist, and of most essential service to Cortés whom she always accompanied." [73]

Montezuma gave Cortés one of his daughters, who, baptized as Doña Ana, lived with him in his quarters in Tenochtitlán—along with two of her sisters and another Aztec princess. Doña Ana, then pregnant, was killed in the causeway at the *Noche Triste*. It is said that two of Montezuma's daughters bore him sons and one a daughter. In his will, he mentions another natural daughter by Leonor Pizarro, who later married Juan de Salcedo.

At the crest of his fame, Cortés was married in Spain to Doña Juana de Zuñiga, of the high nobility of Castile. "She was a good wife," says his biographer, "and loved him just as Catalina Xuárez and all his mistresses, while his uxorious instincts made it equally easy for him to be happy with all of them. He was affectionate and tender, devoted to all his children, distinguishing but little between his legitimate and his natural children in a truly patriarchal fashion. For the latter he secured bulls of legitimacy from the pope, and provided generously in his will." [74] Though the scope of their affections may not have ranged so far and wide, many thousands of Latin American men have since followed the example of the Conqueror in all these respects.

As also happened in Peru, there were many other liaisons between Spaniards and high-born Indian women. The alliance between Cortés and the "republic" of Tlascala was sealed by the gift of five daughters of the local rulers. According to Bernal Díaz, they were "handsome in comparison to the other women of the country, well dressed, and each attended by a female slave." [75] The ceremony of presentation only took place after they had been "converted" to Christianity and baptized with proper Spanish names. Cortés, who showed unusual restraint on this occasion, turned over Doña Luisa, daughter of the top-chief Xicotenga, to Alvarado; Velásquez de León received Doña Elvina, most beautiful of the five. Bernal Díaz had forgotten the names of the others, but he said, "they were all *doñas* (and) were assigned to Olid, Sandoval, and Avila." Doña Luisa, who apparently had very regal ways and was a person of much consequence in the Tlascalan state, gave Alvarado a son, who was also called Pedro, and a daughter, who was named Doña Leonor. Doña Leonor, "an excellent lady," married Don Francisco de la Cueva, cousin of the Duke of Albuquerque and so a relative of both of Alvarado's wives. In other words, she married into the *grandeza*, the highest peerage of Spain. She had four or five sons, "all worthy cavaliers." Probably the most married of the Aztec "princesses" was Doña Isabel, widow of Cuautemoc, hero of the Mexican resistance to the Spaniards. Herself another daughter of Montezuma, she had previously been the wife of Cuitlahuatzin, also an important leader of the Aztecs. After the execution of Cuautemoc by Cortés, she married in succession three of the Spanish conquerors. Her fourth husband, Juan Cano, said of her that she could hold her own in intelligence and charm with the noblest ladies of Spain.[76]

Though Francisco Pizarro, the conqueror of Peru, was in a position to take his pick of Inca princesses, there was nothing in his relationship with women to redeem his personal character from the infamy it deserved. His partner and rival, Diego de Almagro, at least had a fine half-breed son, who revered his father and died to avenge his execution by Pizarro. But it is probable that no woman or child ever loved the Marques Pizarro. Doña Inés, a sister of the Inca Atahualpa, was his mistress and bore him a daughter, who was named Francisca. The *coya* Azarpay, who was also sister—and wife—of Atahualpa and one of the greatest ladies of the kingdom, was garroted by Pizarro's orders after she was betrayed by the mistress of the conqueror. According to Pedro Pizarro, who was secretary to the Marqués, Pizarro had a wife of the rebel Manco Capac tied to a stake, beaten and shot to death with arrows because the Inca had sent Indians to abduct him and had stolen a horse and a Negro slave that belonged to him.[77] Of the other Pizarro brothers, Hernando married a *coya*, who shared his long semi-imprisonment in Spain and evidently managed to hold the affection and respect of her violent and imperious husband.

By reason of its results, the most important of the affairs between the Spanish conquerors and Indian women in Peru was the union of Garcilaso de la Vega with the *coya* Doña Isabel Chimpu Ocllo, a niece of Atahualpa.[78] He was one of the more respectable captains of the Conquest, scion of one of the most distinguished families of Spain, and one of the few gentlemen among the Spanish forces in Peru. Doña Isabel lived with him for many years in the fine house that still stands in Cuzco and was hostess in the home that was known for its hospitality. There she bore her Spanish lord the son who was to be famous as the Inca Garcilaso, and there the boy grew up with other sons of the conquerors, some mestizo like himself. He was to be the chronicler of his mother's people and historian of the deeds of his father's people in Peru—and in the southern part of the United States.[79] When his father married, it was into the Spanish aristocracy where his roots were so deep. The brilliant and sensitive son had a profound hurt in his soul that never healed, a split personality whose two sides he could not reconcile, and an inferiority complex that became the stigmata of the mixed peoples in the New World. Though he was honored in literary and scholarly circles in Spain and lived a life of solid respectability, he never quite arrived at the high goal that he set for himself.

Philip Ainsworth Means recounts a story which deserves repeating in his words as an illustration of the various possibilities and ramifications of these interracial affairs: "The Inca Sayri Tupac and his wife had but one child, the Princess Doña Beátriz Clara. After her father's death she, a great heiress with three estates on which were more than 16,000 tribute payers and 9,000 ordinary Indians, was placed with her mother in the house of a *vecino* (resident) of Cuzco named Arias Maldonado, so that the influence of his wife and daughters should hispanicize her thoroughly. Maldonado permitted his brother, Cristóbal, to rape the girl when she was less than ten in order that she might be forced to marry him. She did so, but the marriage was annulled later. When fifteen years old, the Princess chose as her husband her first cousin, Prince Felipe Quispi Titu—and for this match a papal dispensation had to be obtained. After the death of Prince Felipe, Princess Beátriz Clara married, in 1572, the captor of Inca Tupac Amaru I, Don García Onaz de Loyola, nephew of Saint Ignatius Loyola, founder of the Jesuits. Their daughter, Doña Lorenza Ana María de Loyola Coya, was taken to Spain by order of the king and there she married Don Juan Enríquez de Borja, son of Saint Francis of Borja, receiving, in 1616, the title of Marchioness of Oropesa. A son and a daughter of theirs married into the house of Idiáquez, Dukes of Granada, to which belonged Saint Francisco Javier. Thus did the blood of the Incas mingle with that of Saints. Let us hope that they are all cozy and happy in Heaven." [80]

Though thousands of mestizo children ran wild and loose in the new cities and towns of the Indies, with only such care and control as their too pliant mothers gave them, many of the Spaniards made provision for their casual offspring, sometimes in their own homes and with their legitimate children. A man who accepted the responsibility for the fruits of his dalliance was one Diego de Ocana. Among the several bequests and arrangements made in his will there appears this item: [81]

"I say that I once had relations with the said Antonica, who bore a child named Alosico. But she was ill-watched, for she also had relations with an Indian of my household. However, judging by the color of the child, everyone declares that he seems to be the son of a Christian. It seems so to me, for it may be that he is my son; and since in case of doubt it is better to acknowledge him than to ignore him, I command my sons to bring him up, have him indoctrinated, and do something good for him, for I believe that he is a son of mine, and not of an Indian."

Caught in a new shadow world between the two races, both of which spurned them, the more sensitive or aggressive of them were liable to become "juvenile delinquents." To give these foundling boys an anchor in society, the good Viceroy Mendoza established the orphanage-school of San Juan Letrán in Mexico City. In Paraguay, the half-breed sons of the conquerors, claimed or unclaimed by their fathers, were eventually to take over the colony as theirs and, fortunately for Spain, the king's.

The situation in Chile was probably fairly typical of that which prevailed generally in the Spanish colonies during the period of the Conquest. There was the same tendency to amative anarchy and genetic variety. The unsettled conditions of life in Chile were not yet conducive to the observances of rules and customs which regulated and stabilized the relations between men and women in Spain. Even the more staid and respectable matrons of early Chilean society seem occasionally to have indulged in love affairs "that resulted in the creation of much new and Christian lineage in the colony." [82] Meanwhile, the usual *rapprochements* had early been established between the conquerors and the Indian women roundabout. There was seldom any sentiment involved in these casual and ephemeral affairs on either side. However, they were frequently productive of hydrid children, and Spaniards often formed life-long attachments with mestizas, who with each generation became progressively lighter in complexion and, in general, more attractive.

The 150 founding fathers of Chile sired a total of 226 mestizo children, *whom they recognized*. [83] Fifty of these were claimed by the exuberant Francisco de Aguirre, as his own progeny which reduces considerably the per capita figure for his companions. According to Thayer Ojeda, it is more likely that each Spaniard was responsible for an average of one mestizo child a year. This rate would have yielded a grand total of 20,284 by 1565, by which time 1,532 Spaniards had settled in Chile. Cristóbal de

Molina wrote in that year that mestizos were very plentiful in Santiago and that there were from two to eight in each house in town.

Of the original 150, Rodrigo de Araya was married in Chile to Magdalena Fernández, a Spanish woman. He had a daughter by her and a mestizo son. Santiago de Azoca had five legitimate children and four mestizos. Pedro Bonal married Barbola Flores, one of the mestizo daughters of Blumenthal, the German. Pedro de Cisternas had ten legitimate children and only one mestizo. Alonso de Córdoba had two sons by his Spanish wife in addition to three children by Indian women and one mulatto child. Juan Dávalos Jufre married Catalina de Mello, a *mulata*, probably Portuguese, and had a quadroon daughter by her. Garcí Díaz de Castro, an Andalusian hidalgo, who had first come to Chile with Almagro, had married Barbola Díaz la Coya, an Inca "princess" in Peru, and had four sons "of noble blood." Juan Gallego de Rubias on his deathbed married an Indian woman in order to legitimize their son. Giraldo Gil, Andalusian tailor, married Juana de Lezcano, a freed Moorish slave, who had been branded in the face. They had two children and he had two more by Indian women. Garcí Hernández married a mestizo daughter of Diego García de Cáceres, one of his companions, who gave him ten children. Juan Jufre, one of the leaders in the colony, married Constanza de Meneses, daughter of Francisco de Aguirre, who came from Spain with her mother. Nine children resulted from the marriage. Jufre had two older children by Indian women. Pedro de León, one of the Andalusian brothers in Valdivia's force, had married María Muñoz in Spain and had two daughters by her. When in his dotage, he married an old Araucanian squaw, with painted face, later went crazy and lived to be over a hundred. Gabriel de Salazar had seven mestizo children. Diego Sánchez married Doña Inés de León y Carbajal and had six children in wedlock and three outside. Luís de Toledo, of Seville, married Isabel Mejía, mestiza, who made him a family of eighteen or twenty children. Francisco de Villagra, who was one of the early governors, had one son by his Spanish wife, Cándida de Montesa. He had three more by another Spanish woman and one by an Indian woman.

The Spanish Woman in the Colonial Period

During the colonial period, Latin American society took the form that it was to keep until well into the republican period. Then new influences were to modify its structure and standards, and to change some very deep-seated habits, wherever society lay open to the play of new and strange social forces. This was particularly true of the large port cities, like Buenos Aires, Havana, and Rio de Janeiro, where customs grew increasingly apart from the old way of life that still prevailed in the back country. Hence, the deep estrangement between metropolis and provinces, as in Argentina, and the widening "cultural lag" on which Sarmiento commented in his *Civilization and Barbarism.* Meanwhile, the old ways have survived much as they were in places that lie off the beaten track—like Mérida in Venezuela, Cuenca and Jaén in Ecuador, Moyobamba in Peru, Sucre in Bolivia, Pasto in Colombia, and Cuyabá in Brazil. By their very isolation these communities were immunized against the innovations that threatened the integrity of the old order.

By the middle of the sixteenth century, the great adventure of the Conquest was over. Except along the edges of the new frontiers, where the exposed nerve ends of war had not yet grown over with the flesh of peace, as in Arauco and the wild Carib and Chichimec lands; in the tumultuous mining camps like Potosí; or on the pirate-haunted coasts, there was an end to the excitement and violence. There was time now for settled living; for making love to a woman of one's choice, instead of grabbing any likely female who was handy and forgetting her as quickly; for raising a family that would carry on after a man was gone; for building a competence against the future; for just sitting and talking with friends and for enjoying the other quiet pleasures and satisfactions. Except for the Indians and Negroes who were all about and for the differences in the physical setting we might imagine we were in some Spanish town.

It was not an heroic age. But it was a good time for quieting overwrought nerves and for the prosaic job of building a new society. The routine of life was punctuated at regular intervals by family celebrations and the festivals of the Church, and daily by the dual rituals of the siesta, that further slowed down the tempo of living, and of the parade around the plaza at dusk. So it was in the average colonial city. In the great capitals, like Lima and Mexico City, there was much more variety and choice of activity. Sometimes there was boredom and restlessness in the vegetating towns. They led to feuds between families, to long-drawn-out lawsuits that helped to relieve the monotony of existence, to amorous intrigues and escapades that defied the tightening conventions of society. Those who felt too confined or had too strong an urge for the old times escaped to the frontier, beyond the reach of the bishop and the corregidor, and out where a man could still do as he wanted, if he was willing to pay the price; if they stayed at home, they might become *bravos* or town brawlers, and so be threats to law and order in a well-behaved community. Sometimes people with too much time on their hands and who saw too much of their neighbors were liable to take out their frustrations in envy and spite—those twin serpents in the garden of Spanish individualism.

In the quiet centuries that followed the noise and tumult of the Conquest, a new civilization was a-making. The ingredients that went into it were what the Spaniard and the Portuguese brought to it with them and what the Indian and the Negro added to it in their own ways. At times there seemed to be little conscious effort put into the process. The pot just simmered on the great stove. People appeared afraid to poke it or stir it too much and hoped that what came out of it would be good—and that the taste of the stew would be more Spanish than Indian.

The Conquest had been men's work, but when it was ended, they were tired from the effort, as Spain herself was. But it must have been hard for them to relax, and their minds were so full of memories that many of them doubtless used to pace about at night from sleeplessness, as old Bernal Díaz did in Guatemala. The new generations who came after them wanted only to keep what their grandfathers had won for them. There was glory enough in the family to last for a long time and there was enough land and what it yielded for everybody. So they slowed down and took it easy, and too many of them went into convents, when there was so much work that needed doing on the outside.

But the women were not tired, and the long apathy of their menfolk created a vacuum into which they moved unobstrusively and effectively with all their unspent resources of energy and devotion. This was their time, though they never told anyone so, their men least of all, and they made the most of it. The two great institutions of the new society—the family and the Church —were theirs. The one was in a very real sense of their making, and they nurtured it and managed it once it was formed. The other lived by their patronage and support. Outwardly passive and deferential from respect for the Spanish tradition of male supremacy, women remained the conservative and stabilizing force in colonial society. In the meantime, the men were free to wander in both a physical and a spiritual sense. While they strayed, the family—and their interests in it—were in safe and competent hands.

Social habits were crystallized during these centuries between the Conquest and the Independence. Sometimes the habits brought from Europe were preserved much as they were, if they served the purpose of the new societies. Climate changed some old habits and so did the isolation of communities, which often became ingrown. But the presence of Indians and Negro slaves and the whole business of race probably did more than anything else to alter the patterns of living imported from the Peninsula. In Spain there had been class lines, but all, *arriero* and *grandee,* were Spaniards and respected one another as men. In the New World, it was very different. There were slaves of another race and color to serve one. And there was a host of mixed breeds of various shades and degrees of hybridization who were lower in the social and economic scale. The borders between the various racial categories were liable to be tighter drawn than the class lines in Spain, for they were marked by physical differences. So those who were white were set apart and above those who were colored. But those who were born in Spain were of a higher caste than their children who were born in the New World. Only they were eligible to high office in the imperial service, and other privileges were reserved for them.

So the creoles became a frustrated lot. Their grandfathers had been mighty men in the land and by their enterprise had given these kingdoms to Spain. Now they were political eunuchs and could never expect to be a corregidor or a judge, or a governor or a viceroy. There was no proper outlet for their ambitions for eminence or power, no congenial field for the full exercise of their Spanish individualism. So they often turned their energies into channels that were unworthy of them, or they became sluggards and triflers. In either event, the women suffered because of their men's frustrations and because too often life in the colonies did not bring out the best in them. So their own tasks of holding the family and the home together were made harder. For sometimes the men went afield on ventures to rebuild their sagging egos and shirked the domestic responsibilities they had shared in creating.

People had more of the material things than they had in Spain. It was a frontier world, where there was much to be had for the taking and others to do any hard work that had to be done. There was more to eat and more land to own and more of nearly everything else but political freedom and privilege. Out of their new bounty, men became more liberal and open-handed, because they could afford to be more indifferent to money where there was so much natural plenty.

In these years the simple routines of daily living took shape. For example, the habit of sleeping in a hammock in the hot lands. The word itself was Arawak and the Spaniards readily adopted the woven bed, because on warm nights the air circulated all around them. Sometimes the combination of tropics, hammocks, and servants made the creole women lazy, and with their Arabic addiction to sweets they tended to overweight. Juan and Ulloa wrote of the women of Cartagena that "in the house their whole exercises consists in sitting in their hammocks, and swinging themselves for air; in these they pass the greater part of the day." In one house at Guayaquil, another hot city, Captain Hall found three generations of women in hammocks that were suspended from the ceiling twenty feet above.[84] "The whole party," he said, "was swinging away at such a furious rate, that at first we were confounded and made giddy by the variety of motions in different directions."

Similarly, the habit of the siesta after the midday meal, a beneficent custom which has spread beyond the bounds of the more torrid regions. The siesta is a concession to climate, which, by breaking up the day into four parts instead of two, spreads the tensions and fatigues of the working hours over a longer period and so eases their burden. M. Depons, who was in Vene-zuela in the first years of the last century, wrote: "No custom seems to have taken a deeper root in the Spanish manners than that of the nap, which they take after dinner. There is not a single individual in the Spanish settlements who is not in the habit of appropriating two, three, or sometimes four hours of his time every day to sleep, be his repast heavy or light." He remarked that foreigners generally give up their efforts to stay awake while the rest of the population is asleep, and end by adopting the cus-tom with enthusiasm, as Captain Hall did on the road between San Blas and Tepic.[85]

Among the indulgences, smoking was much more common with women in colonial times than it is today.[86] They smoked small cigars, a habit which they acquired from their Negro house servants. The gradual trend to a greater refinement of manners and foreigners' disapproval of the habit led to a general abandon-ment of cigar smoking, except in Paraguay, where it is still widely practiced by the women. Peruvian women of all classes were accustomed to carry with them a small roll of pressed tobacco, which they rolled against their teeth to clean them! Women of the lower class, who, according to Juan and Ulloa, "generally pervert the best things" kept a wad of tobacco in their mouth, "affecting to distinguish themselves by its largeness." [87] In the colonial period, ladies of quality were much given to gambling in their houses, particularly in New Spain. At one time the vice reached such proportions in Mexico City that the king ordered the viceregal authorities to use rigorous measures to stop the habit. Thomas Gage, the English friar, said: "Gaming is so com-mon to them that they invite gentlemen to their houses for no other end." [88] In fact, a lady "of great birth" hailed Gage and another friar from her window and bid them inside for a game.

The Limeña

As time went on, diversification developed in the pattern of woman's life and place in society. Perhaps the most distinctive of the local types to be evolved was the woman of Lima. Since the Limeña exacted the admiration and interest of foreign ob-servers who visited Peru in the eighteenth century and the early part of the last, there is a considerable literature about her.[89] Unfortunately, changing fashions and the pressures of uniformity were responsible for the passing of this unique and intriguing figure, who eventually went the way of the Incas, and the Argentine gaucho. While she had her fling, she gave a special and quite Andalusian flavor to the viceregal capital, and Lima was the drabber for her eventual going.

The secret of her attraction and her power was her peculiar costume, within which she lived as behind a mask. In some of its features it was obviously derived from the Moors, whose women it was designed to protect from masculine eyes; with the Limeña it served an entirely opposite purpose as a cover for coquetry and an impenetrable disguise for impishness. The language of women's dress is a foreign tongue to men, but of those who tried to describe the alluring masquerade of the *tapada* or "veiled one," probably the most articulate was Captain Basil Hall, of the Royal Navy, who spent several years on the west coast at the end of the colonial era. "In the cool part of the day," he wrote, "for about an hour and a half before sunset, the ladies walk abroad, dressed as far as I know unique, and certainly highly characteristic of the spot. This dress consists of two parts, one called the Saya, the other the Manto. The first is a petticoat, made to fit so tightly that being at the same time quite elastic, the form of the limbs is rendered distinctly visible. The Manto, or cloak, is also a petticoat, but, instead of hanging about the heels, as all honest petticoats ought to do, it is drawn over the head, breast, and face, and is kept so close by the hands, which it also conceals, that no part of the body, except one eye, and sometimes only a small portion of one eye, is visible. A silk colored handkerchief, or a silk band and tassel, are frequently tied round the waist and hang nearly to the ground in front. A rosary, also, made of beads of ebony, with a small gold cross, is often fastened to the girdle, a little on one side, though in general it is suspended from the neck."

Max Radiguet, the Frenchman, made no effort to analyze the construction of the *saya*-and-*manto*, but went off into raptures about its revelations.[90] Some foreigners were concerned about the propriety of the Limeña's ensemble which, according to W. B. Stevenson, "sits close to the body, and shews its shape to the utmost possible advantage." [91] Jorge Juan and Antonio de

Ulloa, the Spanish naval officers, said: "Their dress is very different from the European, which the custom of the country alone can render excusable; indeed, to Spaniards at their first coming over, it appears extremely indecent." [92] After commenting on "its indelicacy to an European eye," Captain Hall criticized travelers who judge foreign customs by their home standards, and added: "To us, who took all things as we found them, the Saya and Manto afforded much amusement; and, sometimes, not a little vexation." For the *tapadas* had the embarrassing habit of accosting foreigners who had been in Lima for some time and reminding them of things they might have preferred to forget. So they delighted, too, in embarrassing husbands, lovers, rivals, the people of pomp and power—and pretense—all who were vulnerable to their barbs and pleasantries. Anonymous and mysterious, they kept Lima in a *carnavalesque* ferment with their frolicsome sallies. One of them would lure her husband into a flirtation and when he had committed himself to a rendezvous, she would pull the *manto* from her face as the ultimate rebuke to his indiscretion. Sometimes they broke uninvited into exclusive parties and probably enlivened the affair with their gay and irreverant presence, or they looked through the windows and commented on the guests and their frills and foibles. There was no defense against their impertinences and intrusions, and, anyway, there might be some great lady behind the disguise. But since women of all classes indulged in the custom, it was probably the most democratic institution in the proud city. And from among the *tapadas,* of his time, the Viceroy Amat took as his mistress Micaela Villegas, better known as La Perricholi, a popular actress of the Lima stage, and made her the most famous woman of eighteenth-century Peru.[93] But not all men could be viceroys, and it was the men of Lima who were the principal butt of their women's escapades. So there was a saying that Lima was a paradise for women, a purgatory for men, and a hell for burros. Juan and Ulloa said that the Limeñas were so vain and haughty that they "will scarce stoop to the will of their husbands. Yet by their address and insinuating compliance, they so far gain the ascendancy over them as to be left to their own discretion. . . . And with regard to the independence they affect, it is no more than a custom long established in the country." [94]

In spite of the liberties which the Limeñas took to themselves in public, there was probably little more license in Lima than in any other colonial metropolis, though the sexual atmosphere must have been more highly charged than in such sedate places as Córdoba and the cities of the Andes. Contemporary observers were inclined to criticize the Limeñas for their prodigality rather than for any libertinism. For those who could—and some who could not—were inclined to spend vast sums on clothing and jewels and exotic perfumes that would further embellish their already beautiful persons. For example, Captain Frézier, the French engineer, who was on the west coast of South America between 1712 and 1714, made some caustic comments on the extravagance of the Limeñas. In addition to their outlay for "the richest Silks" and "a prodigious quantity of Lace," they were "insatiable as to Pearls and Jewels for Bracelets, Pendants, and other Ornaments," all to the ruination of "the Husbands and the Galants." "We saw Ladies," he said, "who had about them above the value of 60,000 Pieces of Eight in Jewels"; [95] and added that "they are generally beautiful enough, of a Sprightly Mien, and more engaging than in other Places." He considered the Limeñas as graceful of carriage, with sparkling eyes, and of "pleasant Discourse." They approved of a "free Gallantry" on the part of the men, to whom they made witty and sometimes off-color replies. When the men made "scandalous proposals" to them in public, the women only thanked them for the compliment to their attractions, and then went about their errands. Captain Frézier remarked that at social functions the women of Lima often displayed their breasts, "which Spaniards look on with indifference," but are in love with little feet. The Limeña, too, was very proud of her tiny feet and sometimes spent a small fortune between the shoemaker and the jeweler for their adornment.[96] The Frenchman also reported the existence in Lima of a refuge for divorced women, which had been established by a former bishop. He said that the occupants had been divorced for "Complaints of Misunderstanding, or Want of Health or Satisfaction; and, it is still more amazing, they afterwards marry others."

Though the city of Guayaquil is one of the least attractive of South America, it has long been noted for the beauty and charm of its women. Two seagoing Englishmen have paid tribute to the Guayaquileñas. One of them, Captain Basil Hall, said of them: "They were by far the merriest and lightest-hearted people, besides being the fairest and handsomest, we had met with in South America." Captain Woodes Rogers, who went a-privateering in the Pacific a century earlier, wrote of his sailors' goings-on at Guayaquil. "The Houses up the River were full of Women," he wrote, "and particularly at one place there were above a Dozen handsome genteel young Women well dress'd, where our Men got several Gold Chains and Ear-rings, but were otherwise so civil to them, that the Ladies offer'd to dress 'em Victuals, and bought 'em a Cask of good Liquor. Some of their largest Gold Chains were conceal'd, and wound about their Middles, Legs, and Thighs, etc. but the Gentlewomen in these hot Countries being very thin clad with Silk and fine Linnen, and their Hair dress'd with Ribbons very neatly, our Men by pressing felt the Chains, etc. With their Hands on the Out-side of the Lady's Apparel, and by their Linguist (interpreter) modestly desired the Gentlewomen to take 'em off and surrender 'em. This I mention as a Proof of our Sailors Modesty and in respect to Mr. *Connely* and Mr. *Selkirk* the late Governor of *Juan* Fernandoes who commanded this Party.[97] For being young Men, I was willing to do 'em this Justice, hoping the Fair Sex will make 'em a grateful Return, when we arrive in Great Britain, on account of their Civil Behaviour to these charming Prisoners, they call'd at this House for Provisions as they return'd down the River, and being so civil at first, they gave their fair Landladies no Uneasiness nor Surprize at a 2nd Visit." Captain Rogers very self-righteously contrasted the restraint of his blushing boatmen with the conduct of "the French Buccaneers, alias Pirates."

Though Mexico City never developed a distinctive type of woman, as did Lima, social life in the capital of the northern viceroyalty never lacked for unusual women. For example, there was old Doña María de Mendoza, mother-in-law of the Viceroy Luís de Velasco, who tried to run the viceregal household and the government of Mexico, and who was never silenced until one day the long-suffering viceroy knocked her out with a silver candlestick.[98] Many of the *virreinas*, too, were interesting women in their own right, as was the gay Doña Blanca de Velasco, Marquesa de Villamanrique.[99] Once the abbot of a convent at

Xochimilco, Fray Pedro de San Sebastián, gave a Boccaccian
fiesta that lasted over two week ends. There was much drinking
and feasting, and hilarity and other carryings-on. The virreina
and one of the friars threw oranges at one another from boats
on the canal, and then everybody bombarded everybody else with
ears of corn, until one caballero was hit on the nose and others
began to topple into the water. Two centuries later, the reigning
beauty of Mexico City was "La Güera" (Rodríguez), a member
of old and distinguished families in the capital.[100] After flirta-
tions with some young officers of the Grenadiers' Regiment,
"La Güera" and her sister were ordered to be married by the
scandalized viceroy, the great Revillagigedo. That was in 1794.
"La Güera" married José Jerónimo López de Peralta de Villar
Villamil and outlived two more husbands to die in 1851. She had
three beautiful daughters, all of whom made good marriages.
She is believed to have been the only woman for whom the
famous Alexander von Humboldt ever forsook his scientific pur-
suits. When Madame Calderón de la Barca, the American wife of
the first Spanish Minister to the Mexican Republic, received a
call from "La Güera" in 1840, she found her still beautiful and
attractive.[101]

Five Women of the Colonies

The Spanish woman of the colonial period who deviated farthest
from the national ideal of her sex was, of all things, a man-at-
arms, named Catalina de Erauso, but better known to history
and legend as "the Nun-Ensign." [102] She was born in San Sebastián, in the Basque country, in 1585. When she was only four
years old, her parents put her in a Dominican convent, from
which she escaped eleven years later, to take the disguise that
became the mark of her fame. When she was eighteen, she took
ship at Seville for the Spanish Main, where she began a career
of adventure that lasted for twenty-one years. During much of
this time, she served as an ensign or standard-bearer in the royal
forces, and for a while she did duty under her brother's command
on the Araucanian frontier in Chile. Flat-chested, hipless, and
muscular, she was able to preserve her pretense until she voluntarily renounced her masculine disguise, only to resume it for the
rest of her unwomanly life. A brawler by disposition and deft

with either sword or dagger, she swaggered and swashbuckled her way through the cities of the Andes. Finally, after a particularly noisome scrape in Guamanga or Ayacucho, where she fell afoul of the corregidor's guard, she realized that the game was up and unburdened herself to the local bishop. Ill at ease, in the unbecoming garb of a nun, she was harbored in the local convent of Santa Clara until arrangements could be made for her transportation to Spain. She later visited Italy where she was received by the pope and became the sensation of Southern Europe. After the novelty of being on her good behavior had worn off and she had written her autobiography, she became restless and eventually returned to the New World. She ended her days in the northern viceroyalty, where she owned and operated a train of pack mules on the *camino real* between Veracruz and Mexico City. The years did not tame the belligerent spirit of the famous muleteer, and her quick temper became as familiar a hazard in the roadside inns of Mexico as it had been in her more nimble days in Peru.[103]

At the end of the colonial regime, Stevenson encountered an interesting woman in the valley of Chancay, in Peru.[104] She was known locally as *La Niña de la Huaca* and was respected and feared by everyone in the neighborhood. "She stood six feet high," he said, and she was "extremely fond of masculine exercises. Nothing was more agreeable to her than to assist in apprehending runaway slaves, or in taking the robbers who sometimes haunt the road between this place and Lima. She would mount a spirited horse—astride—arm herself with a brace of pistols and a lance, and with three or four men she would scour the environs of the valley and the road to Lima, where she became more dreaded than a company of *encapados,* or mounted police officers. I visited her at her residence, and found her better instructed in literature than the generality of the native females; she was frank, obliging, and courteous, managing her own estate, a sugar plantation, to the best advantage superintending the whole of the business herself."

Doña Catalina de los Rios de Lisperguer, better known in the chronicles of infamy as "La Quintrala," lived in Chile in the sixteen hundreds.[105] She was an encomendera in the rich lands of the Central Valley, and a woman of importance in the rural society of what is now the province of Aconcagua. She was a mixture of three peoples—Indian, Spanish, and German—and the strains seemed to run at cross purposes in her nature. She was a descendant of Bartholomeus Blumenthal, one of those stray Germans who occasionally turned up in the Conquest. In order to identify himself more closely with his Spanish colleagues the Nuremberger changed his name to Flores. He had three mestizo children by Elvira de Talagante, who was the daughter of a Mapocho chief in the neighborhood. Somewhere in the interval between Blumenthal and Doña Catalina, a Spanish branch was grafted onto the family tree, and what the hybrid tree finally bore was poison fruit.

A sadistic killer, "La Quintrala" murdered her father, a priest who was her lover, and a number of other citizens who had the habit of not leaving her house alive. In a community that still took death quite casually, the lethal consequences of her displeasure eventually became a public scandal and led to her trial before the supreme court of the *Audiencia*. But the judges were very lenient with the murderess, who had influence in high places, and only sentenced her to stay home for a while. There she fell into her old ways again, but henceforth her victims were the lowly dependents of the encomienda, who had no friends in high places. When she died, her evil hands were folded across her bosom and she was laid away in the Augustinian church in Santiago. But for a time, life was safer in Chile.

Juana de Asbaje y Ramírez de Santillana was born in 1651 in a Mexican farmhouse near the village of San Miguel Nepantla. Today, on the highway that goes from the capital around behind the volcanoes and down to Cuautla in "the hot country" there is a sign by the roadside that reads "Nepantla de Sor Inés." For to God, to whom she dedicated the prime of her brief life, and to the learned and worldly circles, to whom she consecrated the fruits of her poetic genius, she is Sor Juana Inés de la Cruz, nun, and "the most important literary figure of colonial Hispanic America." [106] She was a precocious child, with an insatiable curiosity in every field of knowledge. As she grew to womanhood in the city, it was only the vitality of her mind and the freshness of her imagination that saved her from becoming a bluestocking in an environment that was already pedantic enough. In spite of her contemporary fame, there are large gaps in the story of her life, so that she has been the subject of much speculation and controversy. In 1665, when she was only fourteen, she became a favorite lady-in-waiting to the Virreina, Doña Leonor Carreto, Marquesa de Mancera, and years afterwards, when she was a nun, she was to be friend and confidante of another vice-queen, the Condesa de Paredes.[107] In 1667, she first entered a convent and two years later she took the veil in the Hieronymite order. She was still only eighteen, and spent the remaining twenty-six years of her life in the convent. She brought in with her as much of the world she had already graced and charmed as the prioress and the bishop and her confessor would permit. In her cell, she composed a large quantity of poems—lyrics that were long and religious in their inspiration, short playlets for special command occasions, and *villancicos* or Christmas carols to be sung in the Cathedral. She also served as bookkeeper and archivist for the convent, and did her share of the charitable work that fell to the sisterhood.

Her life never seemed to be of a piece or to be her own for long. Too many conflicting influences impinged on her personality —the Church, the viceregal court, the deep-seated prejudices and traditions of Spanish society. Intellectually she was superior to the society in which she moved, whether inside or outside the convent.[108] She had a congenial mind only in Carlos de Sigüenza y Góngora, first scholar of the viceroyalty. "Study is dangerous to a dullard," she once wrote, "for it merely places a sword in the hands of a brute; thus education, that noble instrument of defense, becomes in his hands his own nemesis; and that of many others." She was a feminist before her time, in a man's tight world, and bitterly resented her helplessness to change things for women, "those poor souls who are generally considered so inept." Perhaps, in the few years before she became a nun, she never met a man for whom she would be willing to sacrifice some of the independence she managed to preserve from the manifold compulsions that pressed in on her proud spirit. Like Santa Teresa de Avila, her emotional life must finally have found its home in her religious devotion. The fervent love poems which she wrote may have been addressed to some dream lover she never met.

Manuela Saenz was most famous of the hetaerae.[109] Mistress of Simón Bolívar, the Liberator, though by no means the only lover of that great philogynist, she was certainly the most enduring. She was born of "good family" in the city of Quito in 1797. When she was twenty she was married to James Thorne, an English merchant and ship operator, who lived in Lima. In those years of Spain's fading power in Peru she learned much of men and women, a knowledge which she was later to place at the disposal of her illustrious paramour. Meanwhile, instinctively a rebel, she plotted with the patriot underground in Lima, much to the displeasure of her husband.

She first met Bolívar in her native Quito at a ball which celebrated the victory of Pichincha over the royalists. That was in 1822. For the eight years of glory—and ultimate grief—that remained to him, Manuela, his "lovable fool," was the one indispensable woman for him, whatever his more ephemeral philanderings.[110] Bold and resolute herself, with no thought for her own comfort or convenience, she was the ideal companion for a restless and high-strung warrior like Bolívar. Uncommonly intuitive, in turn self-effacing or assertive as the occasion demanded, she protected his interests and his life against his many enemies open and concealed. The last twenty-one years of her life, she kept a tobacco shop in the dreary port town of Paita in Northern Peru. Among those who visited her there were Simón Rodríguez, the eccentric tutor of her famous lover; Alexander Ruden, of Cincinnati, the local American Consul; Giuseppe Garibaldi; and Herman Melville.

When she finally broke with her English husband in 1825, the year after Ayacucho, she wrote this letter to him: [111] "Sir, you are excellent, you are inimitable. But, my friend, it is no small matter that I leave you for General Bolívar; to leave a husband without your qualities would be nothing. Do you think for a moment that, after being beloved of this General for years, and with the security that I possessed his heart, I would choose to be the wife even of the Father, Son, or the Holy Ghost, or of all three? I know very well that I cannot be united with him under the laws of honor, as you call them, but do you believe that I feel less or more honored because he is my lover and not my husband? I do not live for the prejudices of society, which were invented only that we might torture each other.

"Let me be, my dear Englishman, let me be. Let us instead do something else. We should marry when we get to heaven; but on this earth—No!—In our heavenly home we shall lead entirely spiritual lives. There everything will be quite British, for monotony is reserved for your nation in love, that is, for they are much more avid in business. You love without pleasure. You converse without grace, you walk unhurried, you sit down with caution, you do not laugh even at your own jokes. These are divine attributes, but I, miserable mortal who can laugh at myself, laugh at you too, with all this English seriousness. . . ."

WOMAN AND THE FAMILY IN THE REPUBLICS

With independence and the republics there began a new era in Latin American society. The changes came slowly, but they came earlier along the coasts, where foreign influences had freer play. They reached Buenos Aires long before they reached Córdoba and Salta, and Guayaquil before they reached Quito or Cuenca. In spite of the shock of the *Independencia*, some of the colonial ways and patterns that were identified with Spain were too deep-seated to change suddenly. Many of them served their purpose too well to be discarded just because they were reminders of Spanish domination. Also, there were conservative elements in the new societies that were bent on keeping as much of the old regime as possible. So the lag in change was due to satisfaction with the old customs, to the traditional conservatism of the Church, and to the passive force of inertia and isolation. But the important thing was that the restraints and repressions imposed by Spanish law and authority were gone now, and that the gap which they left could be filled by something of the people's own choice and making.

The principal difference was in the new spirit that came over the liberated peoples. Often, like the unaccustomed thing that it was, it was not clearly felt for a time. Then it gradually dawned on them that they were free to remake their world if they wished. At last the creoles had come into their own. Men had a new sense of importance. They were no longer subjects and second-class Spaniards, but now they were citizens and of a country that was theirs and not the king of Spain's.[112] New fields opened up to their ambitions, and life itself took on greater meaning to them.

It had become more than a pattern of pleasure and pain woven into the fabric of time—something more than just a way of spending the interval between birth and death. There was also a new tolerance of the mixed peoples, the realization of a sense of brotherhood that was actually Christian and Spanish, but which had been thwarted before by political considerations. Now the mestizos and other hybrids began to find the place in society and the state that their services and their talents merited. Women, too, profited from the new sense of importance and the new interests of their menfolk, as well as from the general vitalizing of society which eventually followed the Independencia.

During the present century, there have been increasingly strong pressures on the customary pattern of relationships between men and women, and on the traditional family system in general. Some of these represent the accumulated force of trends which had long been developing under the republics; others are relatively new and more revolutionary in character. The status of women within the family and in relation to the larger community is being subjected to a number of influences, both foreign and domestic in their origin.

The growing number of American or western European women who reside in the Latin American countries or travel in them inevitably affect by example the attitudes and habits of local women who observe them or meet them in a social way. This influence extends not only to externals like dress and fashions in "beauty treatments," but to such activities as drinking and cigarette smoking, driving cars, indulgence in sports, the protocol of mixed dancing, and generally to a more open disregard of old taboos. The cosmopolitan atmosphere of the local diplomatic colony and of the country club serves as a potential catalyzer of social customs and leveler of prejudices.

Similarly, foreign influences came in through the medium of Latin American women who lived or traveled abroad. Many who were educated in convent schools or lay colleges in Europe or the United States, have brought with them a store of extracurricular ideas for experimental purposes. The wives and daughters of diplomats and of business and professional men are accustomed to go far from home on shopping forays, and on prolonged vacations in lands of unconventional ways. As they tend increasingly to travel untended by their menfolk, they are liable to learn much of direct interest and applicability to their own living problems. Though in a more dramatic form and artificial setting, much the same impressions may be acquired from foreign movies while remaining at home. Though the full extent of its influence on custom is debatable, there can be little doubt that the impact of Hollywood on the man-woman relationship in Latin America is considerable. The wide circulation of American magazines, particularly of the Spanish and Portuguese editions of *Readers Digest* is also a factor in inducing social changes.

Large cities are the natural enemy of the traditional Latin American family. The growth of such metropolitan monsters as Mexico City and São Paulo bodes no good for the old-fashioned patriarchal home.[113] Its natural setting, where it flourished best, was in a sleepy colonial town like Arequipa or Bahia. In the big impersonal city, the institution lost much of its power over its members. It had to compete with the appeal of extraneous loyalties and attractions, such as commercialized pleasures, and it was particularly exposed to the disintegrating effects of foreign influences. Though it survived in much of its original strength in the quieter eddies of population, it felt outdated in the new cities, especially where the younger generations were concerned.

The new mechanics of living were not compatible with the old ways. The tempo of life had been easygoing and unhurried and spacious; it has become more complex and cramped and urgent. In the "big houses" of the old regime there was time for everything and room for everybody—the immediate family, grandparents, occasional stray relatives, and servants. There were often quarters for married sons, where they could live with their brides until they were able to establish a home of their own. In addition to their primary purpose, they fulfilled the functions of an hotel, a court of domestic relations, and a social security system. The overcrowding of cities has forced people into small apartments and uncomfortable houses called *villas*. The patio and everything it represented is disappearing and instead there are front yards as in American towns, in which nobody relaxes or plays, as they once did in the patio that was like an all-embracing womb and refuge deep within the protective body of the house. So, because of a revolution in housing, fewer people live under the same roof, and families that once lived together as a self-sufficient clan now tend to be scattered about the city and the country. In Rio de Janeiro, one may observe the transformation in the contrast between Laranjeiras and Copacabana, and, in Mexico City, in that between Coyoacán and the Lomas de Chapultepec.

In Latin America, as in other parts of the world, the repercussions of economics have also affected the status of woman and the family. The new industries have offered many jobs to women. Many of these factory workers come from villages in the provinces and would otherwise enter the ranks of house servants in the cities. Whatever their source, their employment in industry tends to create a shortage of household help and to raise the wages of servants. Of the professions, women first went into teaching in large numbers, and the expansion of public school education has opened many opportunities to them. Nursing did not attract them until much later, but thousands are now engaged in hospital and public health nursing. Women office workers are everywhere an accepted commonplace in business and government, and saleswomen are increasingly the rule in retail stores.

The "career woman," as she exists in the United States—the woman, single or married, who for one reason or another (economics, boredom, ambition, the spirit of 1776, or indifference to men) goes her own way in business or the professions—has appeared in Latin America. However, the atmosphere is not yet propitious to her full flowering, and she is still uncommon enough to be a subject of comment among her more conventional sisters.

There are communities where women, usually of the lower classes, are the mainstay of the local economy or of an important segment of it. Sometimes the women are only transferring to a new and more advanced order the division of labor which had been customary among the Indians. Sometimes the decimation of the male population by war or migration had left the responsibility of community survival to the women. This happened in Paraguay after the war against the Triple Alliance of Brazil, Argentina, and Uruguay. The same circumstances probably help to account for the superiority of the Tehuana women of southern Mexico.[114] In fact, it would be difficult to imagine Mexico without the steadying and stabilizing influence of its women on men by nature so capricious and violent.[115] In the capital of Bolivia, too, the upper level of *cholas* or mestizo women are much superior to the men of the same class. As in Paraguay, the operation of a large variety of small business in La Paz is virtually monopolized by these sturdy and self-reliant females in lacquered derby hats and high-buttoned shoes.[116] In the Tupiza region of Bolivia, the strong-minded women generally boss the men and run the business of the locality. Sometimes, the domestic informality of the male population has placed the burden of holding the family—and the local community—together squarely on the dependable shoulders of the womenfolk.

An omnivorous state has intruded into the province of the family, that inner sanctum of Spanish life and proverbial refuge of Spaniards from the raids of the world on the human soul. It professes its purpose to be a benign one—the sponsorship and protection of this basic institution of Spanish society, and of its ancillary paraphernalia, such as marriage and the education of children. However, as in Communist countries, the logical end of this trend under the new and more possessive dictatorships would certainly be the deliberate weakening of the family as a rival for the loyalty of the individual citizen.

The most recent crop of national constitutions shows much concern for the salvation of the family. "Matrimony, the family, and maternity are under the protection of the State" reads the basic law of Bolivia.[117] The constitutions of Cuba and Peru, and the Central American republics, express the same idea in much the same terms. El Salvador promises the enactment of "laws and provisions" for the "moral, physical, economic, intellectual, and social improvement" of the family and for the "promotion of matrimony." Several countries announce themselves as the friends of matrimony and facilitate the legal transformation of concubinage into common-law marriage. While the Brazilian constitution declares that marriage is indissoluble, the Cuban Constitution makes provision for divorce. "Marriage," it says, "may be dissolved by agreement of the husband and wife, or on the petition of either of the two." Though several countries recognize the juridical equality of the sexes, the Cubans are particularly emphatic in the matter. According to the Cuban document, "the married woman enjoys the full advantages of equal civil capacity, with no necessity for marital permission or authorization in order to manage property, freely to engage in trade, to enter industry or a profession, to practice an art, to hold office, and to dispose of the product of her work." On the other hand, the Nicaraguans hedge on the problem of equal rights and after proclaiming the principle of equality, they add the waiver "except in regard to women on account of the differences inherent in their nature or where the good of the family is concerned." According to the Paraguayan constitution, "The civil rights of women shall be regulated by law, taking heed of the unity of the family, the equality of woman and man, and the diversity of their respective functions in society."

Several of the republics show much interest in the economic security of the family, and take steps to secure the family patrimony against attachment or alienation. In probably no other part of the world is so much solicitude displayed by the State for protecting the integrity of the homestead. This is reflected in tax schedules and revenue laws that are liable to be highly favorable to the home owner, and which in actual operation virtually ensure residential property against seizure for nonpayment of taxes. A common phase of this jurisprudence is represented in a clause of the Paraguayan constitution which declares that "Every Paraguayan home should be located on a piece of owned land." The fierceness with which Latin Americans guard the precincts of the family against all the intrusions of government and public is well expressed in the words of the Brazilian constitution: "The home is the inviolable asylum of the individual."

Many of the constitutions express the deep concern for the welfare of children that is so strong a sentiment among Latin Americans. The constitutions of Cuba, Panama, and Uruguay are particularly explicit in this regard. Says the Cuban constitution: "Parents are obliged to support, tend, educate, and instruct their children, and the latter to respect and assist their parents." Thus, the obligation within the family is reciprocal. The Cuban law goes on to declare that "Children and youth are protected from exploitation and from moral and material neglect." The language of the Panamanian constitution is quite similar to that of the Cuban. According to the Uruguayan constitution, "The care and education of children until they reach their full physical, intellectual, and social capacity, is the duty and right of parents. . . . The law shall provide the necessary measures for the protection of infants

and children against parents or guardians who neglect them physically, intellectually, or morally, as well as against their exploitation and abuse."

Many of the republics prescribe equality of treatment for
legitimate and illegitimate children. Since the rate of illegitimate
children is very high in most Latin American countries,[118] a provision of this kind has far-reaching social consequences. The
words of the Bolivian constitution, "the law does not recognize
inequality among children," are typical of the general tenor of
the constitutions. The constitution of Panama specifies that "Parents have the same duties toward children born outside of wedlock as towards those born in it." In cases of intestate succession,
all children share equally in Panama. In Ecuador, an illegitimate
child must receive at least one-half the portion of a legitimate
child. There is everywhere a humane tendency to do away with
all discrimination against "natural" children, which may go to
the length of removing from their birth records any imputation
of illegitimacy that might later be a handicap to their advancement.

As reflected in the new constitutions, there is a general trend
toward granting the vote to women. The female suffrage movement is not sponsored or promoted by any militant group of
women, for they do not exist in Latin America, but it has the
backing of liberal elements in whatever political parties there
may be. The Inter-American Commission of Women provides a
continental rostrum for agitation by a few leading and lonely
feminists, but it has probably had very little to do with the advances which Latin American women have made in the political,
legal, and social fields. As a rule, women are not yet "politically
conscious," and where they do avail themselves of the privilege
of voting, the net result is liable to be only to double the customary confusions of politics. However, the suffrage has given women
an instrument with which they can exert pressure on national
legislators to enact much-needed welfare legislation. On several
occasions they have not hesitated to browbeat and intimidate
reluctant lawmakers by threatening to unseat them at the next
elections. Of all the republics, women have made most of their
political opportunities in Chile, where they not only vote in con-

siderable numbers, but many of them hold public office, even attaining seats in the national congress.

The electoral provisions of nine republics expressly provide for universal suffrage, without distinction as to sex. Whereas any Guatemalan male, eighteen years old, has the vote, a woman must be able to read and write before she is admitted to the polls. In neighboring Honduras, the suffrage is limited to men. Peruvian women may vote only in municipal elections. Although the Mexican constitution of 1917 clearly included women as voting citizens, the Congress thereafter took a grudging stand on the implementation of the constitutional provision and the necessary enabling legislation was only voted in 1953.

Though threatened by new forces that are afoot, the pattern of the Latin American family has changed remarkably little in the essentials. It still has a strength and solidarity seldom found among old American stock in this country. It is ruled by an accepted and well-balanced set of responsibilities and authorities, except among the lower classes, in whose domestic arrangements there is likely to be considerable latitude for individual caprices and idiosyncrasies. At this level of society there is little respect for tradition, and there generally exists a free and easy pragmatic attitude toward social conventions and rules of conduct. In fact, the formality of marriage is commonly dispensed with and there is no double standard as among their social "betters."

Marriage serves its proper purpose much better than in the United States. It is not entered into lightly or frivolously, or very romantically, but circumspectly and seriously and with much hope of deep and life-long satisfactions. It is much more than the door to a honeymoon. In spite of the efforts of the State to break the Church's monopoly of the wedding ceremony, even to offering bargain rates in competition, the average woman believes that she is not really married unless with the full ritual of the sacrament and with the blessing of the priest. The persistence of this conviction probably does much to account for the durability of marriage and the willingness to make the most of its possibilities.[119]

The Latin American woman is better educated and better informed with each year. She moves about more on her own, and the old taboos do not bind as tightly as they once did. She keeps busy with children and the management of her home, perhaps includ-

ing the direction of some of the world's most exasperating servants. If she participates in more outside activities than formerly,
it is not out of boredom or restlessness. She has no need to fill
emotional gaps in her life with the nirvana of alcohol, the endear-
ment of dogs, or the mock battlefield of the card table. Her life
has many rewards, and it is doubtful if she has an urge to rebel
against anything in particular. Foreign women who sometimes
would like to make her unhappy with her lot are likely to find
her quite unco-operative.[120] In a world in ferment, it is encourag-
ing to find so large a segment of humanity which does not aspire
to carry banners or march in protest. She avoids masculine roles
and manners—and she knows more about her husband's business
and interests than the average American wife knows about what
goes on inside her husband's head or in his office. In this respect,
it is significant that on his death she frequently takes over the
management of his business as the "Widow of Fulano de Tal."

A man is still a very important object in Latin America. He
has not yet been swallowed up by large corporations or the other
organizations that devour men's souls for breakfast. Government
is trying subtly to enslave him with offers of a "better life" or
boldly to impress him with its power to discipline the refractory.
In the long run, he is probably fighting a hopeless battle against
the inevitable, and one of these days he will most surely be tagged
and put "in his place."

Meanwhile, he is lord of the Latin American share of creation,
or at least thinks he is; which, after all, is probably the important
thing. If sometimes his supremacy is an illusion, all the appearances are so deftly observed that the results have the effect of
reality. He is still somebody in his own home and family, where
he is treated with respect and consideration. If he signs as head-
of-the-family, he does not have to put the proud fact in quota-
tion marks. At least within this inner circle of intimacies, for the
time being he may feel that he is *"yo el rey"*—or *el reyezuelo*.

Sometimes he philanders. It may be very casual, or it may go
on for years and have an air of permanence or even of staid respectability about it. By an apparent paradox, incomprehensible
to other peoples, he can meanwhile remain a "good family man"
and a loving and tender husband.[121] The strong ties of his children
and the good name of the family mark the limits to such affairs

that are fixed by a strict protocol. Though he may wander afield at times, the chances are that in middle age he may become the most uxorious of husbands. While the American is prone to consider the Latin American man as a shamelessly immoral person, to the Latin American, the American, by virtue of easy divorces, only takes his adultery in a series of chronological sequences.

The folklore and jurisprudence of sex in Latin America start with the very plausible assumption that no woman can safely be left alone with a man for ten minutes. On this basic distrust, there is overlaid a body of law and custom designed to safeguard the family and society from the consequences of unrestrained biological impulses. While people do not always observe these rules, they do respect them and they do not debate their propriety. They have a singularly honest and unhypocritical approach to the whole question of sex. They have pretty well settled the problem of where it belongs in their civilization, so they talk little about it and write less. Books on the subject are rare in their bookstores, and these are generally the works of foreign "experts" in the field. There are no "Advice to the Lovelorn" columns in the newspapers, because, if love is lorn, one would not go to a professional soothsayer of amor for counsel or comfort.

The presence of sex has long since been gracefully accepted along with such other elemental forces as weather and government, and, like them, to be made the most of within the accepted rules. They do not agonize over the right and wrong of sex or of its various manifestations and even what the U.S. State Department has called its "deviations." Since sex is generally a very personal affair, there is a healthy principle of Latin American law to the effect that what two persons do without damage to society is a matter that concerns only themselves and their consciences.

NOTES

1. Cristóbal Bermúdez Plata, archivist of the *Archivo General* de Indias, is the principal editor of the *Catálogo de Pasajeros a Indias* (2 vols., Seville, 1940-1942).

2. Samuel Eliot Morison, *Admiral of the Ocean Sea: A Life of Christopher Columbus* (2 vols., Boston, 1942), II, 172.

3. Simone de Beauvoir, *The Second Sex* (tr. from the French, New York, 1953).

4. Antonio de Herrera y Tordesillas, *Historia General de los Hechos de los Castellanos en las Islas i Tierra Firme del Mar Océano* (8 vols., Madrid, 1722–30), VI, 153. One of the most interesting pictures of the man-and-woman relationship among the Indians of the New World is found in the account of the buccaneer, Lionel Wafer, *A New Voyage and Description of the Isthmus of America* (3d ed., London, 1729), pp. 359, 366.

5. The Anonymous Conqueror, *Narrative of Some Things of New Spain And of the Great City of Temestitan, Mexico* (tr. from the Spanish, New York, 1917), p. 75.

6. Frederick Boyle, *A Ride Across a Continent: A Personal Narrative of Wanderings through Nicaragua and Costa Rica* (2 vols. London. 1868), I, 266, quoting Herrera, *op. cit.*, and Pascual de Andagoya, *Relación de Sucesos de Pedrarías Dávila en las Provincias de Tierra Firme.*

7. Nearly all the chroniclers of the Spanish Conquest recount stories of female warriors among the Indians. Oviedo, in particular, refers to them frequently. Of the armies of the Mexican Revolution, Anita Brenner wrote: "Almost every troop had a famous lady colonel or lady captain, a husky earringed girl, armed to the teeth, and among headlong, reckless fighters one of the first." *The Wind that Swept Mexico* (New York, 1943), p. 42.

8. Herrera, *op. cit.*, III, 169.

9. Gonzalo Fernández de Oviedo y Valdés, *Historia General y Natural de las Indias, Islas y Tierra Firme del Mar Oceano* (4 vols., Madrid, 1851–55), p. 422.

10. *Ibid.*, III, 126.

11. *Ibid.*, II, 141.

12. *Ibid.*, II, 354.

13. Charles L. G. Anderson, *Life and Letters of Vasco Nuñez de Balboa* (New York, 1912), p. 163.

14. Herrera, *op. cit.*, VI, 412.

15. *Ibid.*, VI, 332.

16. *Ibid.*, VI, 319.

17. Oviedo, *op. cit.*, II, 254.

18. *Ibid.*, III, 133.

19. Pedro Pizarro, *Relation of the Discovery and Conquest of the Kingdoms of Peru* (tr. from the Spanish, 2 vols., New York, 1921), II, 406 ff.

20. Oviedo, *op. cit.*, IV, 37.

21. *Ibid.*, IV, 102.

22. Bernardino de Sahagún, *Historia General de las Cosas de Nueva España* (5 vols., Mexico, D. F., 1938), II, 209.

23. See Oviedo, *op. cit.*, III, 135, on the bathing habits of the Indians in the Urabá region of Colombia.

24. Sahagún, *op. cit.*, I, 531-43.

25. Herrera, *op. cit.*, VI, 447.

26. Havelock Ellis, *The Soul of Spain* (Boston and New York, n.d.), p. 65.

27. See the remarks of Giovanni Battista Gonfalonieri, Venetian Ambassador at the Spanish Court (*Memoria de alcune cose notabili . . . 1592*), quoted in Santiago Magariños, ed., *Alabanza de España* (3 vols., Madrid, 1940), II, 168.

28. Ellis, *op. cit.*, p. 64.

29. Giacomo Casanova de Seingalt, *Memories,* VII, chaps. 13-16. On the typical Spanish attitude toward sex, see Somerset Maugham, *Don Fernando; or Variations on Some Spanish Themes* (Garden City, N. Y., 1938), pp. 122, 193.

30. Salvador de Madariaga, *Englishmen, Frenchmen, Spaniards* (tr. from the Spanish, London, 1928), p. 224.

31. "The reckless self-abandonment sometimes shown by the advanced woman in pursuit of impersonal ends, her tendency to unsex herself by imitating masculine methods, are profoundly antagonist to the temperament of the Spanish woman, whose energy and good sense are too solidly personal to be easily turned aside into artificially masculine lines." Havelock Ellis, *op. cit.,* p. 105.

32. Gonzalo de Correas, *Vocabularia de Refranes y Frases Proverbiales y otras Fórmulas Comunes de la Lengua Castellano* (Madrid, 1924), *passim.*

33. *Leys de Indias, libro 9, título 26,* no. 24.

34. *Ibid.,* law no. 25.

35. *Ibid.,* law no. 28.

36. Tomás Thayer Ojeda and Carlos J. Larrain, *Valdivia y sus Compañeros* (Santiago, 1950).

37. Bermúdez Plata, *op. cit.*

38. Thayer Ojeda and Larrain, *op. cit.,* p. 36. See also Ida Weldon Stevenson Vernon, *Pedro de Valdivia, Conquistador of Chile* (Austin, Texas, 1946), *passim.* Stella Burke May, *The Conqueror's Lady* (New York, 1942) is a fictionalized biography of Inés Suarez.

39. See above, Bermúdez Plata, *passim.*

40. Herrera, *op. cit.,* VI, 130-32.

41. Bernal Díaz del Castillo, *The True History of the Conquest of Mexico* (tr. from the Spanish, New York, 1927), pp. 533-42, and *passim.*

42. *Ibid.,* p. 478.

43. Garcilaso Inca de la Vega, *Historia General del Perú* (3 vols., Buenos Aires, 1945).

44. Bernard Moses, *The Spanish Dependencies in South America* (2 vols., New York and London, 1914), I, 311.

45. Garcilaso, *op. cit.,* p. 104.

46. *Ibid.,* II, 273.

47. John Eoghan Kelly, *Pedro de Alvarado, Conquistador* (Princeton, N. J.), pp. 173, 205.

48. Bermúdez Plata, *op. cit.,* entries for 1538.

49. Garcilaso, *op. cit.,* I, 113.

50. Morison, *op. cit.,* II, 397, C. S. Forester's novel *To the Indies,* treats of this phase of the Spanish Conquest of the New World.

51. See Oviedo, *op. cit.,* I, 97.

52. Oviedo, *op. cit.,* quoted by Carlos Pereyra, *Las Huellas de los Conquistadores* (Madrid, n. d.), p. 261.

53. Oviedo, *op. cit.,* I, 97.

54. Charles L. G. Anderson, *op. cit.,* pp. 222-23.

55. Oviedo, *op. cit.,* I, 544.

56. Anderson, *op. cit.,* p. 330.

57. Oviedo, *op. cit.,* III, 122.

58. *Ibid.*, III, 122.

59. Philip Ainsworth Means, *Fall of the Inca Empire and the Spanish Rule in Peru: 1530-1780.*

60. See Pedro Simón, *Historia de la Expedición de Pedro de Ursua al Marañón y de las Aventuras de Lope de Aguirre* (Lima, 1942), pp. 74-5, 178; and Adolpb F. Bandelier, *The Gilded Man and Other Pictures of the Spanish Occupancy of America* (New York, 1893), p. 101.

61. Carlos Pereyra, *op. cit.*, p. 260.

62. Juan Bromley and José Barbagelata, *Evolución Urbana de la Ciudad de Lima* (Lima, 1945), p. 38.

63. Juan Rodríquez Freile, *El Carnero: Conquista y Descubrimiento del Nuevo Reico de Granada de las Indias Occidentales del Mar Océano y Fundación de la Ciudad de Santa Fé de Bogotá* (Bogotá, 1942), p. 93 (note).

64. Germán Arciniegas, *Knight of El Dorado* (tr. from the Spanish, New York, 1942), pp. 216, 223.

65. Oviedo, *op. cit.*, IV, 141.

66. See A. Curtis Wilgus, ed., *Readings in Latin American Civilization* (New York, 1946), p. 51, and Augustin Zapata Gollán, *Las Puertas de la Tierra* (Santa Fé, Argentina, 1941), pp. 23-28.

67. Gilberto Freyre, *The Masters and the Slaves* (tr. from the Portuguese, New York, 1946), pp. 84-85.

68. Pedro de Cieza de León, *The Travels of, A.D. 1532-50* (tr. from the Spanish, London, 1864).

69. Ulrich Schmidel, *Viaje al Rio de la Plata* (tr. from the German, Buenos Aires, 1942).

70. Arciniegas, *op. cit.*, pp. 122-23.

71. Bernal Díaz, *op. cit* p. 526.

72. *Letters of Cortés* (tr. from the Spanish, 2 vols., New York, 1908), I, 217.

73. Bernal Díaz, *op. cit.*, pp. 76, 79.

74. Francis A. Mac Nutt, in *Letters of Cortés, op. cit.*, introduction I, 42.

75. Bernal Díaz, *op. cit.*, p. 140.

76. *Letters of Cortés, op. cit.*, II, 263 (note).

77. Pedro Pizarro, *op. cit.*, II, 405-6.

78. See William Hickling Prescott, *History of the Conquest of Peru* (Everyman Edition), p. 177. Garcilaso's works include: *Comentarios Reales de los Incas* (Lisbon, 1609). English translation published by the Hakluyt Society, 2 vols., London, 1869, 1871; *Historia General del Peru* (Cordoba, Spain, 1617); *La Florida del Inca* (Lisbon, 1605). English translation published by the University of Texas Press, Austin, 1951.

79. The *Comentarios* were reprinted in Buenos Aires in 2 vols. in 1943, and the *Historia General* in 3 vols. in 1946.

80. Philip Ainsworth Means, *op. cit.*, p. 134 (note).

81. Herbert Ingram Priestley, *The Coming of the White Man 1492-1848* (New York, 1929), p. 111.

82. Thayer Ojeda and Larrain, *op. cit.*, p. 16.

83. *Ibid.*, p. 18.

84. Jorge Juan and Antonio de Ulloa, *A Voyage to South America* (tr. from

the Spanish, 4th ed., 2 vols., London, 1806), I, 33; Basil Hall, *Extracts from a Journal Written on the Coasts of Chili, Peru, and Mexico in the years 1820, 1821, 1822* (2 vols., Edinburgh, 1824), II, 108.

85. F. Depons, *A Voyage to the Eastern Part of Tierra Firme, or the Spanish Main, in South America, during the Years 1801, 1802, 1803, and 1804* (tr. from the French, 3 vols., New York, 1806), I, 122. Basil Hall, *op. cit.*, II, 191.

86. Juan and Ulloa, *op. cit.*, I, 38.

87. *Ibid.*, II, 109.

88. Thomas Gage, *A New Survey of the West Indies, 1648* (New York, 1929), p. 85.

89. The rich legendry of colonial Peru is lavishly portrayed in the literary tapestries of Ricardo Palma's *Tradiciones Peruanas*, which first appeared in 1872. As Librarian of the National Library, Palma had access to much original documentary lore on the early history of the country. Of the several editions available, I have used the illustrated six-volume edition published by Espasa-Calpe in Madrid and Barcelona in 1930. A selection of the anecdotes has been translated by Harriet de Onís and published under the title *Knights of the Cape* (New York, 1945).

90. In Raul Porras Barranechea, ed., *Pequeña Antología de Lima (1535–1935)* (Madrid, 1935), p. 288.

91. N. B. Stevenson, *A Historical and Descriptive Narrative of Twenty Years Residence in South America* (3 vols., London, 1825), I, 300.

92. Juan and Ulloa, *op. cit.*, II, 55.

93. Jorge Basadre, *Peru: Problema y Posibilidad* (Lima, 1931), p. 224. For the origin of the name by which she is best known, see Stevenson, *op. cit.*, I, 230. See Thornton Wilder's novel, *The Bridge of San Luis Rey*.

94. Juan and Ulloa, *op. cit.*, II, 61.

95. Amédée François Frézier, *Relation du Voyage*, etc. (English tr., London, 1717), pp. 219, 257. According to Juan and Ulloa, "A lady covered with the most expensive lace . . . and glittering from hand to foot with jewels, is supposed to be dressed at the expense of not less than 30 or 40,000 crowns, a splendour still the more astonishing, as it is so very common." *op. cit.*, II, 60.

96. Juan and Ulloa said that one piece of Cordovan leather served for both sole and upper. Buckles were set with diamonds or pearls, as were also their garters. "The shoemakers," they wrote, "who are no strangers to the foible of the sex, take great care to make them in a manner very little calculated for service." *op. cit.*, p. 58.

97. Woodes Rogers, *A Cruising Voyage Round the World* (London, 1928), p. 131. Alexander Selkirk was the original of Defoe's *Robinson Crusoe*. He had been marooned on the Island of Juan Fernandez several years before and had only recently been rescued by Capt. Rogers.

98. Lesley Byrd Simpson, *Many Mexicos* (New York, 1941), p. 58.

99. Manuel Romero de Terreros, *Bocetos de la Vida Social en la Nueva España* (Mexico, D. F., 1944), p. 18.

100. *Ibid.*, p. 210.

101. Francis Erskine Inglis de Calderón de la Barca, *Life in Mexico during a*

Residence of Two Years in that Country (1st ed., London, 1843), (Everyman Edition), p. 87.

102. See the English translation and notes by James Fitzmaurice-Kelly, *The Nun-Ensign* (Boston, 1899). There is a French tr. by the Cuban-born poet, José María de Heredia, *La Nonne Alferez* (Paris, 1894).

103. Simpson, *op. cit.,* p. 147.

104. Stevenson, *op. cit.,* I, 362.

105. Agustín Edwards, *My Native Land* (London, 1928), p. 62.

106. Arturo Torres-Rioseco, *New World Literature* (Berkeley and Los Angeles, 1949), chap. III. See the new edition of the works of Sor Juana Ines, edited by Alfonso Méndez Plancarta. The first volume of this series was published in Mexico in 1951, under the subtitle *Lírica Personal.*

107. Irving A. Leonard, *Books of the Brave* (Cambridge, Mass., 1949), p. 408.

108. "Her life is a prodigious tale of devotion to knowledge." Pedro Henriquez Uréna, *Literary Currents in Hispania-America* (Cambridge, Mass., 1945), p. 76.

109. See Victor W. von Hagen, *The Four Seasons of Manuela: A Biography* (New York and Boston, 1952).

110. When Bolívar was going to visit a certain town in Peru, an officer from Lima is said to have called on the head man of the town with a requisition for "lodging, food, a good bed, etc., etc.," The mayor interpreted the three "et ceteras" as *"tres muchachas"*; Luís Alberto Sánchez, *Vida y Pasión de la Cultura en América* (Santiago, 1935), p. 81.

111. Von Hagen, *op. cit.,* p. 148.

112. "It is said that when a creole mother in this country (Peru) holds her baby between her hands . . . she addresses a boy as 'My dear little Bishop' or 'My President,' " William Lewis Herndon and Lardner Gibbon, *Exploration of the Valley of the Amazon* (2 vols., Washington, D. C., 1854), I, 56.

113. "In Mexico City . . . the old family home is breaking up and is disappearing." Herbert Cerwin, *These are the Mexicans* (New York, 1947), p. 278.

114. [In Tehuantepec] "the woman—she is the loveliest in Mexico—is the head of the house." John L. Strohm, *I Lived with Latin Americans* (Chicago, 1943), p. 343. "As in Tehuantepec, the heart and soul of the town (Juchitán) is the buzzing market, and its life and heart are its women, ever active, good-natured, but relentless in business, a fair match for the commercial cunning of the foreign merchants." Miguel Covarrubias, *Mexico South* (New York, 1946), p. 159. See Covarrubias' account of the famous Tehuana, Doña Juana Cata Romero. *Ibid.,* pp. 149, 226-37.

115. "Mexico is a man's country. In all matters they are the heads of the families. But women . . . cleverly accept the role of more or less passive resistance and then proceed to do as they wish and get what they want. A Mexican woman in a temper is not something to tangle with." Herbert Cerwin, *op. cit.,* p. 28. "However much the men like to think otherwise, the *molinera* (the Indian woman) . . . subtly rules him and the family." Olive Floyd, *Doctora in Mexico* (New York, 1944), p. 248.

116. Of the Costa Rican women, John Stephens wrote: "In San José . . . all the ladies were what might be called good businessmen, kept stores, bought and sold goods, looked out for bargains and were particularly knowing in the article

of coffee." *Incidents of Travel in Central America, Chiapas and Yucatan* (2 vols., New York, 1841), I, 373.

117. Russell H. Fitzgibbon, ed., *Constitutions of the Americans* (Chicago, 1948) p. 52.

118. About 25 per cent of the children born in Chile in 1942 were illegitimate. The rate for Santiago was 20 per cent, and in the northern Department of Huasoo over half of all births were illegitimate. Republic of Chile, Dirección General de Estadística Demografía y Asistencia Social Año 1942 (Santiago, 1945). Of 176, 431 births in Peru during the year July 1942-June 1943, about 45 per cent were illegitimate. The rate for Lima was slightly less, and in Cuzco about 51 per cent of births for the year were illegitimate. In a population of over 7,000,000 there were only 20,261 marriages during the year. Republic of Peru, Dirección Nacional de Estadística, *Extracto Estadístico del Peru 1943* (Lima, 1951). John W. White quotes A. F. Bunge to the effect that "the rate of illegitimacy (in Argentina) is on the increase, while the birth rate itself is declining." According to White "The rate of illegitimate births in the city of Buenos Aires is 12 per cent, and it reaches 43, 44, and 46 per cent in the Provinces of Tucumán, Salta, and Jujuy respectively. In some of the national territories more than half of the births are illegitimate and in the territory of Formosa the rate is 66 per cent. The rate for the country at large was 28 per cent in 1938. *Argentina: The Life Story of a Nation* (New York, 1942), p. 297. T. Lynn Smith says that "Brazil's population lives in the married state in a much less degree than that of the United States." Of Brazilians over fifteen years of age in 1920, 44.9 per cent were married whereas in the United States the percentage was 59.9. *Op. cit.*, p. 217.

119. See Olga Briceño, *Cocks and Bulls in Caracas: How We Live in Venezuela* (Boston, 1945), p. 59; and Charles Macomb Flandrau, *Viva Mexico!* (New York, 1909), pp. 92-93.

120. "There is probably no need for any extension of sympathy to the Hispanic American women on account of their state. They seem to be happy and to have the kind of life they want. And are they really the submissive servants of the men?" Charles E. Chapman, *Republican Hispanic America: A History* (New York, 1937), p. 15. When Mr. and Mrs. John Biesanz conducted a poll among Costa Rican women, the results showed that young women placed faithfulness in fifth place among the traits desirable in a husband. Married women ranked it fourteenth! The most important quality was declared to be culture (*cultura*), i.e. "manners, courtesy, some degree of formal education." John and Mavis Biesanz, *Costa Rican Life* (New York, 1944), p. 62. On marriage in Latin America, see Elizabeth Borton de Treviño, *My Heart Lies South* (New York, 1953), the acute and amusing observations of an American woman who married into a large, emotional, and warm-hearted Mexican family.

121. "Contrary to our highly colored picture of the guitar playing caballero, our Latin American neighbor finds his fulfillment in the high respect he feels for his wife and the adoration with which he cherishes his children." Kurt Severin, *To the South* (New York, 1944), p. 203.

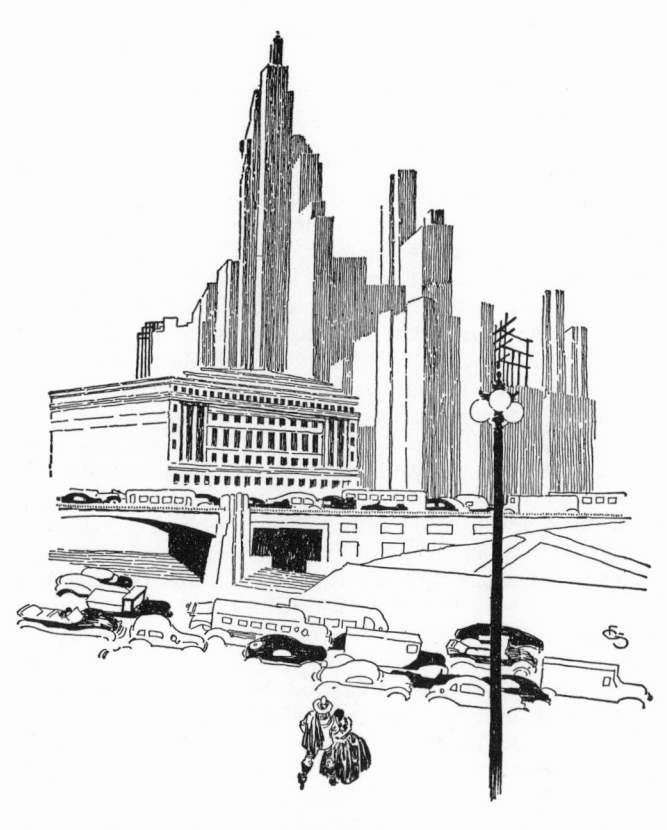

Chapter IX

THE CITY

THE CIVILIZATION of Spain was an urban thing.[1] From
the time when the Greeks and the Punic peoples settled in
Iberia, Spaniards had lived in cities and shunned the open countryside. If they did not dwell in cities, they grouped themselves
in towns and villages for sociability and protection. Only in the

northwest—in the Basque country, and in Asturias and Galicia—did Spaniards tend to spread out over the land, as did the Portuguese. There the cities are mostly ports, like Vigo and Coruña and Bilbao, and of no particular charm or flavor, but good places to tie up fishing boats. It is from that part of Spain that the shepherds came to tend the sheep of the Mesta, and still migrate to the far west of the United States to follow one of the most solitary of occupations. The Romans, too, were a city people, and their long stay in the Peninsula only confirmed the Spaniards in their natural urge toward urbanization. And when the Moslem came, the Arabs forgot their deserts and the Moors their mountains, to add a new splendor to Córdoba and Granada and Seville.

When the Spaniards came to the New World, they brought their urban instincts and leanings with them.[2] Since they could not conceive of a civilization that was not built around cities, they literally started founding cities as soon as they landed. Two of the most prolific of the early city builders were Sebastián de Benalcázar, who left a trail of incipient cities behind him on his march from Quito north to Cali in Colombia; and Pedro de Valdivia, conqueror of Chile, who laid out a number of settlements and garrison posts that were to become the principal cities of that country. Cortés halted his march on the Aztec capital to go through the formalities of establishing the "city" of Veracruz, for he would not have felt quite Spanish if he had left a municipal void behind him. The notary drew up the necessary proclamation and articles of incorporation, and read them aloud to the assembled soldiery. The names of the mayor and board of aldermen were announced, and Father Olmedo, the chaplain, blessed the unborn city and called down the divine favor on its future. The site for the all-important central plaza was marked off and lots were distributed among the founding citizens. Only then could Cortés go about the business of conquering Mexico. Later, men came back from the interior or from the islands and settled there.[3] When its original location was found to be unsuitable, it was moved to another site before the end of the century, as happened with several other colonial cities.[4] It has ever since been the principal port of entry of Mexico, and has survived the visitations of pestilence and piracy, the disruptions of revolution, and its occupation by American and French forces. In the meantime, it was the last, as it was the first, seat of Spanish power in Mexico. The same ceremony, and with similar details, came to be repeated many times during the Conquest, as when Pizarro founded San Miguel de Piura in the coastal desert of northern Peru, and again at Lima. And when Diego de Almagro broke with his partner, he went through the motions of making *his* city farther to the south, though he died too early for it ever to become a reality of streets and houses.[5]

Some of the Indian peoples, like the Aztecs, the Mayas, and the Incas, had been great city builders on their own account. Some of the Indian cities were long since dead, like Tula of the Toltecs, Machu Picchu and Tiahuanaco in the Andes, or even buried in the jungle, like Chichén of the Itzás, Copán and Palenque, and a host of other Mayan cities, most of which were not even found or uncovered until our own time.[6] But some were alive and full of activity, like Tenochtitlán and Cuzco. These the Spaniards took over for their own and built new Spanish cities on the sites of the Indian capitals. In a fury of vandalism and iconoclasm, they razed what of the Aztec city survived the long siege, though Cortés and his captains had seen and marveled at its wonders.[7] But much of the cyclopean stonework of Cuzco proved unmovable, even for the superior mechanics of Europeans, so they just laid their lesser stonework on top of the Incaic foundations, and made a hybrid city of it.[8]

Tenochtitlán lay on a lacustrine island in a mountain bowl that was "the Valley of Mexico," and connected with the mainland by long causeways. The situation was to produce serious drainage problems for the Spanish city which took its place. After a series of long and disastrous inundations, a canal was tunneled through the mountain rim to the west to relieve the pressure of the flood waters.[9] But the subsoil remained spongy, to create new dilemmas for Spanish and Mexican builders, and leaning and lopsided structures, whose foundations have found no bottom in the ooze. In every other respect, it is an ideal site for the great city that it is.

Like Mexico City and Cuzco, most Latin American cities, except on the east coast of South America, are located in highland or mountain basins or valleys. That is particularly true of Mexico, Colombia, and Ecuador. It is also the case with Guatemala City

and San José in Central America; Caracas and Valencia in Venezuela; La Paz and Cochabamba in Bolivia; Santiago in Chile, and
São Paulo in Brazil. Cities, like Potosí and Guanajuato and
Taxco, sometimes grew up around mines, and have preserved the
profile and characteristics typical of hill towns. Havana and Cartagena and Rio de Janeiro were built on superior harbors, and
Arequipa, Mendoza, and Tucumán in natural oases that favored
large-scale irrigated farming. Of the two capitals on the banks
of the River Plate, Montevideo has a better site than Buenos
Aires. The Portuguese, a coastwise folk, laid out a series of port
towns on the bays and estuaries of the Brazilian *marinha,* which,
with a few exceptions, gave excellent anchorage for ships all the
way from Belem south to Rio Grande. Besides Rio, they included
São Luiz, which the French held for a while; Recife, a channel
behind an exposed reef; Bahia, with its vast expanse of protected
water; Vitoria, a little Guanabara; and the serpentine tidal river
that winds across the coastal plain at São Vicente—Santos.

Various considerations influenced the selection of the site of
Lima, which was destined to be the capital of Spanish South
America. Of the alternatives, Cuzco was too high—and too Indian, and it lay on the wrong side of the Cordillera. For a while,
the Spaniards were tempted to set up their government and its
appurtenances in the attractive valley of Jauja, which lies in the
basin of the Mantaro on the highroad to Huancayo. Instead, they
chose a location on the narrow shelf of desert land between the
gray Andean foothills and the Pacific, near where the River
Rimac debouches from the mountains on its torrential way to
the sea. They corrupted the Quechua name of the stream into
Lima, for the "City of the Kings" proved to be only a ceremonial
appellation. Here there was plenty of water for the needs of a
large population and for irrigating the coastal lands nearby. The
gorge of the Rimac provided a convenient link with lofty Indian
lands of the Sierra and southward across the Apurimac into
Cuzco. The site was far enough from the ocean to discourage the
English sea rovers, even if the city had no wall for its defense.
Yet it was only a few miles from its port at Callao, which was
protected from the open Pacific by the island of San Lorenzo.
The city paid for the obvious advantages of its geographical position with relation to the rest of Peru and to its strategic sea

routes with a disagreeable fogbound winter climate, though a few miles to the west, in the Chosica gap, there is unbroken sunshine and moderate temperatures all the year.

SPANISH CITY PLANNING

The government of Spain took an active interest in the location and planning of cities in the colonies.[10] An early law of 1523 prescribed the conditions for laying out new cities. First, they were to be situated in the proximity of water and building materials, and there should be pasture lands and a source of firewood nearby. Then it went on to order that "sites for settlement are not to be selected in very high places, because of discomfort from the winds and difficulties of service and transportation, nor in very low places, near swamps and lagoons, because they are generally unhealthy, but they are to be located in moderate altitudes, and in places where winds from north and south blow freely." Places subject to fogs were to be avoided, and if built on a river, the location should be such that the rising sun would shine first on the town and not reflect from the surface of the water in the eyes of the inhabitants. Slaughterhouses, stockyards, fish markets, tanneries, and "other dirty and ill-smelling businesses" were to be placed outside the precincts of the town, preferably on the other side of a river or on the seashore.

Once the site for the town was agreed upon, the most suitable place for the plaza was chosen. Working out from the plaza, as the heart of the town, men measured off the site with cord and rule, and drew up a street plan and plot of the future building lots. Cities were not to grow helter-skelter, as they had in Spain, with no two streets running in the same direction, but according to a uniform geometrical pattern fixed in advance. So the checkerboard street plan was imposed once for all, and where there have been variations from it, they have been because the lay of the land made it impossible to follow the official plan.[11] Not only were streets to be parallel to each other, but they were to run east and west, or north and south, and at uniform distances from each other, so that the intervening *manzanas* or blocks were all of the same size and shape. In cold country, streets were to be wide, and in hot climates, they were to be narrow, as they are in Cartagena.

Much attention was given to planning the plaza. As the city grew, there might be more plazas to take care of the needs of the population, so then the original plaza was known as the "plaza mayor" or the "plaza central," or the "plaza de armas," where troops might drill, as in Lima. The regulations stipulated that the plaza should be half again as long as wide, so that it would be better adapted for fetes of horsemanship. As for dimensions, it should be at least 200 feet wide and 300 feet long, and not over 532 by 800 feet, depending on the anticipated importance and magnitude of the city. The four principal streets and as many minor streets should lead off from its corners, and crowding the plaza on the wider thoroughfares were to be the *portales* or porticos, that have ever since been the delight of Latin American promenaders and shoppers. Around the plaza itself, were the locations reserved for the government buildings and the cathedral or principal church.

Half of the twenty national capitals of Latin America bear Indian names. The names of five have a religious connotation. It was customary to include the patron saint in the official title of the city, as San Cristóbal de la Habana, San Francisco de Quito, or São Sebastião do Rio de Janeiro, but in common parlance the saint's name was omitted. Three of the capitals were named by the discoverers from their first impressions of natural features, actual or illusory. Like most peoples who migrate far from home, the Spaniards, in their nostalgia, recalled the names of places that were familiar to them. As so many of them came from Estremadura, there are Medellíns and Méridas and Trujillos strewn about the map. There is a Guadalajara, a Córdoba, and a Valencia, but there is no Toledo or Madrid or Seville of importance. Nor is there a Lisbon or Oporto in Brazil. In spite of Santos and São Paulo, Belem and the Concepcións, the Church probably left more of its holy nomenclature in California than it has in any other area of equal size to the south. Where a locality was already identified by a native name, the Spaniards frequently retained it, though they might corrupt it, as they did the originals of Mexico and Lima. Since most of the towns in Mexico and Peru were predominantly Indian anyway, they kept the Aztec place names with their *tls* and other combinations of consonants that sound so harsh and unpronounceable to foreigners, and the smoother-flowing *huas* of the Quechua—the Huánucos and Huachos and Huancayos. In Chile, the Tehuelche names, like Cauquenes and Loncocho, Taltal and Llai-Llai, outnumber the Spanish Valparaisos and Coronels.[12] Hundreds of Brazilian towns and cities bear such distinctive Tupí names as Aracajú and Caxambú, Araraquara and Pirapora, Mogy-mirím and Paraguassú. The Brazilians have also had the habit of using two names for some of the old state capitals of the northeast, one of them the name of the particular state. Thus, São Salvador is Bahía, Recife is Pernambuco, Belem is Pará, and Fortaleza is also Ceará.

STREET NAMES

Much history is written in the street names of the Latin American cities. The demands of politics and patriotism, and the urge for modernity, have sometimes wiped out these picturesque reminders of other days from the faces of cities. Worthies of the republics and national holidays have often been conveniently honored by rechristening old streets for them. Thus, in Lima, Avenida Colmena (beehive) becomes Nicolás de Pierola (former president of Peru); in Santiago, Calle Las Animas (spirits) is now Alonso Ovalle; and in Havana, Calle Obispo was officially changed to Juan Clemente Zenea, but to the Habaneros it is still Obispo. Sometimes, it is a foreign dignitary, like George Washington or Woodrow Wilson or Franklin D. Roosevelt, who is honored. However, out of long habit, the people may go on using the old street names, to the confusion of taxi drivers and mail carriers and the irritation of government at the stubborn conservatism of the citizenry. Days of the year are also applied to streets to commemorate some notable event in a nation's annals, a device whose possibilities are limited only by the length of the year. So, among the streets and boulevards, there is a 5th of May in Mexico City and a 25th of May in Buenos Aires, an 18th of July in Montevideo, and in Rio there is a 1st of March and a 7th of September.

In Mexico City, the street names are even more diversified than they are in Buenos Aires. Few of the colonial names have survived the pressures of change. Among the exceptions are La Corregidora alongside the Zócalo and Donceles and Isabel la Católica—all women; and, as lone tributes to the conquerors,

Velásquez de León, killed by the Aztecs on the *Noche Triste,* and Puente de Alvarado. The Aztecs fare better. Cuauhtemoc rates a wide avenue in the city that he defended so heroically, and the ill-fated Montezuma a lesser thoroughfare. To the northwest, beyond the Calzada of Melchor Ocampo, there is a maze of Tizocs and Xolotls, and Axayacatls and Cacamatzins. Quetzalcoatl has his street, but Huitzilopochtli, the sanguinary war god, does not. To the southeast of the center of the city, off San Juan de Letrán, a street is dedicated to the culture hero, and monotheistic King of Tezcoco, Netzahualcoyotl. Few Spaniards are honored: Fathers Motolinia and Las Casas, because they were kind to Indians, and two of the later—and better—viceroys, Bucarely and Revilla-gigedo. There are streets for leaders of the Independencia, like Hidalgo and Iturbide, and for liberal statesmen of the republic, like Juárez and Lerdo. Of the heroes of the Revolution, Madero draws the principal shopping street of the city, Obregón, a very wide avenue, and Emiliano Zapata, an honor he would not have desired for himself. Of foreigners who have been decorated with street names, the most important and meritorious is the great Humboldt, who has been honored on land and sea from California to the Antarctic. Among others have been notables as far separated in time as Herodotus and Sir Walter Scott, and a galaxy of assorted Frenchmen that includes Renan and Flammarion, Sadi Carnot and Michelet. Honor is also paid to the Mexican bards, Sor Juana and Amado Nervo, and among national scholars, to Justo Sierra and Icazbalceta. There are whole series of streets named for foreign countries and cities and rivers, and for Mexican states and rivers and trees. And there are streets of the Sun and the Moon, of Liberty and The-Man-who-was-Strangled—and of Schultz and Sullivan.

In the cause of convenience and order, a numerical system for distinguishing the streets of Bogotá and Caracas has supplanted the picturesque and romantic street names of the colonial cities. Part of Carrera Séptima, or Seventh Avenue—the forum of loquacious Bogotanos, was once, by some strange stroke of fancy, known as Calle Caliente, or Hot Street, certainly a misnomer when the drizzling fog rolls down off Monserate at dusk. Carrera Octava, or Eighth Avenue, was formerly the Calle del Amor. There was also a Calle del Afán, or Street of Anxiety, a Calle del

Descuido, or Street of Carelessness, a Calle del Consuelo, or Consolation, and a Calle del Suspiro, or Street of the Sigh. The extremes of biblical nomenclature were probably found in Caracas, where there were once streets of the Encarnation of the Son of God, of the Circumcision and Baptism of the Infant Jesus in the Temple, of the Seizure of Jesus Christ, and of the Last Judgment.[13]

The street names of Rio de Janeiro strongly reflect the latent nostalgia of the Cariocas for the period of the empire. Dom Pedro II has *his* street, and so do many of the imperial nobility. Among them are the Barão de Petropolis, the Marquez de Olinda, the Conde de Bomfim, the Visconde de Albuquerque, the Duque de Caxias, and a score of others. The principal thoroughfare of downtown Rio was named for the Baron of Rio Branco, the first of Latin American diplomats. Of other streets of the Brazilian capital, there is one—Ouvidor, the favorite promenade of its people—that, like Obispo in Havana, Florida in Buenos Aires, and Agustinas in Santiago, will always resist any official demands for change.

Probably nowhere were the street names so colorful or so reminiscent of the living history of the place as in colonial Lima. Time and the republic have taken their toll of them, but some have persisted into the present as relics of the rich blazonry of the old city. As they still do, the names of streets might change with each block, and even in the colony the names would shift from one era to another. The Jirón Unión, that goes from the Plaza San Martín over to the Plaza de Armas, where the city had its birth, and the streets that cross it, were the seats of crafts and trades that ministered to the needs of the Spanish population. Sometimes by command of the viceroy, sometimes for the advantage of their business, the different trades tended to concentrate in a particular block. Thus, there were "streets" of the silversmiths and the swordmakers, of the hatters and the dyers, of the guitar makers and the featherworkers. There was a Junk Iron Street and a street of the secondhand clothing dealers, which was decreed as a means of controlling the sale of their masters' apparel by Negro slaves. There were streets of the ducks and the burros and the roosters, of the lettuce patch, or Lechugal, and of the "broken mill" or Molino Quebrado. There was a street of the miracle and one of bitterness, or Amargura, where the stations of the Cross were painted on the walls of the houses. The Calle de los Siete Pecados commemorated seven young women who had sinned, and the Calle de las Siete Jeringas because a doctor had saved a wounded man with seven enemas. The Calle del Huevo celebrated the feat of a hen that laid a big egg, and the Calle Ya Parió was so dubbed in honor of a woman who was a long time in giving birth.[14]

COLONIAL LIMA

Though Lima was larger and more important than any other New World city, except for Mexico City, in nearly every respect it was representative of other cities.[15] In fact, it may still be considered as the most typical Latin American city—the true *Ciudad Criolla,* or creole city. Because of its political position as capital of the viceroyalty and the efforts of its merchants, it became a very rich city of sumptuous and lavish living. Even members of the Spanish nobility who resided in Lima entered the field of trade. A Portuguese Jew who lived in Lima in the early seventeenth century wrote that "everybody, to the highest nobles, dedicates himself to commerce . . . and they are so skilled at every kind of trading that no people are superior to them." [16] Several had a working capital of over 1,000,000 pesos and many had over 500,000. At that time the wealthiest merchant in Lima was a Corsican, and it is interesting to note that among the foreigners in the city were Frenchmen, Italians, Germans, Flemings, Greeks, Dalmatians, Genoese, English, Hindus, and Chinese. Over a century later, Juan and Ulloa drew a similar picture, but reported that "the wealth of most families terminates with the life of him who raised it." [17] They said: "The inhabitants of Lima have a natural aptitude and disposition for commerce, and the city may be considered as an academy to which great numbers repair to perfect themselves in the various arts of trade. . . . There are many families who support a proper splendor entirely by the revenue of their estates, without joining in the cares and hurry of commerce. But a greater number with estates add the advantages of commerce, in order to preserve them."

Independence brought a good many changes in the life of Lima. The mines in the sierra no longer yielded the returns which they once had. With the disappearance of the Spaniards, the creoles took over the direction of the city's business life, as well as that of its politics. Captain Basil Hall, who visited Lima during San Martin's occupation of the city, wrote: "All was doubt and despair. In the former times, said the Limenians, our city was that in which pleasure held her court; wealth and ease were our attendants; enjoyment was our only business; and we dreamt of no evil but an earthquake. They had yet to learn that there are moral and political, as well as physical earthquakes, which, though they leave churches and dwellings undestroyed may lay the whole fabric of society in ruins." [18] When Charles Darwin visited Lima, he remarked that, though it "must formerly have been a splendid town," it was then in "a wretched state of decay." "The streets are nearly unpaved," he added; "and heaps of filth are piled up in all directions, where the black gallinazos, tame as poultry, pick up bits of carrion.[19] E. G. Squier saw Lima in the 1870's, when the economy of Peru had been given a new lease of life by the guano boom. Of "the old viceregal, luxurious, bigoted, and corrupt capital of Peru," he said: "The ancient city of the Kings is still rich, still gay, still flourishing, and more luxurious than in its proudest colonial days." [20]

When the ceremony of the founding of Lima took place on January 18, 1535, only Francisco Pizarro and eleven Spaniards were present. More soon came in from the interior and by the end of the year the City of the Kings, as it was then known, had a population of 69 *vecinos,* that is, citizens who were registered before the *Cabildo* or city council as qualified to receive allotments of land within the limits of the new municipality. The growth of the city, and the relative proportion of different elements in the population at various periods are shown in the table on page 350.[21]

The most noteworthy fact brought out by this chart is the progressive mestization of the population. The unrestrained mixing of the three basic ingredients produced before the end of the colonial period the complex of hybrid groups that still characterizes Lima, as it does many other Latin American cities.[22] As a result of the successive crossbreedings among the various groups, the ethnic composition of the population was in constant flux, so that there was never a normal type. Moreover, the gradations

Year	Total	White	Indian	Mestizo	Negro	Mulatto	Other mixture
1599	14,262						
1614	25,434	12,134	1,978	192	10,386	744	
1700	37,234						
1755	54,000						
1791	52,627	17,215	3,210	23,233	8,960		
1812	63,900	18,210	10,643	4,879	17,881	10,231	2,056
1839	55,627						Asiatic
1876	100,156	42,694	19,630	23,120	9,088		5,624
1908	130,289	55,918	19,878	43,559	7,275		3,572
1920	173,007	70,350	18,248	71,688	6,608		5,673
1931	275,908	94,998	15,719	144,527	8,244		12,417
1940	402,976						

of admixture were so many and confusing, and their respective physical markings so deceptive, that there was no certain formula for determining exactly to what particular group one of the mixed bloods might belong. The elaborate terminology that was devised to differentiate and distinguish all the possible admixtures was of only very limited value in practical usage. For, since white blood was at a premium as the ultimate and supreme desideratum in all colonial society, the light-complexioned mestizo or mulatto very naturally moved himself over in the social spectrum to the chromatic equivalent, whenever there was occasion to identify himself. If his coloring were light enough, nobody asked any questions, and the individual had arrived among the elect of the community, at least in so far as ethnics were involved. The rest was a matter of manners and economics, though in a snobbish society the lack of pedigree was always a handicap. For such purposes, the blood of the Incas qualified one for the aristocracy, as happened with the Ampuero family [23] and the chronicler, Garcilaso de la Vega. Sometimes socially ambitious people bought patents of *blancura* or whiteness from a hard-pressed treasury, that left no legal doubts of their right to belong, whatever the biological facts might be in the case. This became a fairly common practice in Brazil, where there was much less color prejudice than in the Spanish colonies.

In a society so constituted, deep grudges and resentments among the socially underprivileged, in other words, the mixed peoples, were inevitable. Pure bloods were arrayed against mixed bloods, whose only escape was by way of a series of fortuitous reincarnations that would gradually ensure descendants the coveted status of whites. The only alternative was the achievement of some superior personal distinction by his own efforts that would compel the recognition of his social superiors. To the zambo, mixture of Indian and Negro, and without the saving elixir of white blood in his veins, the social prospect was almost hopeless.

The Spanish rulers condoned, at least tacitly, these divisions and antagonisms within colonial society. For their perpetuation assured that the mixed breeds would not unite, to pool their frustrations and turn their discontents against the white minority and the authority of Spain, which the whites represented. Government was concerned only with keeping their explosive possibilities under control, and with preventing any one segment of the population from asserting itself to the detriment of the common interest. In time, the various categories of racial combination became so well blended that they were all treated indiscriminately as "colored people," or mestizos in the generic French sense of *métis*. There was then a solid majority of mestizos, who might also be partly mulatto in their racial make-up. The change has become quite evident within the present century, and is recognized by the grouping of all mixed breeds in the official Peruvian statistics. Neither the other Europeans who came in after Independence or the Orientals who began to arrive after the middle of the last century, have materially affected the miscegenative process. Unlike Argentina, Uruguay, and southern Brazil, where non-Hispanic Europeans have been a major formative factor, it has been exclusively a national problem, with roots deep in the history of Peru.[24]

Today the average Limeño is a mestizo. He has the same inferiority complex, the same unfulfilled aspirations, the same vague sense of not "belonging" that generally characterizes his mestizo fellows elsewhere. In Mexico, the mestizos have come into their own by the violence of revolution, and in Asunción and San Salvador by a natural evolution. In Peru, there is much greater opportunity, at least in the economic field, than there ever was before, and few doors—and those, mostly little doors—are closed to the ambitious and the talented. But among the majority of mestizos there is an apparent paralysis of will and an inclination to wait for the State to do things for them. Their minds are full of "unfinished business" that, for lack of straight thinking and of confidence in themselves, they seldom get to. So, as in all places where they have not found a settled place in society, they become the raw material of revolution and the darlings of the demagogues who would interrupt the orderly evolution of the nation for their own glory. They represent a great reserve of intelligence too little drawn on, as those who have broken out of the leaden ring of inertia to attain high place in the community have amply demonstrated.

In the meantime, the basic texture of society has changed surprisingly little in Lima. There is still the same predominantly white upper class, habituated to command by centuries of experience, with its own ideas of what is best for Peru—and generally right. There are the same Indians, some in "store clothes" and some fresh from the sierra, but all ill at ease in the city that does not belong to them. Since there is no source of replenishment, as with the Indians, Negro blood is gradually being "absorbed" into the mestizo mass, so that the blacks have become increasingly scarce.

Lima has always been a seat of political power, ever since Pizarro and his little band of companions founded it over four centuries ago. The Peruvian state, whether represented by a viceroy, a republican dictator, or a constitutional president, has always spoken with great authority. Colonial Peru was a kingdom, like New Spain, or old Spain itself, and its government was, in its spirit, if not in its form, a replica of the metropolitan government. As the title implies, the viceroy was the king's alter ego in his overseas dominions. He was surrounded by pomp and ceremony that awed the impressionable masses of the country. Men did not lightly contradict him or oppose him and expect to go on living. All his agents and underlings—captain generals and governors, corregidors and judges—stood in the long shadow of his omnipotence and shared in his immunities. It was only when the creoles or colonial-born Spaniards grew so numerous and bold in the late eighteenth century that the stage was set to challenge the ancient and august pretensions of Spain in the Americas.

During the Wars of Independence, Lima played a hard-to-win game with the patriots. There were deep-seated attachments to

Spain that were not easy to eradicate, and there was a reluctance to give up the imperial prerogatives of a viceregal capital for the limitations of a republic shorn of the outer provinces. The appetite for intrigue of a volatile and pleasure-loving populace, without many convictions, except as they affected one's personal interests, bewildered the straightforward mind of San Martín and exasperated Bolívar, himself no stranger to artifice or pretense. But Lima had the habit of rule, so after Ayacucho it continued to dominate the new and curtailed Peruvian Republic. The republicans did not put on such a good show as the Spaniards had, and some of the new politicos were upstarts with very unregal manners, but Lima endured the blustery generals and the stodgy civilian presidents because she was still mistress of Peru—and Peru was no trifling morsel for any city to reign over.

Colonial Lima was much more than the capital of the largest viceroyalty in history. It was the scene of the vivid and dramatic life whose follies and crimes, and comedy and tragedy, Ricardo Palma has evoked so brilliantly in his *Tradiciones Peruanas,* that is the favorite reading of literate Peruvians.[25] Somehow the intensity of passions of the Conquest left its mark on the spirit of the city, and the recurrent earthquakes reminded its people of how ephemeral were all their hopes and satisfactions. The pulse of the city beat faster than it did in Mexico City and in Bogotá. So there was a tendency to take their pleasures while there still was time, and night and fog and the heavy doors of castellated houses hid their amours and intrigues, their *engaños* or deceits and their revenges. The victim might be a too concupiscent viceroy, like the Conde de Neiva, or the too insistent suitor of a lady beyond his social pale. The day was reserved for the obligations of piety and charity, for display and promenade and talk, and for the work of managing the business of city and viceroyalty.

Some of the colonial cities and towns have survived into the republican era as museum pieces and monuments of antiquity. Perhaps the mines on which they depended for their brief glories have been worked out, as at Ouro Preto in Minas Geraes, or the economics of the republics have found no other sustenance for them. So, if they are accessible by modern transportation, they become tourist attractions and objects of local veneration. First of such places is Cuzco, former capital of the Inca Empire, where the principal event of the year is the Inti-Rami, or Indian festival.[26] An archaeological and historical prodigy, it has few visible means of support and is a hardy beggar at the doors of the national treasury, while the UN has also sent a group of international experts to plan measures for its rehabilitation. Among others in the same category are Potosí, once one of the largest cities in the hemisphere; Loja, hidden away in a mountain corner of Ecuador; and, for that matter, Quito, too; Popayán in Colombia; Guanajuato in Mexico; and Trinidad in Cuba. Long after independence, many cities that lay off the main lines of travel kept their rustic and easygoing atmosphere. Though capital of an independent nation, Asunción has changed remarkably little with the years. Isolated, in spite of airlines, in the plains of eastern Bolivia, Santa Cruz de la Sierra still conserves much of the Arcadian air that Herndon and Gibbon found a century ago in that "frontier town of the Spanish race." [27] Its people lived independent of the outside world and with little effort enjoyed the fruits of a bountitiful nature. Moreover, the American naval officers encountered "a degree of kindness and politeness seldom met with in fashionable parts of the world."

POTOSÍ

Though silver has long since given way to tin as the source of its local economy, the famous mining city of Potosí is only a shell of its former self. It was founded in 1545 at the foot of the conical *cerro* which appears on the coat of arms of the republic of Bolivia. It quickly became the richest mining camp in Peru, and in all the world, and made the fortunes of several of the early conquistadores. From the beginning it was a turbulent place and its chronic disorders and street battles several times challenged the power of the viceregal authority.[28] Its miners and merchants lived sumptuously and violently in an atmosphere of tensions that seemed accentuated by the peculiarly trying climate of its 14,000 feet altitude. Father Acosta called its mines "the greatest treasure that ever was in this world." [29] Father Vázquez de Espinosa, who saw it in the early seventeenth century, said that it was "the largest settlement to be found in all the Indies." [30] Among its permanent residents were more than 4,000 Spanish mine- and mill-owners, and merchants. There were also many of the veterans known as *soldados honrados,* of whom Father Vázquez wrote: "The truth is that many of them are lost souls; it would be better if they would work or try to make a living some other way, for they are the chief cause of the troubles that are apt to arise in that kingdom." In addition to the silks and other luxuries which he saw for sale in the shops, he said that the taverns of the city dispensed annually over a million and a half jugs of wine. The Frenchman, Acarette du Biscay, who visited Peru by way of Buenos Aires during the years 1657–59, reported that between 300 and 400 Spaniards capable of bearing arms, and about as many mestizos, lived in Potosí.[31] He found its inhabitants quarrelsome and arrogant, and given to display. He said that it was customary to wear three or four leather vests as protection against sword thrusts. There was still great wealth in the town after over a century of working the mines, and many individuals had fortunes of three and four million pesos. Women were kept indoors "to a much greater extent than in Spain," and were reported to keep themselves "intoxicated" with coca. When the itinerant "Inca" Concolorcorvo saw Potosí in 1770, there were only about 12,000 people in the city, and the mines were in decay.[32] He said that "in spite of so much wealth, there is no sumptuous building in the town, with the exception of the mint—which is truly magnificent." The inhabitants were so contentious that two men seldom remained friends for a week. The only constancy appeared to be in the pursuit of "the amorous passions," from which lucrative occupation several of the local harlotry had recently retired to live munificently after forcing their current paramours into marriage. Joseph Andrews, who saw Potosí at the end of the colonial period, said: "It looks like the city of a prince of sin, strange, deserted, solitary, mysterious, a place of evil enchantment."[33]

There are a good many new cities in Latin America. Some were drowsy *pueblos* that vegetated through the colonial period, but took on a fresh lease of life in the last century to become places of importance like Montevideo and Rosario, now the second city in Argentina. Some are brand-new cities, created to satisfy some specific need in a nation's economic or political life. Of these are Antofagasta, the principal port of northern Chile, not founded until 1870; La Plata, in Argentina, founded in 1882, and already rechristened as Evita Perón; Torreón, a bustling commercial center in northern Mexico, only seventy years old; and, even younger, Manizales, an important provincial capital and coffee market in Colombia. Belo Horizonte and Goiania, capitals respectively of the Brazilian States of Minas Geraes and Goyez, are fiat cities, made to order after a preconceived plan, like Washington and Canberra. With a population of over a third of a million people, Belo Horizonte is one of the most attractive cities of South America. The government of the Brazilian republic has long considered the establishment of a new federal capital in an area reserved for the purpose on the far plateau of Goyaz, where the Arcadian environment would presumably be favorable to the improvement of the public service. Though the proposal to transfer the seat of government from Rio de Janeiro is revived from time to time by some Catonian legislator as a cathartic for the political morals of the country, no concrete steps have yet been taken in that direction. And meanwhile, the government continues to erect more buildings in the present capital to house the federal bureaucracy whose members would be very reluctant to accept the alternative of a purifying exile in the *sertão*.

In certain Latin American countries there has evolved a trichotomy of cities—a triple pattern of urban functionalism. The three basic purposes of the city—political, economic, and social or cultural—are represented in an unusual degree by as many different cities, instead of being concentrated in a single metropolis, as is still the rule in most of the republics. Whatever the other functions which it may serve, one city is essentially a political capital, a seat of government. Another is, above all, an economic city, a center of industry and business, and devoted primarily to the creation and distribution of wealth. The third is literally the urbane city, a center of civilization, that specializes in the arts of living. It may excel in cultural attainments, but not necessarily so. It is liable to be the favorite city of a whole people—the *ciudad querida,* or beloved city—the place which they prefer to visit in their leisure. Its deepest attachments are not of interest, but of sentiment, and its most cherished values are of the spirit. In Spain itself, the threefold pattern exists in Madrid, Barcelona, and Seville. Though the pattern is not as clear in its details, it is represented in Italy by Rome and Turin and Florence. In Latin America, a classic example is found in Brazil in the urban triad of Rio de Janeiro, São Paulo, and Bahia. Other examples are Mexico City—Monterrey—Guadalajara, in Mexico; and in Colombia, the trichotomous division of cities appear in Bogotá, Medellín, and the gracious old colonial city of Popayán.

THE CAPITALS

The normal tendency in the republics is for the capital to dominate and dwarf all other cities. This monopolistic condition is a heritage of the colonial regime, when, to serve the purposes of imperial policy, power and wealth and culture were encouraged to gravitate to the seat of government. The design has persisted in its original simplicity in Argentina, Chile, Costa Rica, Cuba, the Dominican Republic, Paraguay, Peru, Uruguay, and Venezuela. No secondary city approaches in influence or population the commanding position of the capital in any of those countries. A similar situation exists to a more incomplete degree in the Central American republics of Guatemala, Panama, and El Salvador. It does not prevail in Bolivia, Ecuador, Nicaragua, and in the three major nations listed above, that is, Brazil, Colombia, and Mexico. The Bolivian cities—Cochabamba, Oruro, Sucre, Potosí, Santa Cruz—isolated from one another by long distances, went their separate ways, and developed characters of their own. They became ingrown and particularistic in their attitude toward each other. Though La Paz came to fill a certain political void among all these centrifugal leanings, and supplied an artificial cohesion to their divisions, the other cities have tended to regard it as a parasite that preys on the puny wherewithal of the country.[34] In Ecuador, Quito is not even the largest city of the republic and is forced to treat Guayaquil with the respect and consideration due its superior enterprise and vitality. As for Nicaragua, León and Granada would never willingly acknowledge the supremacy of Managua, the parvenu capital, which owes its position to their own bitter and irreconcilable rivalry.[35]

The predominant position of the average capital can be expressed in terms of the wide disparity which generally exists between its population and that of the larger provinvial cities. While metropolitan Lima has a population of over 600,000, Arequipa,

the second city in Peru, has less than 80,000 inhabitants. Cuzco
has over 45,000, Trujillo less than 40,000, and Chiclayo about
33,000. In Chile, of about 6,000,000 people, well over 1,000,000
live in Santiago. In the port city of Valparaiso, which is really
an economic appendage of the capital, as Callao is of Lima, there
are about 200,000 people, and Concepción, the third city of Chile,
has less than 90,000. About 660,000 Cubans live in Havana, but
only about 120,000 in Santiago, and 80,000 in Camaguey. In
Uruguay, the contrast is even greater, for Montevideo has about
750,000 inhabitants, or almost a third of the total population of
the country. Paysandú, the second city, has only some 46,000
people and Mercedes about 35,000. None of the Paraguayan cities
are large, and Asunción and its suburbs have less than 150,000
people. Villarica, the second in size, has only about 28,000, including those in its "municipal district" which corresponds to an
American county. Of about 18,000,000 Argentines, nearly 5,000,-
000 live in metropolitan Buenos Aires, a serious disproportion in
what is largely an agricultural country. Four other cities—
Rosario (465,000), Córdoba (350,000), La Plata, or Evita Perón
(217,000), and Santa Fé (168,000)—add approximately an ad-
ditional 1,200,000 to the urban population of the republic.

The capital, in the centralized republics like Peru and Chile,
by a descending hierarchy of provincial governors, departmental
prefects, and "political chiefs," controls the political life of the
country as effectively as any Spanish viceroy or captain general
ever did. The ultimate repository of power at the bottom of the
pyramid is the *jefe político* or local boss, who delivers the votes
in one direction and, in the other, transmits orders and favors
from the capital to the citizenry. The facilities of modern transportation and communications have strengthened the hold of the
metropolis on the rest of the country. The radio carries the voice
of authority to the ends of the republic, perhaps to blare out of a
loud-speaker in the plaza and disturb the long siestas of a provincial town. Planes carry newspapers that embody the current
thinking of the capital, the *papeleo* of administration, and im-
portant-looking bureaucrats on inspection junkets to the interior.
For example, whereas Peruvian government officials formerly
went to Iquitos by way of the Panama Canal and the Amazon,

with sometimes an incidental side trip to New York, they can now fly to the city on the Marañon in a few hours.

The capital becomes the show window of the country. It is modernized and glamorized with electric lights, wide boulevards or *granvias* and Paris-like promenades, and impressive public buildings. Airports like Limatambo, and Ministro Pistarini at Buenos Aires would be the envy of New York or Chicago. Private interests contribute to the general effect with attractive shops, neon lights, and monumental apartment houses. It is a mecca of money and men. As the banking and financial center of the country, riches flow naturally to it, for investment or for keeping or spending. For those who make their riches in the provinces are inclined to spend it in the capital, where they are likely to maintain their homes for much of the year. The more ambitious and promising youth of the country are accustomed to go to the capital for their education. Too often, lured by the spell of the big city, and the far greater opportunities for advancement—and fame, they do not return to their home towns to apply the fruits of their training to the needs of an often backward community. Thus, there are liable to be too many physicians and other professional men in the capital and often there are too few in the provincial centers, to take care of the minimum needs of the local population.

THE PROBLEM OF URBANIZATION

With a few exceptions, like Brazil and Peru, Latin America is overurbanized, especially when one considers the basic nature of its economy and the current state of its development. In most countries there is not enough public money to go around, in order to finance the modernization of all the cities at one time. So the provincial towns are skimped and what money there is is liable to be lavished on the capital and whatever other cities can exert enough political pressure on the national treasury. If anything, there are not enough cities in Brazil to furnish the essential cultural and economic services a society has a right to expect of them. So there is a very wide cultural lag between Rio and São Paulo and the southern coastal zone in general, on the one hand, and the vast hinterland, on the other. In Minas Geraes, an important state of 8,000,000 people, Belo Horizonte is the only city of over 100,000 inhabitants. Juiz da Fora, the second city of the state, has less than 90,000. In the state of São Paulo, conditions are much healthier, for the large interior towns like Ribeirao Preto have had not only the local pride and initiative, but also the resources necessary for making them attractive cities in their own right. As it is, Brazil has one of the highest ratios of rural and village to urban population of any country in the world. The nation's fundamental problem in this connection is not an excess of city population but the too rapid growth of Rio and São Paulo in relation to that of other cities and to the accommodations which they are able to offer to the horde of newcomers from the rest of the country. In Peru, the persistent tradition of Lima as a viceregal capital explains her extraordinary position in every field of the national life. Moreover, the masses of conservative and village-minded Indians in the sierra have proven to be a brake on any general movement of people to the capital. Lima draws rather on the coastal regions to north and south for the accretion of her population than on the mountain lands to the east.

Much of the early history of the Argentine Republic was bedeviled by the bitter struggle between Buenos Aires and the provinces. The issue at stake was whether the country should be ruled from "the Port" by a centralized form of government, as in Chile and Peru, or by a federal system, such as Mexico had early adopted. For a long time there were intermittent civil wars between "unitarians" and "federals," that delayed the economic development of the rich interior. It was only when a suitable formula was worked out which would recognize the unusual position of Buenos Aires and include her in a "federal district," instead of permitting her to use the all-important province of the same name as the instrument of her ambitions for domination, that domestic peace came to the federalized republic. Domingo Faustino Sarmiento, who was president from 1868 to 1874, described the intervening strife in *Facundo,* or *Civilization and Barbarism.* In Sarmiento's book, Buenos Aires was the exclusive seat of civilized customs in Argentina while the interior was backward and rustic, with rude and uncouth manners personified in the gaucho.

Until independence, a dull provincial town of no particular

distinction or charm, once the heavy hand of Spain was removed from the young viceroyalty of the River Plate, Buenos Aires quickly came into her own. As foreign goods poured into the promising city, ideas and habits accompanied them. So there was a new air of sophistication about the place, as the port city looked irrevocably toward Europe and snobbishly turned its well-tailored back on the vulgarities of the interior. A deep-seated social incompatibility gradually developed between the cosmopolitan splendor of Buenos Aires and the modest airs of even the more progressive provincial cities that only time can eradicate.

The process of excessive urbanization which has characterized most of the republics and affected chiefly the growth of capital cities like Caracas and Santiago has been promoted by a variety of factors. A network of paved roads converging on the local Rome and the cheap busses which use them on long interurban runs have brought the experience of travel within reach of the poorest segments of the population. Also, word has reached the remotest corners of the land that in the great city there may be jobs for the taking in the new industries or on the public works projects of government. Also, the other attractions of the capital are better advertised than ever: the bright lights, the tinny pleasures, the fancy store windows, the daily ceremony of changing the palace guard, even the noises of progress.

The larger cities have sometimes flourished unduly because they satisfy deep human and social needs which should be filled by the satisfactions of rural and village life and by the cultural offerings—in the wider sense of the term—of the lesser cities and towns. The spread is now too great between the two extremes, and only by much intelligent and patient effort by government, communities, and individuals, can the gap be more nearly closed, to the progressive enrichment of the national life. This end can be accomplished without the violence of a social revolution dictated by political considerations. In other words, the forced partition of large properties, as is now occurring in Bolivia and Guatemala, is not the proper answer to the problem. For the peasant farmer, unprepared for the responsibilities of ownership and management, may only be exchanging an easygoing King Log for a politically rapacious King Stork, with the national economy the ultimate loser.

CITY *vs.* COUNTRY

Latin America has failed to make rural life attractive. The gradual breakdown of the old hacienda system was not only caused by the superior lure of the city that tended to make an absentee landlord of the *hacendado*.[36] For too many of the old semifeudal lords of the land, or their descendants, have preferred to live on the Avenida Alvear and in Lima's San Isidro or in the Vedado, and visit their estates only occasionally. They often maintain show places on the Pampa or in the Central Valley of Chile that may be little more than sumptuous vacation resorts for their families and friends. Thereby they tend to forego their natural role of leadership in the local community and the responsibility for its development that goes with their superior position and preparation.

But the whole latifundian system had been in a state of flux for some time. By removing the traditional labor base, the emancipation of the slaves in 1888 broke down the pattern of large fazendas that had characterized northern Brazil since early colonial days. In Mexico, the system was liquidated by the Revolution of 1911, only to creep back later in places under new ownership. In parts of Bolivia, landowners, increasingly distrustful of the *indiada*, spent less and less time on their lonely estates. In the tropical countries, efficient company plantations pointed to new roads in the production of export crops. In the meantime, hacienda agriculture, formerly a very gratifying way of life— but scarcely a business—was forced by a chain of circumstances to enter the realm of economics. New competitive conditions in world markets—as for cacao and sugar, rising costs of operation, and growing restiveness of farm workers, accounted for most of the pressure for change in large-scale agriculture. If they expected to survive under the changing order of things, the hacendados would have to spend some time on the farm and maybe wind up by settling down there permanently, and visiting the city only when there was nothing else to do.

The category of middle-class farmers or rancheros is not yet strong enough or numerically important enough to be a major factor in the rural society. This promising element has limited strongholds of influence in the Argentine *colonias*, in some of the

Mexican valleys, in the newer irrigated zones of the Peruvian littoral, in wide areas of Brazil, and among the *finquero* class in the "mild" coffee countries about the Caribbean. The farther extension of its preponderance would be the strongest guarantee of social and economic improvement in the rural life of Latin America.

A much more difficult phase of the whole problem of city *vs.* country consists of the millions of subsistence farmers.[37] Their status varies greatly, but the majority of them have a common denominator in poverty. Many of them live outside the conventional economic system altogether. Their problem cannot be solved by giving each of them forty acres and a tractor and a loan from the agricultural bank. It is something much more fundamental, for large numbers of them represent a major human reclamation problem. In other words, they may first have to be rescued from disease and ignorance, from chronic nomadism and the curse of primitive farming methods. Yet, since there are so many of them and fundamentally of good human raw material, they are well worth whatever efforts may be required for their redemption from backwardness.

The above are some of the factors involved in striking a better balance between the urban and rural sides of Latin American civilization. Other factors are more roads and schools, rural electrification, public health clinics, and something like the American institution of the county agent. A good deal is being done by some of the governments themselves, by the initiative of private corporations like the United Fruit Company, and by means of the co-operative technical programs which are sponsored jointly by the Institute of Inter-American Affairs and the participating country.

The too rapid growth of their populations creates many acute problems for the cities. Public utilities frequently find the demands of industry and domestic users on their facilities beyond their actual or potential capacity, with the result that water and electricity are rationed and only available at certain hours of the day. Shortages of both are liable to be among the principal harassments of city living in Latin America. Heavy inflation of prices, usually beginning with rents and spreading to foodstuffs and clothing, normally accompanies any large and continued influx of population from the interior. The work of the social agencies of government, including the police and charitable establishments, is greatly intensified. Provincials, like the Indians who migrate to Lima from the mountains, bring their bacilli with them and serve as new foci of infection that add to the burden of the public health department. Similar attendant problems affect the national government as well. For example, any considerable dislocation of rural population and its transplanting in a metropolitan center reduces the available food supply of the country proportionately, as each former producer of food becomes only a consumer of the things he grew before. In the same way cities may outgrow their customary, and sometimes precarious, sources of foodstuffs, a hazard that in the case of Rio, is sometimes aggravated by the breakdown of local produce transport.

THE CITY IN LATIN AMERICAN CIVILIZATION

The civic sense in Latin America, as in Spain, is a matter of municipal pride. It takes form in devotion to a city and a desire for its glorification and beautification. The nation does not arouse the same sentimental attachment, for popular distrust of the national government is widespread and deep-seated. National patriotism tends to be a high-sounding abstraction that is taught in the public schools and cultivated in army barracks. It has definite overtones of bellicosity toward the neighbors, and in the new welfare states it implies a certain interested enthusiasm for the supreme giver of handouts. The republic is a relatively new and artificial entity, set up more or less arbitrarily by drawing certain lines on a map and then warning strangers to keep outside the lines. For the process to be complete, there must be a flag, a song which no one would ever sing of his own free will, an army, a constitution, and a president, who is preferably a general. To attract friends, it ultimately learns the trick of giving things away: wage increases, price controls, subsidized housing, land that it has taken from someone else.

The cities were created long ago because a Spaniard was liable to be unhappy without them, as the Paraguayan was without his orange tree or the Chilean countryman without his fig tree, and they grew because they fulfilled the deep aspirations of his spirit. They represented an unbroken tradition that survived wars and natural cataclysms and the overthrow of states. They were of a size to be easily encompassed by the eye or that any man could traverse by his own locomotion. The sight of Rio seen from Sugar Loaf or Corcovado, from some point of vantage on the Tijuca road or from across the bay; of Santiago at sunset from the Cerro of Santa Luzia or the higher level of San Cristóbal; or of Mexico City from the passes over the surrounding heights, is enough to lift the heart of one who dwells there. He could well salute his city with the same awe and reverence as the subject of the Inca, on entering Cuzco, bowed to the imperial capital and repeated a prayer to its guardian deities. To the citizen, the city is his; the country belongs to the government. The country is usually too big, and too much of it is likely to be forbidding and unfriendly. There are too many mountains, too much desert or jungle, or too much emptiness, as on the Pampa, where there is nothing to hitch one's heart to. There is nothing to be cherished as a city plaza of his own making can be. The average inhabitant of a Latin American city knows remarkably little about his country that lies beyond the immediate horizon and off the beaten tracks. And the beaten tracks are liable to be short and narrow and uncomfortable, so one ends by staying home. For his city is something intimate and endearing that he can feel an affection for and in whose accomplishments he can take pride. It is no wonder that the city is almost uniformly better governed than is the country.

The citizens commemorate with pomp and splendor the centenaries of their cities, many of them anniversaries of four centuries of communal life. They celebrate the long milestones of their history with pageantry and oratory, and their scholars write beautiful books as mementos of the city's greatness, as Daniel Samper Ortega did of Bogota.[38] And the municipality may publish the records of the colonial Cabildo, to preserve for future generations the moving human drama of its memorabilia, as Lima did.[39]

So the cities are forever striving for their greater adornment and distinction. To that common end, their administrative leaders, and their artists and architects and engineers combine their efforts in the tasks of city planning.[40] Dictators and presidents, and mayors like Pereira Passos, Rio's great perfect, make it their particular ambition to leave the city a more imposing and stately thing than they found it. If what they leave is a monument to themselves, and perhaps to their individual vanity, its usufruct belongs to the city and its citizens. It is seldom that their personal vainglories overreach themselves, though other crying needs of the country may have to be sacrificed to provide the all-important metropolis with new avenues and monuments and sumptuous public buildings, and such practical accessories to its daily life as markets and waterworks and sewage systems.

ARCHITECTURE OF THE CITIES

The appearance of the major cities has been transformed, often very radically, and sometimes unequally and chaotically, as Mexico City was. Sometimes the face of an urban dowager like Bogotá is gently lifted, or passion of renovation transfigures the heart of a city, as is happening to Caracas. For the most part, the changes in Buenos Aires appear to follow an orderly plan, but the phenomenal growth of São Paulo has an elemental and cosmic quality about it that seems to transcend any human planning. Though four of the Caribbean capitals—Santo Domingo and Guatemala City, Managua and San Salvador—have been largely destroyed or heavily damaged by earthquake or hurricane during the present century, the pattern of their reconstruction has had to be held within the modest limitations of the resources available for the purpose.

The look of the public buildings of Latin America has run the gamut from the severe classicism of the Herrera School through the baroque, then reverting to a neoclassic style and later to a pseudobaroque or "world's fair" type of architecture, exemplified in Rio's Monroe Palace and Mexico's *Bellas Artes*.[41] At present, the most interesting structural developments are in the new prodigies of concrete and glass done in the modern functional style. Some of the Latin American designers like Niemeyer in Brazil have proved to be worthy disciples of Le Corbusier and the other patron saints of the new architectural evangel.[42] French influence has been so strong in Buenos Aires that much of it is very Parisian in appearance. Except infrequently and in minor decorative details, the Indians left no mark on the predominant architecture of Latin America until our own time. On the other hand, in the early colonial period, Arabic or *mudéjar* influence was occasionally seen in the work of the Andalusian builders who came to the New World. Since most colonial architecture was ecclesiastical, the Church was the typical product of the builder's art and on it were lavished the ingenuity and imagination of the designers. With a few exceptions, like the work of Aleijadinho at Ouro Preto, and the distinctive façades of the baroque Jesuit churches, the architecture of colonial Brazil was not noteworthy. As would be expected, there is no more uniformity in the public architecture of the average large city in Latin America, like Mexico City, than there is in London or New York. In São Paulo, above the vestiges of earlier periods, the profile of the restless city is punctuated with tall skyscrapers.

Spaniards brought their residential architecture to the New World, in the sixteenth century, as they brought all their lares and mores. And their descendants and later comers seemed to see no good reason to change it very much until recent times. Externally it was plain and solid, and on the inside it offered privacy and protection for family living. It was usually a one-story house, though if the family were big and affluent enough, there might be two floors. All over Latin America there are still hundreds of miles of streets bordered by such houses. One can still see them in Celaya or Tunja, or Salta or Olinda, or in a thousand other towns, or, for that matter, in Havana and Bogotá and Lima, for they are very durable buildings. The walls were usually of adobe and the roof of red tiles baked in the neighborhood. The front wall was whitewashed and flush with the narrow sidewalk, that was laid of heavy slabs of stone. Women of the house had a habit of leaning on a cushion in the front window and watching the local world go by, and if the windows were barred, the youth of the town courted their *novias* through the *reja,* as their ancestors had done in Spain. The street door was stout and heavy and when it was locked with the big key, only a battering ram could have broken into the security of the interior. If the house was of two stories, there was likely to be a balcony or two. Some of these were only projections over the street from upper bedrooms and guarded by a balustrade. In Lima and Cuzco it was the fashion to build large closed balconies of finely ornamented woodwork. Then the women of the house could observe the passers-by in the street below without being seen, just as one could from behind the jalousies of Venice and the Levant. Survivals of this distinctive feature of Peruvian colonial architecture can be seen in the older parts of Lima. One of the finest examples of this type of construction is the famous Casa Torre-Tagle, which is now used as the quarters of the Ministry of Foreign Affairs. Modern architects have preserved this attractive and distinctive motif in many new buildings, including the city hall or *ayuntamiento* in the Plaza de Armas.

Behind the front entrance and beyond an intervening hallway, there was located the all-important patio or courtyard. The size and layout of the patio varied with the means and position of the owner. It was a very Spanish thing, with Roman antecedents, and it made of the house or *casa* an *hogar* or home. Its adornment and care reflected the good taste and the domestic instincts of successive generations of wives and mothers. For here in good weather the family spent most of its time. All or part of it might be paved with glazed red or figured tiles, as in the beautiful patios of Seville, and, if water were plentiful, there might even be a fountain. There were flowers and shrubbery, and song birds or a parrot to amuse the children with his stream of chatter, and perhaps a mischievous coati or other tamed small animal of the wilds for a pet. Often there were orange trees or other fruit trees, to add to the beauty and delight of the place. Sometimes, to the rear of the kitchen and servants' quarters, there might be a second patio with pleasant walks and seats among shade trees and flowering bushes, as there was in the Casa San Pablo in Caracas. The rooms of the house opened off the main courtyard, and if there were a second story it was surrounded by an open gallery to which stairs went up.

Many of these gracious habitations have survived in the older sections of the cities that were the seats of the colonial aristocracy, as in Botafogo and Laranjeiras in Rio, and in Bogotá, and in quiet old towns like Quito and Trujillo and Arequipa. But the architects no longer build them. For residential construction has gone the way of other building. After all, the "big houses" were made for an age that had more time for the elemental arts of living. They were designed as setting for a patriarchal way of life that placed a high value on space and ease and leisure. So the patio has disappeared from the ground plans of the modern designers, because it occupied too much ground. Other factors which have contributed to the change are: the pressure of high land values and increased building costs; the rise of new moneyed classes who never know the peculiar charm of the old seignorial homes; the arrival of "the servant problem" in Latin America; the craze for the new electrical gadgetry that did not fit easily into old expansive mansions built for an unmechanical age; the competition of the automobile and outside activities that have made the home less important than it formerly was; and the desire to imitate the living habits of foreigners.

Now residential architecture runs to "villa" and "chalets," and to apartment houses that look like those in Bombay or Cairo or Stockholm or Brooklyn. There are new suburbs and "subdivisions" and housing "developments," like Lomas de Chapultepec and the Pedregal in Mexico, San Isidro and Los Angeles at Lima, and Jardim America at São Paulo. They contain houses with yards around them in which nobody ever seems to sit, instead of patios inside which people were always sitting and relaxing. In spite of the revolution in the techniques of living, Latin Americans cannot accustom themselves to taking their informal ease within view of the public. So they may build high walls about the yards to provide the seclusion that the patio once gave them. The houses are full of modern conveniences, there are plenty of electrical outlets, and the plumbing arrangements are the last word, even to the added European feature of the bidet. But the current may be turned off at 6 P.M. or there may not be any water after dark or on Thursdays. Many of these houses are very elegant and sumptuous, and their design and planning provide a perpetual field day for the architects, who in some places like Lima are the pre-eminent artists. They indulge in unlimited experimentation with materials and decorative motifs, sometimes with striking results, and always with a variety of effects.

STREETS AND PLAZAS

The colonial cities required one extra-wide thoroughfare where the members of the local aristocracy could exhibit themselves and their finery and equipages to the best advantage. Avenues and boulevards did not become a pressing matter until the automobile dropped the miracle of multiple horsepower into the eager hands of Latin Americans and thereby created a major traffic problem. The problem was further complicated by the survival of a network of narrow streets and alleyways that had perfectly well served the needs of oxcarts and horse-drawn carriages and mule trains, and it was aggravated by the resistance of an individualistic people to any controls over their right to run down or to be run down.[43] Anyway, to be a city and not an overgrown colonial village, there had to be a local counterpart of Fifth Avenue or the Champs Elysées, or preferably of both.

So the cities set about to refurbish the old broadways or to lay out new and pretentious avenues named for Christopher Columbus and Simón Bolívar, Woodrow Wilson and F. D. Roosevelt, the United States Marine Corps, and a host of local celebrities like Bernardo O'Higgins and José Artigas. The Avenida Rio Branco was slashed through the business district of Rio de Janeiro, not only to facilitate the flow of traffic, but to permit the freer circulation of air from off the bay over the hot city. The gardened Avenida Beira Mar, most splendid of all waterfront drives, follows the long curves of the bay shore for many miles, and beyond the low stone hills which shut off the sprawling bulk of Rio from the sea, reappears as the Avenida Atlantica and its prolongations. In Buenos Aires, the Avenida de Mayo follows much the same Parisian pattern as the Avenida Rio Branco. The government later opened two diagonal avenues—Julio Roca and Saenz Peña—that converge on the heart of the city at the Plaza de Mayo. Intersecting the Avenida de Mayo in an east-west direction is the vast open expanse of the Avenida 9 de Julio, probably the widest street in the world, its crossing a test of the pedestrian's timing and footwork. One of the finest of streets is the wide treelined Avenida de la Reforma, which connects the business district of Mexico City with Chapultepec Park. The principal mark left by Guadalajara's urge for modernity is the bright new Avenida Juárez, that has erased many of the familiar landmarks of the old city.

No phase of the transformation of Guadalajara has been handled with greater good taste than the skilled treatment of the paved plaza in front of the Cathedral, which has made it one of the most impressive spots in any city of the Western Hemisphere. Mexico City's most famous parks and plazas are all part and parcel of the ancient history of the place. Even the trees in Chapultepec are very old, and the Alameda was a favorite promenade in colonial times.[44] The Zócalo was the original site of the Aztec teocalli or sacrificial temple, and from the great square the viceroys long ruled New Spain. Of the other thousands of parks and plazas in Latin America, many are pretty and pleasant places, like São Paulo's little Jardim da Luz. Some are big and varied in their attractions, like Palermo, the Central Park of Buenos Aires. One may have an air of primitive mystery about it, like Los Caobos, Caracas's dark grove of giant mahogany trees. Some are only quiet little corners in a big city, where men may stop to rest on benches. Some are busy centers of movement, from which transportation lines radiate out over the city, like Lima's Plaza San Martín. Some are spots of rare beauty full of old memories, like Santiago's wooded acropolis of Santa Lucía. Sometimes they are surrounded with the stands and stalls of the little merchants of the town and of purveyors of food to the poor, as in the villages of Mexico. Many are only unpretentious open places among crowded streets and houses, where men take the sun on cool days or sit in the shade when it is hot, and where families parade around in the evening, while maybe a band plays waltzes or military marches above the quiet talk of the people, until the town goes home to bed. Like the passing patio of the old houses, they are a lasting source of simple pleasures that fill a very deep need in the lives of the population.

The parks and plazas, the *paseos* and *prados*, are generally punctuated with monuments commemorating something or somebody. The Latin Americans favor equestrian statuary for outdoor use, even though in his lifetime the subject may have been no hippophile and avoided horses like the plague. Maybe it was a gift horse donated by some foreign government that was added to the local collection of oversized bric-a-brac. The best-known statue in Latin American is the so-called "Caballito" or "Little Horse," which stands at the busy confluence of Avenidas Juárez and Reforma in Mexico City. The horse carries on its broad back the unheroic figure of Charles IV, penultimate King of Spain during the colonial regime. Though the Mexicans have long since eradicated all their vestiges of royalty from the republican scene, by some sardonic twist of irony they have preserved this ridiculous symbol of monarchy in their midst. Like the bronze Union generals who appeared in our northern cities after the Civil War, there are many prancing or rampant riders, that include the be-plumed Pizarro which stood so long in front of the Cathedral at Lima, and the dashing Garibaldi and balky O'Higgins in Buenos Aires. Sometimes there is considerable restraint and dignity in the conception of these statues, as in the tired San Martín in Lima, one of the best of the many monuments to the two great liberators of South America. Of sculptured groups, few have any special character or distinction. Among these is the rather flam-boyant Spanish monument on the Avenida Alvear in Buenos Aires. Among the monumental miscellany on the massive side are the modernistic Morelos on the Island of Janitzio in Mexico's Lake Patzcuaro, the lonely Christ atop Rio's Corcovado, Gen-eralissimo Trujillo's big Columbus lighthouse on Santo Domingo, the monstrous four-poster memorial to the Mexican Revolution, and "The Obelisk" in Buenos Aires. Probably the most amazing assortment of statuary in any one place on earth is in Buenos Aires' cemetery of La Recoleta, where are situated the tombs of most of Argentina's great. Besides a path in the forest of Chapultepec, that is frequented by students in late afternoon, is an engaging little fountain overlaid with figured tiles, with open book shelves on its sides, and dedicated to the memory of Miguel de Cervantes, creator of Don Quixote—a thing as unforgettable in its own fashion as is "the Caballito."

As in all places where people insist on living in the mass, there are slums in the cities of Latin America. For example, behind the fancy façades of Mexico and off the familiar tourist trails of the capital, there are human warrens—layers and rows of win-dowless and cell-like compartments that open onto a deep and narrow light well. Over the glamour of Rio, there hang the *favellas*, shack settlements that cling to the bare granite hills above the city's floor and beyond the reach of its water mains and sewers. Their inhabitants resist all the efforts of the municipal authorities to resettle them elsewhere, and, like Villon's vaga-bonds in medieval Paris, compose gay songs in their poverty for the Cariocas to sing at carnival time. In Lima, the lost people who huddle in the dust and dirt of San Cosmé spread their in-fection of crime and disease over the city. Though vast housing projects are being completed by governments, which are aware of conditions and solicitous for their improvement, the problem is sometimes of too great magnitude for any quick solution or even for its radical alleviation by the efforts of humane individuals and organizations.

While Latin American cities now vary greatly in salubrity, plague and pestilence, in the form of epidemics of cholera, small-pox, and yellow fever, have struck many of them in the past.[45] In the Indian countries, where soil and surface water are liable to be perennially polluted and the food supply contaminated, the dysenteries are endemic, as are other gastrointestinal diseases like typhoid. Though the incidence of malaria has been greatly cur-tailed in cities where effective drainage is possible, in places like Managua, Manoas, and Guayaquil, no methods of control have proved efficacious. Because of a combination of climatic and liv-ing conditions that favor infection, the tuberculosis rate in the average city of Latin America is inordinately high. Tropical cities that were pestholes, like Rio and Santos, Havana, Panama, and Guayaquil, have been cleaned up, sometimes by their own public health experts like Dr. Oswaldo Cruz of Brazil, and in certain respects are models of healthfulness. Mosquitoes have virtually vanished, as in Rio, or live on borrowed time, and the once ubiquitous buzzards—the urubu of Brazil and the zopilote of Mexico—that were once important auxiliaries of the public health services, and in Veracruz even protected by law from molestation in the streets, now have the professional standing of witch doc-tors. In all the mechanics of sanitation—water supply, the in-spection of food distribution, hospitals and clinics and dispen-saries, the institutional facilities for professional training, the provision of adequate funds by government—tremendous, even if unequal, progress has been made in the past quarter of a cen-tury. The water supply of Mexico City's three million inhabitants is still very suspect and some of its public markets would have made Montezuma blush with shame.

The cities not only express the peculiarities of the national character, but, unlike the urban centers of more standardized countries, each has a personality all its own, so that an observant stranger who was suddenly dropped into it, would not be liable to mistake it for another. The varied ingredients of their individuality may consist of an extraordinary physical setting, as in the case of Rio de Janeiro; their relative isolation from outside influences, as in Bogotá; the special circumstances of their history and social evolution, as in Lima; and the human amalgam that went into the forging of their population, as in Mexico City —or a composite in different proportions of several of these elements.[46]

MEXICO CITY

Mexicans call it México. To geography and the post office, it is Mexico, D. F. To the Aztecs, it was Tenochtitlán, with its symbolic connotation of an eagle and a serpent, a nopal cactus and a rock. To Cortés and his men it was briefly Colua. Since then, to the rest of the world it has been Mexico City.

It is now the fourth city in the hemisphere. It has more than 3,000,000 people, or nearly ten times its population at the beginning of the century. In the previous hundred years its inhabitants had little more than doubled. It has been an uneven and unhealthy increase. The city has grown beyond its economic foundations, for remarkable as has been the business development of Mexico City in recent years, the solid substance behind the impressive and plausible appearances is still too thin to support so great a city in the style which the rest of the country can afford. Symptomatic of the helter-skelter tempo of its progress is the juxtoposition of deep potholes in busy sidewalks, the steel skeletons of buildings begun years ago and never finished, and a widespread state of disrepair and decay in some quarters of the city, together with ultramodern hotels and restaurants and other pretentious evidences of new wealth and luxury, and such fantastic triumphs of architectural and landscape design as the new University City and the residential development of the Pedregal. Though the new capital of the Revolution is a parvenu, a certain innate sense of beauty and good taste in the race can save its extravagances from the taint of crudity.

In sheer interest, it is the foremost city in Latin America, as the country is the most interesting of the republics. It is not an easy city to understand or to come to terms with, even though it may inspire admiration and a feeling of wonderment. It is unpredictable in its moods and explosive and unserene. Underneath the surface placidity and the courtesy of its people, its temper can be choleric and violent. In this respect, it is very Mexican and in no sense a sophisticated world metropolis. It has rough edges that are chiseled out of obsidian. At heart, it is very provincial and xenophobic, for its roots are deep in the troubled past of Anahuac and it has borrowed only grudgingly from other cultures. A sanguinary thread has run through the dramatic tapestry of its history that has so many memories of stress and conflict. That it lies in sight of sleeping volcanoes has more than a coincidental significance. The president who rules the land from the old palace in the Zócalo sits not only in the seat of the viceroys, but in that of the Aztec "emperors." The low sad undertones of the place are still Indian, though now it belongs to the mestizo, maybe for good, as it belonged for centuries to the Spaniard.

BUENOS AIRES

Buenos Aires is the only real world city in Latin America. It is not a matter of relative size, for Chicago and Berlin are larger, but of the undefinable atmosphere or tone of universality which belongs to the few cosmopolitan metropolises of the planet. It is truly a great and magnificent city, as the king of Spain might call it if it were still his to honor and order about. It is not an Argentine city in the sense that Córdoba or Tucumán is. Nor is it a Spanish-American city, but a European city. Its faces and tongues come from many places—the Mediterranean lands, the so-called Aryan countries of northern Europe, the Slavic world, the Levant. About all its inhabitants have in common is a deep and enthusiastic faith in its future. The people are themselves too "foreign" to distrust the foreigner as the Mexicans do.

Unlike Rio and Mexico City, it owes nothing of its splendor and promise to its site, which is as featureless as that of Calcutta or Houston. But it owes much to its position as the gateway—and chief beneficiary—of the riches of the Pampa, of which it takes a heavy toll for its services as middleman. It is a business city, full of the movement and turmoil of accomplishment and of the material evidences of great wealth. Its people live well and indulge as freely as the law allows in all the amenities of civilized living. It is a great publishing center and all the institutional trappings of culture abound, but its original contributions to the

376 THIS NEW WORLD

intellectual and artistic store of humanity are sparse. The Por-
teños or "people of the port" are a proud and arrogant lot, enterprising and resourceful, and aggressively aware of the immense
latent potentialities of the country. They are not a race, for there
is no Argentine race, as there is a Brazilian or a Chilean race.
There *was* an Argentine race, before the influx of European immigrants swamped the original stock and diluted its blood and
its civilization. Another race is in process of formation, but, despite the official propaganda of *argentinidad*, the elements that are
to go into its making are still far from integration in a definite
racial pattern. In many respects a superior people, the inhabitants
of the Argentine Republic tend to fall a helpless prey to the
machinations of designing politicos, because they have no common
tradition or national "soul" or *alma* to rally around. Much of their
assertiveness and "cockiness" that are often so irksome to well-
disposed outsiders is doubtless an unconscious cover for a certain
confusion of thought and need for self-assurance.

Buenos Aires is not a gay or lighthearted city, as world repute
would sometimes have it. Only in the architectural sense is it the
"Paris of South America." It takes its pleasures rather seriously
and self-consciously, and without the abandon and spontaneity
with which Rio plays and sins its peccadilloes. Most of its citizens
are solid burghers who stay home nights and worry about tomorrow's pesos and politics.

SÃO PAULO

São Paulo is singular and unique among all the major Latin
American cities. It is a wild municipal maverick that carries no
country's brand. The others, whatever their individual peculiarities of temperament, all have telltale earmarks of the same
Hispanic breed. It is a boomtown, rugged and sometimes raw,
and always dynamic. It is self-confident and positive, boastful
and purposeful, and brags of its intention to overtake Buenos
Aires in a few years. Like Saul of Tarsus, for whom it was named,
it is of the head rather than of the heart, and can only be properly
evaluated in terms of statistics. Its people are businesslike and
unemotional, except where their interests are concerned. They
are not given to the moods and tantrums of more schizophrenic
cities, and tend to look down on the Cariocas of Rio as somewhat

lightheaded folk overaddicted to moonlight and fleshpots. In fact, São Paulo is scornful of its more static sisters throughout Brazil. Visiting American businessmen glow with appreciation and understanding as they watch its bustling people dash to and fro in the pursuit of *cruzeiros* and *contos*. They find the local lack of palaver and extraneous "nonsense" a very congenial and refreshing relief from the more oriental protocol of business elsewhere.

São Paulo's dynamism dates from its very earliest times. It was founded exactly four hundred years ago as the Jesuit mission post of Saint Paul of Piratininga. As the priests ranged far and wide in search of Tupi souls to convert, the lay Portuguese and mestizo "Mamelucos" who settled about them on the plateau were even more adventurous and enterprising in hunting down the same Indians and selling them into slavery. As the Bandeirantes, they boldly penetrated the wilderness to the west beyond the Paraná and pushed northwest over the low divide into the basin of the Madeira, and even farther into the vast void of Brazil. They were true frontiersmen, like the early pioneers of our trans-Alleghany West. The Paulistas were never content to sit apathetically with what they had, but always moved to find more. Their restlessness and energy have not been due to the presence of any foreign element in the population—German or Italian—however eagerly foreigners may have entered into the acquisitive atmosphere of the place. They marked the place when it was still a village in Indian country and the only foreigners were the Portuguese.

For a long time, it was only another colonial town, though with more latent promise than the others. Then, in the last century it became the coffee capital of the world and began to grow mightily with the great state behind it. It reached up into Minas and west into Matto Grosso and south into Paraná, to add to the domain of its enterprise. It was built haphazard and without a conscious plan about its low rolling hills and deep gullies. Big business came to settle in the narrow streets of the famous "Triangle," while its operations spread out into the teeming industrial areas of the prodigious city. It makes no claims to cultural superiority, but would resent any imputation of Boeotianism from the neo-Athenians of more bookish places like Bogotá. It has too much on its mind to become a *ville de plaisir* or a center of tourist allurements. To foreigners out to enjoy themselves, it can be a very dull place, indeed.

RIO

For purposes of official publicity, Rio de Janeiro is the *Cidade Maravilhosa*—"The Marvelous City." Estacio de Sa, who sailed between the gigantic headlands at its entrance on a far-flung January morning, mistook the Bay of Guanabara for an estuary and called it Rio de Janeiro. It is not a river, but, like Acapulco, a dead-end indentation in a mountain-rimmed coast. Nor is there anything about its eternal greenery to suggest the midwinter of the north. It is the incomparable harbor of the planet, but it should be the port of paradise. Its overwhelming natural beauty is beyond all hyperbole and any propaganda is understatement. There is too much poetry in its setting for it ever to serve any prosaic purpose. It would be a fit abode for a race of supermen, but its awesome site would only make pigmies of them. It should be the pleasure capital of the world, and have no other function but the dispensation of delights to the human race.

It is the Sybaris of the South, cousin to Corinth and Ptolemaic Alexandria—a hedonistic city and place of languor and uninhibited desire, whose natural bent is for festivity and folly.[47] Its business should be turned over to the competent keeping of São Paulo and the federal government of Brazil removed from its orchidaceous atmosphere to some spot more conducive to sober contemplation and reflection. In spite of the plaintive image of Christ that overlooks the city, and of all those who in the name of St. Peter and John Calvin and Martin Luther have preached His gospel to its people, the Cariocas are Laodicean in matters of the holy faith. One cannot imagine the burning of heretics within their precincts, naturally as it might have come in the Spanish cities. They are pagan at heart, and the rest is a genial mummery of obeisance to the fatherly and forgiving God of the New Testament. After all, He may be one of them, for they say that "God is Brazilian," and they reason that only a divine hand could shield them from the consequences of their errors and frivolities.

Rio is the largest city that lies within the wide belt of the earth between Cancer and Capricorn. Some two million Cariocas cling to the sides of its rocky hills and the narrow shelf of land that skirts the bay and the sea, or swarm over the flats that stretch out to the northwest along the railroads as far as the great swamp of the Baixada. Men have struggled to make the most of the beauty that lies all about them, but at best their works have been a puny effort. Maybe the challenge would be too great for any people. In spite of the spurt that an occasional prefect gives to the implementation of its natural grandeur, the city's man-made splendor sometimes looks shabby and down at the heel. Sometimes the practical affairs of the glamorous city are badly run and the tempers of its temperamental citizens grow short. The Central Railway breaks down now and again and leaves the city isolated from its upcountry sources of fresh food. There is not enough water in the surrounding hills for the hydroelectric plants. The sewage water from the massed apartment houses and hotels in Copacabana runs out onto the crowded beach because there is no other place for it to go. After all, people who dwell in a corner of Eden should not be bothered with such mundane matters.

NOTES

1. On typical Spanish cities, see Walter M. Gallichan, *The Story of Seville* (London, 1910), and R. Trevor Davies, "Madrid under the House of Austria," in Ernest Barker, ed., *Golden Ages of the Great Cities* (London and New York, 1953), pp. 191-212.

2. "In America, also, it is the city that everywhere distinguishes the expansion of Spain. . . . The cities are the most typical, the most truly Spanish, of all the great institutions. The city, with its plaza, its church, its municipal palace, is the nerve center of the community. It is the concrete symbol of Spanish domination in America. Its persistence bears witness to its vigor and its vitality." Richard F. Pattee, *Essai sur l'Evolution Historique de l'Amerique Espagnole* (Port-au-Prince, 1944), p. 17. Manuel Gálvez, the Argentine novelist, said that cultures may be known by the cities they create, "A city is," he wrote, "the material expression of the heart of a people, of their social and individual culture." He called the culture of his own country a "repugnant materialism." Quoted in William Rex Crawford, *A Century of Latin American Thought* (Cambridge, Mass., 1944), p. 150.

3. Thomas Gage said that in 1625, about a century after its original founding, it had a population of about 3,000. "The unhealthiness of the place," he wrote, "is the reason of the paucity of inhabitants." At that time there were several merchants in the town with a capital of from 200,000 to 400,000 ducats. *A New Survey of the West Indies*, 1648 (New York, 1929), p. 35.

4. Other cities which were moved from their original locations included Panama, Guatemala, Havana, and León in Nicaragua.

5. "We do not find this mentioned in the book of foundations, because it did not exist many days. . . . As soon as the foundation was proclaimed, municipal officers were appointed, and a gibbet and pillory were set up. When this was settled, the Adelantado (Almagro) determined to consult with his officers and other people as to what should be done next." Pedro de Cieza de León, *The War of Las Salinas,* p. 106.

6. On the Maya cities, see Sylvanus G. Morley, *The Ancient Maya* (Stanford University, California, 1946), *passim.*

7. On the extensive markets of the Aztec capital, see Cortés, *Letters,* I, 257-58; also Bernal Díaz del Castillo, *True History,* pp. 175-77, regarding the quarter of the artists and the gold—and silver-smiths at Azcapotzalco, the gardens of Montezuma's palace, and the public markets. "We were astonished at the crowds of people," wrote Bernal Díaz, "and the regularity which prevailed, as well as at the vast quantities of merchandise. . . . Each kind had its particular place, which was distinguished by a sign. The articles consisted of gold, silver, jewels, feathers, mantles, chocolate, skins dressed and undressed, sandals, and other manufactures of the roots and fibres of *nequen,* and great numbers of male and female slaves, some of which were fastened by the neck, in collars, to long poles. The meat market was stocked with fowls, game, and dogs. Vegetables, fruits, articles of food ready dressed, salt, bread, honey, and sweet pastry, were also sold there. Other places in the square were appointed to the sale of earthenware, wooden household furniture . . . firewood, paper, sweet canes filled with tobacco mixed with liquid amber, copper axes and working tools, and wooden vessels highly painted. Numbers of women sold fish."

8. "The new kingdoms were in effect grafts of Spain on the Indian trunk. Mexico City, Lima, Cartagena and the other cities of the Tierra Firme were Spanish cities with a New World air, which they owed to the *genius loci* of the different countries, as well as to the temper of the various peoples among whom they grew. Perhaps the city of the Indies most symbolic of this process was the marvelous Cuzco, the Incaic Babylon, on top of whose cyclopean walls the Spaniards raised a Salamanca of pure Castilian character." Salvador de Madariaga, *Cuadro Histórico de las Indias* (Buenos Aires, 1945), p. 47.

9. Alexander von Humboldt, *Ensayo Político sobre el Reino de la Nueva España* (4 vols., Mexico, D. F., 1941), pp. 191, 233-57. On one occasion the city was flooded for five years. During the summer of 1952, about twenty blocks in the business district were flooded for several days. Of the original lake system of the valley only the shallow and brackish sheet of water at Tezcoco remains. The so-called "floating gardens" at Xochimilco are also a survival of the same system.

10. *Leyes de Indias,* section entitled *"De la población de las ciudades, villas y pueblos," tomo* 2, *libro* 4, *título* 7.

11. See Dan Stanislawski, "The Origin and Spread of the Grid-Pattern Town," in *The Geographical Review,* vol. XXXVI, 1946, pp. 105-120; and "Early Spanish Town Planning in the New World," *Ibid.,* vol. XXXVII, no. 1, January, 1947.

12. "Some names (in Chile) reveal the anguish of explorers and adventurers: Pampa Miraje, Llano de la Paciencia, Pampa Engañadora, Cordón Desamparado, Estación Soledad." Benjamín Subercaseaux, *Chile: a Geographic Extravaganza* (tr. from the Spanish, New York, 1943), p. 44.

13. Bernard Moses, *The Spanish Dependencies in South America* (2 vols., New York, 1914), II, 366.

14. T. R. Ybarra, *Lands of the Andes* (New York, 1947), p. 59.

15. There is much interesting material on the history of Lima in Raul Porras Barrenechea, ed., *Pequeña Antología de Lima (1535-1935)* (Madrid, 1935).

16. José de la Riva Agüero, "*Descripción anónima del Perú y de Lima a principios del siglo XVII compuesta por un judío portugués y dirigida a los estados de Holanda,*" in Congreso de Historia y Geografía Hispano-Americanas, *Actas y Memorias* (Madrid, 1914), pp. 347-84.

17. Jorge Juan and Antonio de Ulloa, *A Voyage to South America* (tr. from the Spanish, 2 vols., London, 1806), II, 111-113.

18. *Extracts of a Journal Written on the Coasts of Chili, Peru, and Mexico, in the Years 1820, 1821, 1822* (2 vols., Edinburgh, 1824), I, 97; also, II, 66.

19. *The Voyage of H.M.S. Beagle round the World* (Everyman Edition, 1906), pp. 353-54.

20. *Peru: Incidents of Travel and Exploration in the Land of the Incas* (New York, 1877), p. 25. James Bryce, who was in Lima early in the present century, wrote: "The City of the Kings retains that light-hearted gaiety and gift for social enjoyment for which she was famous in the old days. Not even political disasters, nor revolutions more frequent than earthquakes, have dulled the edge of pleasure," *South America: Observations and Impressions* (New York, 1916), p. 51.

21. The figures given are extracted from Juan Bromley and José Barbagelata, *Evolución Urbana de la Ciudad de Lima* (Lima, 1945). This book also reproduces a series of maps illustrating the expansion of the city from early colonial days to the present.

22. Basing his calculations on the probable increment since the total of 112,926 determined by the Viceroy Revillagigedo's census in 1790, Humboldt estimated the population of Mexico City in 1803 at 137,000 persons. He classified the total as follows: white Europeans, 2,500; white creoles, 65,000; Indians, 33,000; mestizos, 26,500; mulattoes, 10,000. *Ensayo Político, op. cit.,* II, 219. Father Vázquez de Espinosa, who was in Mexico City in 1612 said that in the city and nearby suburbs there were over 15,000 Spaniards, 80,000 Indians, and 50,000 Negroes and Mulattoes. *Compendium and Description of the West Indies* (tr. from the Spanish, Washington, D. C., 1942), p. 156. According to Thaddeus Haenke, who was in northern Argentina in the latter years of the eighteenth century, the population of four important towns in that area was as follows:

Town	Total	Spaniards	Mestizos	Indians	Negroes	Mulattoes
Catamarca	20,390	5,900	4,900	610	834	8,146
Jujuy	19,266	923	3,500	13,570	505	786
Salta	22,389	5,386	4,436	7,620	2,640	2,310
Tucumán	22,809	5,800	7,201	6,508	600	270

23. "To this family the Kings of Spain have been pleased to grant several distinguishing honours and privileges, as marks of its great quality; and many of the most eminent families in the city have desired intermarriages with it." Jorge Juan and Antonio de Ulloa, *op. cit.*, II, 53.

24. On the mestizo in Latin America, see John Gillin, "Mestizo America," in Ralph Linton, ed., *Most of the World: the Peoples of Africa, Latin America, and the East Today* (New York, 1949).

25. Of the several editions of this work, probably the best is the six volumes illustrated edition published in Spain in 1930. A selection of the anecdotes was translated into English by Harriet de Onis, under the title *Knights of the Cape* (New York, 1945). As Librarian of the National Library for many years, Palma had access to extensive manuscript sources of the history of Lima and Peru, on which he drew literally for background material and "local color" for his stories.

26. E. G. Squier, who was in Peru in the middle of the last century, wrote of Cuzco: "The aspect of the place is . . . that of a thoroughly Indian town. There is hardly anything that can be called society, although the better class is hospitable and unaffected, and much more frank and easy in manner than the corresponding class in the towns of the coast, where native manners have been sacrificed in a vain attempt to imitate foreign airs and graces. Some of the old families live in considerable style, and their houses are fitted with real elegance." Squier was amazed at the grand pianos and French mirrors which had been brought up from the coast. This was before the Southern Railway was built between Mollendo and Cuzco. *Peru: Incidents of Travel and Exploration in the Land of the Incas* (New York, 1877), p. 455.

27. *Exploration of the Valley of the Amazon* (2 vols., Washington, D. C., 1854), II, 161-63. Compare Thomas Gage's idyllic picture of León in Nicaragua two centuries earlier: "The chief delight of the inhabitants consisteth in their houses, and in the pleasure of the country adjoining, and in the abundance of all things for the life of man more than in extraordinary riches, which there are not so much enjoyed as in other parts of America. They are contented with fine gardens, with variety of singing birds and parrots, with plenty of fish and flesh, which is cheap, and with gay houses, and so lead a delicious, lazy, and idle life, not aspiring much to trade and traffic . . . especially from the pleasure of this city is all that province of Nicaragua called by the Spaniards, Mahomet's Paradise." *A New Survey of the West Indies*, 1648 (New York, 1929), p. 340.

28. On colonial Potosí, see Bernard Moses, *op. cit.*, II, Ch. 1, "A Mining Town in Upper Peru," and *Crónicas Potosinas* (2 vols., La Paz, 1919).

29. José de Acosta, *The Natural and Moral History of the Indies* (tr. from the Spanish, 2 vols., London, 1880), I, 201.

30. Vázquez de Espinosa, *op. cit.*, pp. 631-32.

31. *Relación de un Viaje al Rio de la Plata y de alli por tierra al Perú* (tr. from the French, Buenos Aires, n.d.), p. 71.

32. *El Lazarillo de Ciegos Caminantes, desde Buenos Aires hasta Lima* (Buenos Aires, 1946), pp. 134, 146.

33. *Journey from Buenos Aires through the Provinces of Córdova, Túcuman, and Salta, to Potosí, etc.* (2 vols., London, 1827), in Tom B. Jones, *South America Rediscovered* (Minneapolis, 1949), p. 174.

34. "Despite the often beautiful weather and the permanent splendor of Illimani, there is something unhomely and mournful about this city. I imagine the Indians sitting around the ruin of the plateau and looking down at it like condors, waiting for it to die." Christopher Isherwood, *The Condor and the Cows: A South-American Travel Diary* (New York, 1949), p. 174.

35. See Frederick Boyle, *A Ride Across a Continent: a Personal Narrative of Wanderings through Nicaragua and Costa Rica* (2 vols., London, 1868), II, 179.

36. On the land systems of Latin America and their economic and social concomitants, see George McCutchen McBride, *The Land Systems of Mexico* (New York, 1923); same, *Chile: Land and Society* (New York, 1936); Robert Swanton Platt, *Latin America, Countrysides and United Regions* (New York, 1942); T. Lynn Smith, *Brazil: People and Institutions* (Baton Rouge, La., 1946); Carl C. Taylor, *Rural Life in Argentina* (Baton Rouge, La., 1948); Nathan Laselle Whetten, *Rural Mexico* (Chicago, 1948).

37. See John L. Strohm, *I Lived with Latin Americans* (Chicago, 1943).

38. *Bogotá 1538–1938: Homenje del Municipio de Bogotá a la Ciudad en su IV Centerario* (Bogotá, 1938). Among other examples of similar commemorative literature are: Carlos Peña Otaegui, *Santiago de Siglo en Siglo* (Santiago de Chile, 1944); Eliecer Enríquez B., ed, *Quito a través de los Siglos* (Quito, 1938). See also, the anecdotal works of Luís González Obregón, *Las Calles de México: Leyendas y Sucedidos* (México, D. F., 6th ed., 1944); and *México Viejo: Noticias Históricas, Tradiciones, Leyendas y Costumbres* (Mexico, D. F., 1945).

39. During the colonial period, the Cabildo or city council was the last refuge of democracy in an otherwise absolutist political system. On occasions of a serious crisis in the city's affairs, a *cabildo abierto* (open council) or mass meeting of Spanish citizens to deal with the emergency. The custom, which is somewhat reminiscent of the New England town meeting, is still found in parts of Latin America.

40. See Francis Violich, *Cities of Latin America* (New York, 1944).

41. There are excellent short sketches of the architectural development of the various republics in Earl Parker Hanson, ed., *New World Guides to Latin America* (3 vols., New York, 1945). On Mexican architecture, see Trent Elwood Sanford, *The Story of Architecture in Mexico* (New York, 1947).

42. Philip L. Goodwin, *Brazil Builds: Architecture New and Old 1652–1942* (New York, 1943).

43. "Buenos Aires is still the only big city without traffic lights; people always laughed them away." Ray Josephs, *Argentine Diary* (New York, 1944), p. 214.

44. "The gallants of this city shew themselves daily, some on horseback and most in coaches, about 4 of the clock in the afternoon, in a pleasant shady field called *la Alameda*, full of trees and walks, where do meet . . . about 2,000 coaches, full of gallants, ladies, and citizens, to see and to be seen, to court and to be courted, the gentlemen having their train of blackamoor slaves, some a dozen. Some half a dozen waiting on them in brave and gallant liveries, heavy with gold and silver lace, with silk stockings on their black legs, and roses on their feet, and swords by their sides." Thomas Gage, *op. cit.*, p. 91.

45. As late as 1779, over 9,000 persons died in Mexico City from an outbreak of smallpox. According to Humboldt, "a great part of the youth of Mexico perished in that fatal year." *Op. cit.*, II, 51. The introduction of vaccination by Don

Tomás Murphy in 1804 prevented the recurrence of such disastrous epidemics. As a result of inadequate food production in Mexico, especially in years of drought, mass starvation in the cities was sometimes as great a catastrophe as epidemics of disease. In the mining center of Guanajuato, more than 8,000 persons died of hunger and attendant diseases in 1784. *Ibid.,* p. 57.

46. During 1929–31, a series of special articles by the writer on the cities of Latin America appeared in the New York *Herald Tribune*.

47. "The atmosphere of Rio de Janeiro is one single aphrodisiac." Herman Alexander (Graf) von Keyserling, *The Travel Diary of a Philosopher* (tr. from the German, 2 vols., New York, 1925), II, 31.

DUARTE COELHO PEREIRA
MANOEL DA NOBREGA
DOM PEDRO II
JOSÉ B. DE ANDRADA
JOSÉ PATROCINIO
RUI BARBOSA
BARÃO DO RIO BRANCO
CANDIDO DA SILVA RONDON
EUCLIDES DA CUNHA
OSVALDO CRUZ

Chapter X

THE BRAZILIAN

THE FIRST Brazilians or *Brasileiros* of modern times were only gatherers of Brazilwood, the dyestuff which on exposure to the air has the color of glowing coals or *brasas*. The country was scarcely considered important enough to have a name of its own and the religious names which were successively applied to it never took root, so it became Brazil and its people, Brazilians.

The early history of Brazil was casual and fortuitous.[1] Since very few of those who took part in it were writing men, we know

385

little about much that went on the length of its seemingly endless coast. Moreover, Portugal, conscious of its weakness in point of numbers, was not given to advertising to the world what it held so tenuously. It had other—and more lucrative—business to attend to in the Orient before it could turn its attention to the development of the vast tropical wilderness that was Brazil. Bound for India in the wake of Vasco da Gama, Pedro Alvares Cabral came upon it by accident in the last year of the fifteenth century. He was making a gigantic tack to the West, in an effort to avoid the difficult sailing conditions off the Guinea coast, and after a perfunctory ceremony of laying claim to the "Island of Vera Cruz," he went on his way to India. It was long before Brazil was brought within the scope of the overseas designs of Portugal, which was preoccupied with its dazzling ventures in Asia.[2] In the meantime, occasional masters of Portuguese trading ships made voyages in search of brazilwood and supplementary cargo, like gaily colored parrots and macaws and playful capuchin monkeys, which was scarcely a trade to distract the interest of the nation from the spices and fabrics and gems that the fleets of carracks brought to Lisbon from the East Indies. In intervals between bartering with the Indians and disporting themselves with their hospitable womenfolk, the Portuguese traders tried to drive off the stray French intruders who early began to make voyages to Brazil out of the ports of Brittany and Normandy.

The French were very persistent in their efforts to establish an "Antarctic France" in Brazil, and made scattered settlements along the coast all the way from the Island of Marajó at the mouth of the Amazon south to Rio Bay. However, France always had too many affairs on her hands in other parts of the world to concentrate her energies against the thin screen of Portuguese who "clung like crabs," as Father Vicente do Salvador said, to the coast of Brazil.[3] Though the Portuguese always seemed half-hearted and haphazard in their activities in Brazil, they had a way of rising to the occasion whenever their hold on the colony was seriously threatened, so that, in spite of the incursions of Frenchmen and Dutchmen, it remained theirs for more than three centuries, or until its own people were ready to take over its rule.

After a lapse of over thirty years, the Portuguese government took the first steps for the occupation of the country. For this purpose, it gave correlative territorial and political concessions to a number of well-to-do *fidalgos* and *cavalheiros,* who were to colonize the lands of their *capitanias* at their own expense.[4] The chain of settlements like Olinda-Recife, Bahia, and São Vicente-Santos that were founded as a result of these arrangements marked the beginnings of modern Brazil. Some prospered more than others, depending on the natural advantages of the locality and on the character of the *donatorio* or concessionaire. A few, like Duarte Coelho, lord of the *capitania* of Pernambuco, were strong men, and skilled from experience in dealing with a tropical environment in the East Indies.[5] Others lacked the necessary capital or qualities of leadership, and their settlements languished through the colonial period.

The principal problems in the formation of Brazil were space and distance, the extremes of nature, the development of an economic base for the colony, and the designs of imperial-minded rivals. The Portuguese did not have to contend with organized military states, as the Spaniards did in Mexico and Peru. The Tupi and related peoples were of a much lower order of civilization than the Aztecs and the subjects of the Incas, and though the Brazilian tribes were warlike in their relations with one another, they were incapable of presenting a united front against the Portuguese. There was some desultory fighting, but the Portuguese came in the role of colonizers instead of conquerors, and avoided open hostilities wherever possible.

When the Portuguese came, Brazil was only a vast emptiness. They had no idea how vast it was until the Bandeirantes pushed out from São Paulo into the far west of the open continent. The Borgia pope had fixed an arbitrary limit to their expansion, which had been pushed out still farther by the Treaty of Tordesillas in 1494. Well beyond the "line of demarcation" the Spaniards had established themselves in the Andes and appeared content to remain there after several disastrous failures to penetrate the Amazonian jungle. Henceforth they showed little interest in the tropical wilderness to the east of the mountains or disposition to challenge the activities of the Portuguese, which were rather in the nature of reconnaissance expeditions than efforts to settle the frontier lands. The first Portuguese effort of this kind was made by a lone adventurer named Aleixo García, who, with a large force of Guaraní Indians, reached the inhabited outskirts of the Inca Empire before Pizarro ever landed on the coast of Peru. The nearest Spanish settlements to the Brazilian coast were at Santa Cruz de la Sierra in the plains of eastern Bolivia and Asunción on the Paraguay. Attempts of the Portuguese to establish a foothold on the River Plate were eventually foiled by the Spaniards from the other side of the river. The east-west connection with the Spanish colonies in Peru by way of the Amazon was not explored from the side of Brazil until 1638, when Pedro Teixeira ascended the river to the region of Quito. This was shortly before the end of the sixty-year Spanish "captivity" of Portugal, during which any controversy as to boundaries was in abeyance. As time went on, the long line of Jesuit missions that extended from the River Plate lands to the upper Amazon came to form a sort of neutral cushion between any possible encroachment of the two powers on each other's borderlands in the interior of the continent.

Brazil was never quite populated or settled, but only occupied, as is true of much of it after four centuries of occupation.[6] From the beginning there was a great urge to move about the country. There were no high mountains to block the way; and none of the other obstacles to travel were entirely impassable. Since most of the navigable rivers of Brazil run in a north and south direction, they were not as important avenues of access to the interior as might have been expected, though the São Francisco was a valuable link between the northeast and the highlands of Minas.[7]

The Indian was always a wanderer in search of food or of refuge from stronger enemies. The *caboclo* or *mameluco,* who was part Indian, and the Portuguese frontiersman, who was *tapuyado,* that is "Indianized," adopted the wandering habits of the aborigines. A seal of restlessness was thereby set on the Brazilian countryman that still marks him, so that it is hard to fix him in one place. Then as now, he felt that farther on things might be better, so that the horizon was always a challenge to him. The climate and the fire, or *roça,* system of agriculture favored and encouraged his nomadism and his vegetative existence.[8] So it was a society that, along its edges, seemed ever to be in motion.

THE POPULATION OF BRAZIL

The settlements were so widely separated that there were frequent occasions for long journeys by land. Communciation by sea was not always safe, and the prevailing winds off the north coast made navigation difficult in one direction. Couriers who carried the official mail between the coast towns kept to the long beaches wherever possible. The cattle for the provisioning of the settlements were often driven great distances from the ranches in the far south or in the hinterland of the sertão. In back country towns that lie on the old trails, one is still aware of the *boiadas* or cattle drives, and of the jingling mule trains that have always been a feature of Brazilian life. The Bahianos who cross into Goyaz or Minas to hunt for diamonds or gold in the river beds are also part of the ancient tradition of vagabondage. But the most itinerant of all Brazilians are the Cearenses, the hardy mestizo folk of the drought-ridden state of Ceará, who have penetrated to the farthest reaches of the Amazon Valley, and more recently have been moving into the industrial areas of the south. Much of the incessant migration within Brazil still moves on foot. There is no railroad to bind together the northern and southern regions of the gigantic country, and the truck road between Rio and the cities of the northeast by way of Teófilo Ottoni is no paved all-weather *camino real*.

There were never enough Portuguese to do all that was needed to open up and bring the country into bearing. It is a miracle that they ever managed to keep the country at all, there were so few of them. Portugal was a very small nation to begin with, and the Oriental ventures took a heavy toll of its inhabitants. The population that was left by the middle of the sixteenth century was spread too thin over the world to hold anything against a strong and determined enemy. So she had to economize her own slender human resources and find other sources of manpower, particularly a numerous and dependable labor force for the plantation system she had in mind. The Indian appeared the logical source of supply. But the Indian had no bent for steady work and was unhappy in the semicaptivity of the *fazenda*. The Portuguese planters early wrote him off as a field hand, and if they could manage to hold him from wandering off into the woods, they used him on less confining tasks for which he had a flair, like those of boatman and hunter. Negro slavery, with which they had long had experience at home, proved to be the answer to their labor problem.[9] The Negro was physically adjusted to the demands of living in a tropical habitat, and he had qualities of temperament that enabled him to accept the burdens of servitude without the hopeless despair or sullen rebelliousness of the Indian. The making of Brazil would have been impossible without the contributions of his body and his spirit.

By the profuse mixing of their own blood with that of both Indian and Negro, the Portuguese also shared in solving the population problem of Brazil. Racial miscegenation was no novelty to them, for particularly those to the south of the Tagus were a hybrid people, and they had no inhibitions on the score of either color, morals, or social difference. Before the systematic occupation of the country was begun, a few isolated Portuguese seamen, who had either been marooned by passing ships or had freely chosen to live with the natives, demonstrated the possibilities of miscegenation on a local scale. The most famous of these advance agents of Portuguese colonization were Diogo Alvares, better known as Caramurú, or "the fire maker," and João Ramalho.[10] The one settled down in the rich lands about the bay of Salvador, where the city of Bahia was to rise. The scene of the other's exploits was far to the south in the Santa Catharina country. Both became chieftains of sorts, and men of substance and prestige among their adopted tribes. Moreover, they both sired a numerous progeny and set a pattern of promiscuity that did much to help fill the genetic void of Brazil. Later, great pioneers of the northeast, like García d'Avila and Jeronimo de Albuquerque, were to become prolific patriarchs in the land.[11] The custom has survived to the present as a seignorial privilege and responsibility, and as an important contributory factor in the progressive whitening of the heavily mesticized population of the more tropical areas of Brazil.

The colony early found a substantial basis for its economy in sugar. The low coastal lands were well adapted to the cultivation of cane, and, since sugar was in short supply in Europe, it was long an extremely lucrative crop, though West Indian sugar was eventually to offer serious competition that reduced the profits of the Brazilian industry. Tobacco, which was grown in the Bahian *reconcavo*, and cotton, planted in the drier zone to the north of Pernambuco as far as Maranhão, provided valuable subsidiary crops.

THE PLANTATION SYSTEM

The life of the colony largely revolved about the big plantations.[12] Whatever its practical shortcomings, in no other European colonies of the time was tropical agriculture carried on so successfully. The members of the slaveholding planter aristocracy were the real rulers of Brazil. Personal prowess was all important in their position, and they were generally shrewd and strong-minded men, but humane in their treatment of their motley armies of dependents, free and slave, and given to a good deal of crude display, particularly when visiting the city with their families and retinues. In the meantime, the governor generals in Bahia [13] and later, the viceroys in Rio were impressive symbols of Portuguese authority. Though some were able and conscientious royal officials, in the last resort, power rested in the hands of the great landowners. Fortunately for the successful working of so easy-going a system, government was much less in evidence and there was much less interference with the lives of the colonists than in the more rigid political atmosphere of the Spanish colonies.

The colony, even in the cities, lacked an air of social refinement. In the beginning it was a male society, because there were few women of their own to share it with. Even when women came out from Portugal, they went into seclusion again. They seemed to have little influence outside the zenana of "the big house," and even that was liable to be diluted by the extramural activities of their robust menfolk. So their rather pallid women were never in a position to give to the life of the colony the tone of graceful elegance that was justified by its wealth and its place in the larger world. The true social level of the colony was one of a rustic epicureanism. It dressed gaudily on parade, and strutted and bowed-and-scraped in the best Lisbon manner, and filled its town houses with miscellaneous assortments of oriental luxuries. But there was mud on its feet and dust in its hair, for it lived close to the earth in spite of all its pretense and posturing, and in its heart it had a common and countrified urge for elemental pleasures and satisfactions.

COLONIAL CULTURE

Its intellectual interests were on as low a plane. The colonists were not given to reading books, and it was late in the colonial period before any books were published in Brazil.[14] There was no university, as in the Spanish cities like Lima and Mexico City, to provide a cover of Old World erudition and pedrantry to its vital and rampageous crudities. Occasionally, some wealthy planter sent a promising son overseas to Coimbra to make a scholar and *doutor* of him. But most of whatever nonfunctional mental activity there was in the colony was due to the Jesuits or to the Sephardic Jews, who had a strong intellectual tradition of their own.

The instrumentalities of the higher cultural life were largely in the capable hands of the Jesuits.[15] But the Jesuits did not see eye to eye with the planter aristocracy on many things of both a spiritual and temporal nature. Moreover, they were too busy trying to protect their Indian charges from the rapacity of the lay element, and to civilize them after their own peculiar pattern, to trouble themselves overly with the intellectual uplift of the colonists. However, some of their leaders, like Fathers Anchieta and Nobrega, Cardim and Vieira, were men of great ability and noble character, who left an enduring mark for good on the early history of Brazil.

Responsibility for the religious ministration of the secular population largely fell to the parish priests of other orders and to the chaplains of "the big houses." They were generally an easy-going lot, who preached a homey and simple Christianity, and in the accepted hierarchy of society showed a becoming respect and deference to the lords of the land, at whose hospitable tables they often ate. On the plantations, they were also accustomed to double as schoolmasters in the rather rudimentary system of primary education which prevailed. They officiated benignly at the frequent religious festivals, in which the saints, like the Greek divinities of old, mingled with their worshipers in an atmosphere of delightful conviviality. They were not exigent in matters of dogma and tolerated the more innocuous of the extraneous elements which Indian and Negro brought with them into this most catholic of Catholic faiths.

For the lush primitive folklore of both races peopled the unseen world of their imagination with a host of goblins and gremlins and other fanciful creatures. Out of the great forest and the rivers of Brazil there came a Pogo-like assortment of animals, such as the *jaboti* or the turtle, the *jacaré* or alligator, and the playful pink *boto* or dolphin of the Amazon, that, for good or evil, were believed to influence the lives of men.[16] Though clerics shook their heads at the maze of superstitions that crowded in on the imagery of the Church to confuse the simple minds of their congregations, the myths were too deeply embedded in popular instinct to yield to reason or admonition. They became the substance of the rich and permanent mythology of Brazil, in which its unconventional fauna play so important a role. They are part of the storied heritage of all Brazilian children, and their elders borrow from them to personify their conceits, like Jeca Tatú, and José Carioca—Joe the Parrot—of Walt Disney's picture, "The Three Cavaliers."

In time, out of all the evolutionary influences that were at work on the raw materials of the Brazilian nation—the racial leavening, the play of natural forces (sun and rain, the jungle and the highlands, and the very immensity of the land), and the processes of historical change—there developed a type that was different from the original Portuguese, but whose core remained Lusitanian. Brazil was so large and its parts were long so isolated from each other that, like the United States, there came to be several regional variations from the basic type. But all the time a Brazilian race was in the making that had a distinctive character of its own, regardless of the differences between Paulista and Nordestino, or between Mineiro and Gaucho.

THE PORTUGUESE

The Portuguese were not altogether like the Spaniards, though they were more like than unlike.[17] And they had more in common with some Spaniards, like the Asturians and the Gallegos, than they did with the Aragonese and the Castilians. All the Peninsula peoples were individualists, but the Portuguese were generally readier to compromise or to yield a point than were the vainer

Spaniards, since they were more practical and cared less for the appearance than for the substance of things. If they could be dogged and stubborn when pushed too far and too rudely, that was also a sign of their essentially peasant character. As a rule, more realistic than the Spaniards, yet on occasion they could be as quixotic, as was demonstrated by some of their fantastic crusading ventures in Africa. They were more sentimental than the Spaniards, as Brazilians are more sentimental than Chileans or Uruguayans. They were given to moods of melancholy that might find expression in singing the rather doleful *fados* or popular ballads of the country. At the other extreme, they might indulge in robust humor and Bruegel-like frolicking, for they were an earthy and unsophisticated folk, whose pleasure ran rather to the organic than the intellectual. They were less military-minded than most of the Spanish peoples, though no less brave in battle when their heart was in the fighting; if it was not, they were liable to show a strong sense of self-preservation. A temperate people by nature, they were slower to resort to violence than the more bellicose Castilians. Nor were they inclined to big pomp and fanfare, since they were aware that they belonged to a little country and had no ambitions to put on the airs of the mighty. They have a strong sense of gain, and respect for money. As a rule, they are better businessmen and financiers than most of the Spanish stocks, and make very solid and conservative storekeepers and traders. Large numbers of them have continued to migrate to Brazil, where, though the butt of caricature and jokes, as the steady and hard-working Gallegos are in Cuba, they are welcomed for their industry and other substantial qualities. In recognition of their value in the development of the country, they are exempted from the quota restrictions of the federal immigration law.

The Brazils and Their Peoples

All Brazil is divided into five parts. If one includes the Amazon Valley as a separate area, there are six parts. The five nuclear parts are: (1) the Northeaest; (2) the state of Minas Geraes; (3) the Federal District; (4) the state of São Paulo; and (5) the state of Rio Grande do Sul. To Brazilians, the human types they represent are, respectively, Nordestinos, Mineiros, Cariocas,

Paulistas, and Gauchos.[18] Neither in terms of geography nor of their distinctive regional cultures are their boundaries fixed. Brazil is still a pioneer country, and the outward movement of people from the old coastal zone of the *marinha* into the hinterland appears sometimes only lately to have begun. Wherever there are railroads or roads to go by and good empty lands to be had for the taking, currents of migration set in toward the interior, as into the basin of the Tocantíns in Goyaz, in the wide strip along the Northwestern Railway in southern Matto Grosso, or the new coffee zone in southwestern São Paulo and the northwest corner of Paraná. The bulk of the migrants may be Cearenses, escaping from the periodic *seccas* of their drought-ridden state,[19] or Bahianos, moving west across the line of the São Francisco, or Mineiros or Paulistas, looking for new opportunities in coffee or rice or cattle. Then, in a sense the newly settled land becomes an appendage of the region from which the majority of its settlers came.

The Northeast is the old Brazil of slavery and sugar. It covers an enormous area, that reaches from the borders of Pará south by "the bulge" almost to the city of Rio de Janeiro. To the west it extends across the sertão until it meets the Amazonian jungle. The sertão is mostly a semidesert of *caatinga* or whitish scrub forest. Sometimes, as in Maranhão and Piauhy, there are great expanses of *palmeiras* or palms. There are also areas of rich farm lands near the coast; and in the southern part, between the Rio das Contas in Bahia and the Rio Doce in Espirito Santo, there is a vast stretch of tropical rain forest that is almost uninhabited. The Northeast is the favorite home of the mixed peoples, the composite of Portuguese, Indian, and Negro. The man of the coastal belt is voluble and expansive and warmhearted. Most of Brazil's favorite orators and lyric poets, like Ruy Barbosa and Gonçalves Dias, come of its exuberant and florid stock. The man of the lean sertão or backlands is as sparse of words as he is of diet and build. There is a strong strain of the mystic in him. He was a partisan of Antonio Conselheiro at Canudos,[20] and has followed the healer-priests who occasionally appear in the sertão, to arouse its simple folk to a frenzy of fanaticism. Distrustful of authority, he is given to hero-worship of those who defy the law, like Lampeão, or "Lightning," the bandit.

The Mineiros are highlanders and have the qualities that are typical of hill peoples.[21] There are some eight million of them, most of whom live in villages in the upland valleys or on small farms. They are set in their ways, and they can say little in many words, while they wait for a stranger to finish talking and show his hand. Conservative and guarded, they are the balance wheel of Brazil. The Cariocas are indigenous inhabitants of Rio de Janeiro, or the Federal District, and of its metropolitan area. They are a somewhat flamboyant and exhibitionistic folk, sharp-witted and sharp-tongued, capricious and volatile, cynical and ironical, to whom the human "show" is the big attraction in life, second only to the annual carnival.

If Minas Geraes is the balance wheel of the Brazilian machine, the state of São Paulo is the motor. The Paulistas are dynamic and purposeful and acquisitive.[22] They think in terms of money and progress. They brought the Industrial Revolution into Brazil and put it to work for their own, and incidentally, the country's, profit and advantage. Their influence and the area of their hegemony extends over the borders of the state into Paraná and Matto Grosso, the Mineiro "triangle" and the contiguous parts of the state of Rio. Since they are the mainstay of the Brazilian economy, they speak with the voice of a majority stockholder, and are accustomed to being listened to. Their state has tended to put on the airs of sovereignty, and when things have not gone to its liking, it has twice revolted against the federal government.

The Gauchos are the people of Rio Grande do Sul, the southernmost state of the republic. It is bordered on two sides by Spanish lands, and reflects their influence in many things, including the local term for its people. The Gaucho is closer in temperament to the Uruguayan than he is to the Bahiano of his own country. He is more the "outdoors type" than other Brazilians. He is more rugged and "red-blooded," and he is at home on a horse, an animal that would be utterly foreign to the temper of the Carioca, while the Mineiro would vastly prefer a sure-footed mule as a vehicle of land transport.

THE BRAZILIAN CHARACTER

The Brazilians are the Chinese of the New World.[23] Chronologically speaking, they are a young people; in a spiritual sense, they are an old race, with roots deep somewhere in time.[24] Of course, the parallel is not complete, and, among other things, the Chinese are the more pragmatic of the two. However, the oriental quality of certain phases of Brazilian civilization is quite evident, and there are areas of thought and conduct in which both peoples are liable to see eye to eye. This is true of the *permanent* Chinese characteristics—pre- and post-Communist—that is, the racial values and habits which, in the long run, are little affected by political change.

An inordinately strong family feeling is common to both Brazilians and Chinese, and in the loose organism of their racial societies, ties of blood are the one binding link.[25] Similarly, each has a distrust of government and believes in the principle of the-less-government-the-better. Both tend to be politically ineffectual, and, in the last resort, it is other forces than governmental coercion which hold the two nations together, and keep them from flying off into political space. Business ethics and methods must have a familiar ring to each other. While the pledged word of honor has much the same binding power with both, the actual conduct of business is practiced in an atmosphere of guile and wile, tempered by good humor and personal good will. Brazilians and Chinese have a deep aversion to war, as a waste of time and money which could be put to better use, and as settling nothing in the end but the fate of those who are killed. Both have a rich sense of humor, and many things in life strike them as funny and ridiculous. They also have a love of talk, and a gift of gab as a pastime. They are loquacious peoples and their crowds are noisy.

What the Brazilians call *sensibilidade* is the key to their national character.[26] It is neither "sensibility" nor "sensibleness," but rather it is sentimentalism, and in motivation implies the predominance of feeling over intelligence. In other words, where the prospect of some action is concerned, the Brazilian tends to think with his heart, more than with his head. Thinking and attitudes are likely to be subjective rather than objective, fo. life is a highly personal matter, made up of relations between individuals. General concepts like "duty" or "morality" are philosophic catchalls, and in serious conversation may be useful as rallying points for lesser ideas, but they are difficult to convert into practical terms where it is a matter of one's own private actions or interests. People are either *simpático* or *antipático;* if they are *simpático,* you like them, but if not, you dislike them.[27] *Amizade* or friendship assumes an importance unknown among the cooler temperaments of northern peoples, and people may be classified as *amigos* or *inimigos*.[28]

The dominion of affective or emotional considerations complicates the conduct of serious affairs, and makes it hard to settle a question on its merits. It has a marked effect on the functioning of the will, and, as with the Spanish-American *gana,* people are liable to act on impulse, according to their emotional reflexes. These internal promptings or motivations may be very violent in their intensity, even if short-lived. Thus, crimes are generally passionate actions, committed on the spur of the moment and without plan or premeditation.

The unpredictability and, what to a more calculating people is capriciousness, that are implicit in so subjective an atmosphere, are further aggravated by an irregular rhythm of effort which Brazilans have in common with Spanish-Americans.[29] Like the build-up of atmospheric pressures in a storm area to the explosive point, these may be relatively long preliminaries of preparation for action. The indolence generated in the process is congenial to the Brazilian nature, even though the actual circumstances of life may be unfavorable to indulgence. The enjoyment of idleness is evidence of superiority over economic pressures, just as white and uncalloused hands are a mark of social category. Over much of the country, it is also a defense reaction against the climate, and so represents an economy of forces, rather than downright laziness or flabbiness of character. On the other hand, there exists no cult of hard work, and popular philosophy is well expressed in the remark of one Brazilian that "Dignified idleness always seemed more excellent and even ennobling than a mad struggle for one's daily bread." More interested in the present than in the distant future, the Brazilians seem, by our standards, an improvident people. On the way to whatever fate the future may hold in store for them, they wish to take time to enjoy the little pleasures and satisfactions by the road.

In the meantime, nobody expects or desires to become rich by hard work.[30] So pleasing an eventuality must depend on either luck or some superior prowess of the individual. Brazilians have much faith in *sorte* or chance. A race of inveterate gamblers or speculators, they are always hoping to win the big prize in the lottery or in the *bicho,* Rio's equivalent of the "numbers" game, in which one bets on some familiar animal or *bicho* (bug). "The *Bicho*" has resisted all the occasional frantic efforts of government to suppress it, and manages to keep the lower classes of Rio in a chronic state of expectation and insolvency. In default of luck and its caprices, one must lean on himself, as it were, and win wealth by some stroke of shrewdness. Thus, business is not business, but a game. The predilection for the brilliant stroke explains the "gimmick" or trick which one is expected to look for in a Brazilian deal. Perhaps no conscious dishonesty is implied, but rather a challenge to a battle of wits. For, except for the petty pilfering which goes on among the lower classes all over Latin America, and which is as much an economic as a moral phenomenon, the Brazilian's standards of personal honesty are probably as high as those of other peoples in a comparable state of evolution.

The possible "antisocial" consequences of the Brazilians' emphasis on sentiment are tempered by the presence of certain other qualities in the national character. One of these is *bondade* or goodness of heart. There is a deep humanity in the people that is Christian in its essence. They are sensitive to the sufferings of others, and are disposed to be open-handed and generous to those in their own circle who are in need of help. If, like the Spaniards, they tend to be indifferent to the miseries of those whom they do not know, it is not from any hardness of heart, but because they are aware of the limits of their capacity to play the good Samaritan. In the back country, there is still much old-fashioned frontier hospitality. However, in Minas there is considerable reserve in the attitude towards strangers. As a rule, the Mineiro does not have a surplus of "the world's goods," so, if he appears at first sight to be inhospitable and parsimonious, it is because he feels in all prudence that he must hold on to what little he has.

There is also in him a certain *desconfiança* or suspicion of the casual outsider that is a holdover from the disorderly eighteenth century, when unprincipled adventurers roamed the highlands in search of gold.

Related to the basic goodness of the Brazilian is his dislike for extreme or violent measures or solutions. If in a given situation, there is no alternative to the use of coercion or physical force, the tendency is to apply it in as benign a form as possible. For example, not only is capital punishment taboo, but the punitive system in general avoids harsh or inhumane penalties.[31] Also, Brazilians prefer to talk themselves out of a dilemma rather than to resort to a contest of muscle. The national reputation for skill at diplomatic negotiation is well-founded and accounts for the strong Brazilian bent for conciliation in international affairs. In ordinary intercourse, they are averse to employing words or expressions that are needlessly rude or offensive. On the other hand, Brazilians are given to the use of diminutives, nicknames, and the familiar given or Christian name, that soften the rough edges of human relationships. Conversation between family members and friends is larded with the familiar and endearing *"nh"* or *"enya."* Thus, it is customary to address one's mother or *mae* as *maezinha* (pronounced "myzeenya"), or to refer to a grandfather as *"avozinho."* Not all nicknames are derisive or derogative, though generally humorous, and they often allude to some physical feature or idiosyncracy of the individual, but without malice.

The habit of referring to persons by their first or given names is universal in Brazil. To begin with, Brazilians have drawn heavily on foreign languages and rummaged through the realms of fantasy and history for their Christian names. The variety is so great that a man is frequently identified by a unique name, which may even appear in its alphabetical place, in lieu of the family name, in the local telephone directory. An example of this widespread custom is *"O Getulio"* or "The Getulio," by which irreverent Brazilians always refer to President Getulio Vargas.

These highly personalized attitudes make manners of supreme importance as lubricants of social functions. There is probably no country on earth where the code of courtesy is more elaborate or better observed.[32] And there is none where a smile wins more or a frown loses so much. Brazilians are easy to lead when sentiment is appealed to; they are difficult to drive against their will. The emphasis on the personal is so deep-seated that it sometimes has the effect of nullifying laws which happen to run counter to established human relationships. Laws and rules do not apply to friends, but are made for dealing with enemies and strangers.

Other restraints on the attitudes which might otherwise lead to a genial anarchy in Brazilian society include the strong sense of democracy which is the deep heritage of a frontier people, a saving sense of humor, and an indifference to things which do not intimately affect one's own happiness. By leveling all men, at least philosophically, regardless of what may be their relative material status, inequality ceases to be a major source of discord in society, by reducing the occasion for both exploitation and envy. The Brazilian's readiness to laugh at the laughable eases the tensions in personal relationships. Sometimes, though, his humor has in it a strong tinge of *malicia,* which is not necessarily malice, but rather mischievousness or a roguish quality, though the temptation to make a joke at the expense of another who has laid himself open to the barbs may be too great to resist.[33] In spite of his sense of humor and of the ease with which he laughs, the Brazilian is often addicted to melancholy moods.[34] Many of his—and his country's—questions are still unanswered, and there may be times when they seem to him unanswerable. Sensitive, he is unusually susceptible to the play of emotions about him, and in the more tropical parts of the country, a too lush and overpowering nature depresses and crowds in on his spirit.

There is, too, a certain indifferentism in the Brazilian's nature which may prevent him from taking anything too seriously, so long as it does not immediately menace the satisfying rhythms of his life. It is a devil-may-care attitude that nothing matters very much provided one can go on enjoying the things that make for his happiness. It tends to make it easier to pardon small offenses and to shorten the life of grudges. There are few expressions that one hears so often in Brazil as, *"Não faz mal"* or *"Não importa"* ("It doesn't matter"). A variation of this easygoing fatalism or resignation is found in another expression which goes, "Leave it as it is, so that one can see how it turns out" (*"Deixa-o como está para ver como fica"*).

The Culture of Brazil

The Brazilian mind is a sharp instrument. It can cut easily and clearly, though when it would dig deeply into the mountains of thought, it may quickly become tired or bored. Its workings are characterized by facility and grace. But it is a two-dimensional mind, and tends to lack depth and persistence, and a feeling for exactness and precision. It emphasizes mental agility and brilliance, and it is likely to put a higher value on the fruits of inspriation and intuition than on the substantial products of plodding and plugging. The Brazilian, particularly the Nordestino, often has a tropical luxuriance of imagination that gives wings to his brain, though they may be the wings of the swallow rather than of the wild goose. The Brazilian also generally has the Cuban's fluency of expression, and the bent for persiflage and pleasantry that enlivens conversation.

Culture in Brazil is a mark of caste.[35] As such, it is as much a social as an intellectual matter. In terms of literacy percentages and school enrollment, Brazilians are not an educated people.[36] Only a small part of the population ever go beyond the primary school, and comparatively few graduates from the *lyceu* or high school. So the number of those who are qualified to enter the universities is insignificant.

As in most of the Spanish countries, the end product of these successive screenings is a cultural aristocracy. Its members are "doctors" or *doutores*. Intellectual distinction is measured by degrees, diplomas, certificates of competence, honorific titles and citations, and all the other tangible insignia of learning. It is composed of persons who read books, often for the pleasure of it, but occasionally for the reason that if one is to be recognized as a cultivated man he must read books and be able to quote from them. Like those owlish folk, the Bogotanos, who are known locally as "The Athenians of South America," many possess an impressive mass of miscellaneous and disconnected knowledge that is the result of much scattered reading. They have evolved culturally far beyond the newspaper, which comprises the reading of the primary school graduate, and beyond the popular magazines including *Selecções*, the Portuguese edition of *Reader's Digest*, that constitute the new frontier country of the public mind. As a rule, they can glibly cite passages from Sartre and Valéry and Mauriac, as their fathers used to display their erudition by quoting from Comte and Taine and Gobineau.[32]

Sometimes, they write books that are very creditable and even distinguished.[38] Their output of serious writing of quality is superior to that of any of the other republics. For example, no other people in Latin America have analyzed themselves so thoroughly and honestly as Gilberto Freyre and Fernando de Azevedo, Alceu Amoroso Lima, and Eduardo Prado; and many others, like Hernane Tavares de Sá, have done. If the total volume of original scholarly creation seems small, as in all Latin America, it is due to the relatively limited public which can read books in Portuguese and can afford to buy them. Writing in Brazil is not a self-sufficient occupation, even for those who have tapped the foreign market for translations of exotic books. So an author must have another source of income to carry the costs of authorship, such as the law or journalism, a post in the bureaucracy or the revenues from family properties. The Brazilians are little inclined to philosophical speculation or scientific investigation, fields of erudition that require more sustained effort and severer self-discipline than the generality of them are willing to accept. They excel rather at literary and sociological criticism and analysis, as they also do at the social novel and the writing of history. There are books which stress the literary artistry of form and language more than intellectual substance. It is like the importance which Brazilians give to the *geito*—the knack or flair for doing a thing in the grand manner, even though intrinsically the occasion may not be of great moment.

NOTES

1. There is no satisfactory short history of Brazil in English. The remarkable tour de force by the English poet, Robert Southey (*History of Brazil*, 3 vols., London, 1810–19), does not cover the imperial and republican periods. The one-volume work of João Pandia Calogeras, Graeco-Brazilian minister of finance, was written in the style of a minister of finance. *A History of Brazil* (tr. from the Portuguese and edited by Percy Alvin Martin, Chapel Hill, N. C., 1939). The excellent *Formação do Brasil Contemporaneo,* by Caio Prado Junior, published at São Paulo in 1942, is still incomplete, and the initial volume on the colonial period has not been translated into English. Another very useful book on Brazilian origins is Sergio Buarque de Holanda, *Raizes do Brasil* (São Paulo, 1948). There is much

sound material on the history of Brazil in Mary Wilhelmine Williams, *The People and Politics of Latin America* (rev. ed., Boston, 1945), pp. 92-101, 143-48, 245-75, 319-23, 753-802. Among other outstanding books on Brazil are: Roy Nash, *The Conquest of Brazil* (New York, 1926); Gilberto Freyre, *Brazil: An Interpretation* (New York, 1945); T. Lynn Smith, *Brazil: People and Institutions* (Baton Rouge, La., 1946); Lawrence F. Hill, ed., *Brazil* (Berkeley, 1947); T. Lynn Smith and Alexander Marchant, eds., *Brazil: Portrait of Half a Continent* (New York, 1951).

2. On the Portuguese enterprises in the Orient see Edgar Prestage, *The Portuguese Pioneers* (London, 1933).

3. See Caio Prado, *op. cit.*, p. 33.

4. "The King of Portuguall gave this land to diverse of his gentlemen to inhabite." Lopes Vaz in Hakluyt, *Voyages*, VIII, 171.

5. Pero de Magalhaes, *The Histories of Brazil* (tr. from the Portuguese edition of 1576, New York, 1922), p. 33.

6. T. Lynn Smith, *op. cit.*, p. 134. According to John L. Strohm, *I Lived with Latin Americans* (Chicago, 1943), p. 26, less than four per cent of the land in Brazil is cultivated.

7. Richard Burton descended the São Francisco nearly a century ago. *Explorations of the Highlands of the Brazil* (2 vols., London, 1869), *passim*. There is a railhead at Pirapora in Minas, from which the river is navigable by low-draft boats as far as the cataract of Paulo Affonso in the state of Pernambuco. As part of a comprehensive plan for the development of the valley of the São Francisco, a hydroelectric plant is being installed at these falls.

8. See T. Lynn Smith, *op. cit.*, pp. 40, 297, 304.

9. On the Brazilian Negro in addition to the works of Gilberto Freyre, see Donald Pierson, *Negroes in Brazil: A Study of Race Contact in Bahia* (Chicago, 1942); and Arthur Ramos, *The Negro in Brazil* (tr. from the Portuguese, Washington, 1939).

10. Ulrich Schmidel, the German *Lanzknecht* who accompanied Mendoza's expedition in the initial founding of Buenos Aires and later participated in the occupation of Paraguay, passed through Ramalho's settlement on the Brazilian coast on his return to Germany. "We then went to a town," he wrote, "which belongs to the Christians and whose chief is called Joao Ramalho. This town is a real den of thieves. We were lucky that the chief was not in the town, but was away with other Christians from São Vicente, making one of the agreements that from time to time they make with each other." Schmidel said that Ramalho could assemble 50,000 Indians under his banner. He continued: "The sons of Joao Ramalho received us very well; nevertheless, we had more fears when we were among them than when we were among the Indians." *Viaje al Rio de la Plata* (tr. from the German, Buenos Aires, 1942), p. 101.

11. See Gilberto Freyre, "Some Aspects of the Social Development of Portuguese America," in Charles C. Griffin, ed., *Concerning Latin American Culture* (New York, 1940), p. 84; and Afranio Peixoto, *Breviario da Bahia* (Rio de Janeiro, 1945), p. 46.

12. On the plantation society of colonial Brazil, see Gilberto Freyre, *The Masters and the Slaves* (tr. from the Portuguese (*Casa Grande e Senzala*), (São Paulo, 1936). "The Portuguese established the first modern society in the tropics which

THE BRAZILIAN

developed national characteristics and qualities of permanency." Percy Alvin Martin, "Portugal in America," in *Hispanic American Historical Review,* XVII, no. 2, May, 1937.

13. William Dampier, the famous English navigator and part-time buccaneer, writes of the Portuguese governor whom he met in Bahia: "The Governour who resides here is call'd Don John de Lancastrio, being descended, as they say, from our English Lancaster Family; and he has a respect for our Nation on that Account, calling them his Country-men. I waited on him several times, and always found him very courteous and civil." *A Voyage to New Holland, &c. in the Year 1699* (3d ed., London, 1703) III, 35.

14. Maria Graham, who was in Brazil in the 1820's, found no bookstore in Recife, and, though there were two booksellers in Bahia, books were "extraordinarily dear." *Journal of a Voyage to Brazil, and Residence there, During Part of the Years 1821, 1822, 1823* (London, 1824), pp. 111, 138. Of Recife she said: "Here the very names of literature and science are almost unknown." Of Brazil in general she commented: "The state of general education is so low that more than common talent and desire of knowledge is requisite to attain any." *Ibid.,* p. 147.

15. "The Jesuits were unquestionably the founders of Brazilian culture." Samuel Putnam, *Marvelous Journey: A Survey of Four Centuries of Brazilian Writing* (New York, 1948), p. 43.

16. See Samuel Putnam, *Marvelous Journey: A Survey of Four Centuries of Brazilian Writing* (New York, 1948), pp. 30, 32; and Erico Verissimo, *Brazilian Literature, an Outline* (New York, 1945), p. 15.

17. On the history of Portugal, see Henry Morse Stephens, *The Story of Portugal* (New York, 1891), and H. V. Livermore, *A History of Portugal* (Cambridge, England, 1947). See also, Aubrey F. G. Bell, *Portugal of the Portuguese* (London, 1915). Gilberto Freyre says of the typical Portugal colonist in the sixteenth century, that he was "like a Spaniard, without his militant orthodoxy; like an Englishman, without his Puritan contours. He was daring, persistent, efficient, but seldom handicapped by inflexible principles, and thus more plastic than the Spaniard or the Englishman . . . notable for a certain power of adaptation and assimilation which set him apart from other Europeans of his time." "Some Aspects of the Social Development of Portuguese America" in Charles C. Griffin, ed., *Concerning Latin American Culture* (New York, 1940), p. 82.

18. Tavares de Sá characterizes these types in the following terms: *Nordestinos* —live mostly on past glories and the public payroll, often wind up on newspapers, glib talkers, quick, scintillating minds; *Mineiros*—love of proportion, unhurried, commonsensical; *Cariocas*—charming, witty, easygoing, volatile, cosmopolitan, given to subtle jokes (*malicia*), the Samba, and carnival; *Paulistas*—"magnificent rascals, hard-bitten, greedy, resilient, pertinacious, dynamic, earnest, hard-working, in a hurry." *Gauchos*—jovial, blustering, fight-loving, equestrian, Hernane Tavares de Sá, *"Brasileiros,"* in *Americas,* May, 1949.

19. See T. Lynn Smith, *op. cit.,* pp. 310-17, and Gilberto Freyre, *Brazil, op. cit.,* p. 83.

20. See Robert Bontine Cunninghame Graham, *A Brazilian Mystic: The Life and Miracles of Antonio Conselheiro* (New York, 1926). Antonio Conselheiro, was the protagonist of Euclydes da Cunha's classic week entitled *Os Sertões,* which was

translated by Samuel Putnam under the title *Rebellion in the Backlands* (Chicago, 1944).

21. On the Mineiros, see Alceu Amoroso Lima ("Tristao de Atahyde"), *Voz de Minas* (Rio de Janeiro, 1945).

22. See above, pp. 513-15.

23. "We are the Orientals of the West . . . [and] the Mineiro is the Oriental of Brazil." Alceu Amoroso Lima, *op. cit.,* p. 91.

24. "The Brazilians do not strike one as a new people." James Bryce, *South America: Observations and Impressions* (New York, 1916), p. 418. Bryce remarked that the Brazilians had less of "the first freshness of youth" than did the Argentines and Uruguayans. Samuel Putnam called the Brazilian nation "at once young and very old." *Op. cit.,* p. 18.

25. "The family attachments here are quite beautiful. They are as close and as intimate as those of clanship in Scotland." Maria Graham, *op. cit.,* p. 226. According to Mrs. Graham, the family feeling was so strong in Brazil that it precluded the formation of other relationships between persons. Roy Nash writes of a "feeling of family solidarity which includes the most distant relations, a kindliness towards the illegitimate child and its mother which is truly Christ-like; and atmosphere where children are very seldom abused or coerced; a paternal reverence which is beautiful even if sometimes undeserved." *Op. cit.,* p. 313. "In the mind of Brazilians the family is the supreme and most venerable unit." Tavares de Sá, *op. cit.,* p. 8. See also T. Lynn Smith, *op. cit.,* p. 633.

26. See Fernando de Azevedo, *A Cultura Brasileira* (Rio de Janeiro, 1943). This work has been translated into English and published as *Brazilian Culture: An Introduction to the Study of Culture in Brazil* (New York, 1950). It contains the most complete analysis of the Brazilian character and of its regional phases to be found anywhere.

27. "[A man] is valued as a personality, and his subsequent position, even if this is official depends very largely on whether his is a congenial character." Konrad Guenther, *A Naturalist in Brazil* (tr. from the German, Boston and New York, 1931), p. 359.

28. "We are not persuaded by force, by money, or by numbers, but we are highly responsive to kindness, courtesy, and suffering. Above will, intelligence, temperament, the Brazilian is a man of the heart. Our civilization rests less upon authority, or obedience, or philosophic principles, or social structures, or rigid traditions, or precise ideology, than upon the fragile and divine basis of friendship; and to friendship the people of Brazil, as individuals and as a nation, dedicate the best of our energies." Alceu Amoroso Lima, in *Tomorrow,* March, 1943, p. 36.

29. See above, p. 132.

30. Commenting on the Brazilian phrase, *"fazer minha independencia"* (to make my independence), Tavares de Sá says there is no equivalent in the language of Brazilians to the American expression, "to make money." "A Brazilian would be appalled by the idea that he would have to devote many years to making his independence, and he would never embark deliberately on a whole life of work, even if it were to bring him wealth; he is always trapped or tricked into it." *Op. cit.,* p. 137.

31. "I believe that the Brazilian code is mild and humane, and I am sure that it is humanely administered. The Brazilians have what I conceive to be a very

proper horror of taking life judicially. They do not shrink in battle; and sudden anger and jealousy will readily induce them to kill." William Lewis Herndon and Lardner Gibbon, *Exploration of the Valley of the Amazon* (2 vols., Washington, D. C., 1854), II, 340. Of conditions in Minas, Richard Burton wrote: "The ratio of crime to population is trifling . . . the law-loving, or rather the kindly though fiery character of the Mineiro is shown by the state of the police. With such and so small a repressive force, most European countries would be uninhabitable." *Op. cit.*, I, 403. "No viceroy of Brazil, no king, no emperor, no president, no bishop has been assassinated in the history of the country." Gilberto Freyre, *Brazil: An Interpretation*, p. 159.

32. Foreigners have always commented on the courtesy of the Brazilians. "Wherever I have met with Brazilians from the greatest to the meanest, I must say I have always experienced the greatest politeness." Maria Graham, *op. cit.*, p. 265. Of "the uniform courtesy extended to one and all," Konrad Guenther said: "This is a trait in which the Brazilian is incontestably superior to the European." *A Naturalist in Brazil* (tr. from the German, Boston and New York, 1931), p. 360. "A general courtesy rules amongst all classes and colours." Henry Walter Bates, *The Naturalist in the Amazons* (Everyman edition, 1910), p. 49. Bates spent eleven years in the Amazon Valley (1848–1859).

33. "Wit of the Cariocas: What Makes them Laugh in Brazil," See Erico Verissimo, in *Vogue,* July, 1946. Verissimo describes *malicia* as "a kind of archness—roguery, and the capacity of never taking persons, things and words at their face values, and of discovering always a double meaning in everything."

34. See Paulo Prado, *Retrato do Brasil: Ensaio Sobre a Tristeza Brasileira* (5th ed., São Paulo, 1944). The first sentence in Prado's book reads: "In a radiant land there dwells a sad people."

35. "[Brazilian] culture has been, and remains very largely to this day, a monopoly of the well-to-do and leisured class; and the same might be said of Latin American culture as a whole." Samuel Putnam, *op. cit.*, p. 45.

36. "Even today, probably more than two thirds of all Brazilians are illiterate," T. Lynn Smith, *op. cit.*, p. 665. Hernane Tavares de Sá said that in 1947 the illiteracy rate was at least one-third higher than the official estimate and that 3,000,000 children between the ages of seven and eleven had no schools to attend. *Op. cit.*, pp. 64-65.

37. Spix and Martius, the German scientists who were in Brazil during the years 1817–1820, commented on the predilection of the Brazilian intelligentsia of that period for French literature: *Viagem pelo Brasil* (tr. from the German, 3 vols., Rio de Janeiro, 1938), II, 103. On the decline of French cultural influence, see Tavares de Sá, *op. cit.*, p. 24.

38. On the literature of Brazil, see: Isaac Goldberg, *Brazilian Literature* (New York, 1922); Ronald de Carvalho, *Historia da Literatura Brasileira* (Rio de Janeiro); Erico Verissimo, *Brazilian Literature: An Outline* (tr. from the Portuguese, New York, 1945); Harriet de Onis, ed., *The Golden Land: An Anthology of Latin American Folklore in Literature* (New York, 1948); Samuel Putnam, *Marvelous Journey: A Survey of Four Centuries of Brazilian Writing* (New York, 1948); Arturo Torres Tioseco, *New World Literature: Tradition and Revolt in Latin America* (Berkeley and Los Angeles, 1949), *passim;* Pedro Henrique Ureña, *Literary Currents in Hispanic America* (Cambridge, Mass., 1945).

EPILOGUE

THERE ARE twenty nations in Latin America. For the present, all are republics, though in their brief careers three have been monarchies. They lean naturally to the republican form of government, even though democracy may not be of the essence of their political life.

Perhaps there should not be more than fourteen. For nationhood is a costly business, and the others cannot afford or justify the luxury of an independent and sovereign status. Six are in reality only provinces that go through the motions of being nations, and they serve no particular purpose beyond perpetuating an original error. If so desired, one of them might even become one of the great powers of the earth, but it has no interest in power for its own sake.

In spite of a certain reputation for turbulence, these twenty nations actually form the most peaceful international community in the world, and they have developed the most effective machinery of any group of states for settling their differences. Although there are surface bickerings and grudges and tensions, these are not old and deep-seated, like those of Europe, and nations manage to live together in remarkable harmony. Because, in an international sense, they are generally so well-behaved and have so little "nuisance value," we tend to ignore them for more contentious peoples who disturb our peace of mind. In what used to be known somewhat euphemistically as the "concert of nations," they play in tune and without discords.

Meanwhile, they are not impressed with the way the older countries manage the affairs of the world and tend to draw within themselves in self-protection. If they write their peaceful principles into their constitutions they have been sincere about it.

Their armed forces, relatively small as new-style mass armies go, are sometimes little more than praetorian bodies. As such, their role is probably more important as a decisive pressure group in the domestic politics of their country than as an instrumentality in foreign relations. In 1953, about half of the Latin American presidents were military men, at least half of whom had risen to power by the time-honored technique of the *coup d'état*. The fundamental weakness of some of these military establishments was demonstrated in the collapse of the regular Bolivian army in the internal disturbances of 1952. Its normal function as a substitute for the presidential electoral machinery of the country has been repeatedly exercised in some of the republics, most recently in the return of General Fulgencio Batista to power in Cuba and in the political overturn in Colombia in 1953. There is a tendency in the smaller republics about the Caribbean to eliminate the standing army altogether, or, at least, to reduce it to a small skeleton organization that could serve as a nucleus for national mobilization in the event of an international emergency. Instead, responsibility for the maintenance of internal order and for repelling any local invasion of the national territory is placed in a constabulary force or in the national police, which may be potentially a more formidable fighting force than the country's army.

These are transitional cultures. While they vary in the degree of their evolution, none of them has the air of completeness or finality that one might find in Europe or Asia. They are societies in the making, and at times one has the impression that the process has begun only lately. It is not only because, in a chronological sense, they are relatively young and have not yet had time to develop the bone-and-flesh structure of national maturity. It is mainly because the diverse ethnic elements which go into their making have not been amalgamated. One civilization has often to be compounded of two, or even three, or four different cultures. The formula of fusions runs: Spanish (or Portuguese), plus Indian (or Negro), or mestizo or mulatto, or any mixture thereof = the "new race." It may not be the "cosmic race" of which José Vasconcelos wrote, but the resultant will be a people unlike any of its separate ingredients.

Because they represent accumulated stresses in their relations with each other, the component cultures cannot exist indefinitely side by side in harmony, on one side or the other. The stresses are derived from memories of past wrongs, habits of rule, vested economic interests, revolutionary agitations. Meanwhile, in default of a democratic social system, acceptance of the equality which is a prerequisite to the harmonious coexistence of disparate cultures becomes impossible. Therefore, there cannot be a single

national conscience in any of these countries until the miscegenative process is completed, and the existing impediments to cultural unity disappear with their social causes. It is a radical solution, but in the long run it offers the only effective end to the
dilemma, as the Brazilians have recognized. If the pressures of
class conflict and international discord were not so acute as they
are today, another answer might be possible, short of tearing
down a house that has been thrown together by several builders
each with ideas of his own and rebuilding it of the same materials.
In the meantime, the biological preliminaries to the formation of
a single people in the mixed societies are nearly everywhere incomplete. Until that time, most of the national cultures are "split
personalities" and do not speak with one voice, but often at cross
purposes.

The level of mutual assimilation of the different racial elements in the population varies greatly from one country to another. The strength of the middle class, which serves as the major
catalytic agent in the process of social evolution, is in proportion
to the numbers of the white or the light mestizo segments of the
population. Where either predominates, as in Uruguay, there is
relative social peace and a sense of people having arrived in sight
of their national destiny, that is, of a civilization which satisfies
basic needs and aspirations. In spite of a lower standard of living
and a backward political situation, somewhat similar conditions
prevail among the long-mesticized inhabitants of Paraguay. In
Argentina, although the intrinsic quality of the population is
superior, it is split psychologically by a schism between the original Spanish element and the demands of the European newcomers
to the country. As a result, the so-called "typical Argentine" is
an unintegrated cross of two divergent personalities. The ultimate
national psyche of this promising people will be the product of
the reconciliation of the claims of both to a proper recognition of
their particular individualities. In Chile, the growing ascendancy
of a vital and intelligent middle class which draws its membership
both from above and below in the social scale of the traditional
hierarchy of classes offers the prospect of a peaceful evolution of
a well-balanced national society free of catastrophic stresses and
strains.

The evolutionary process is much more complicated in the

countries which have inherited a large Indian population. Here, an aristocratic form of society, based on the Indians' acceptance of white supremacy, has survived from colonial times. The middle class is still small and weak, and its members tend to be dependents of the ruling upper class. Where the Indians comprise a numerous and compact block of inhabitants and constitute the bulk of the population over a large area, they tend to be inert and resistant to any overtures or proposals for fuller incorporation into the national culture. In the meantime, their only concern is to be left to themselves and to adhere to the residuum of their own civilization which they have managed to salvage from the wreckage of their long-lost political independence.

In Bolivia the white leaven is too small and ineffectual, and its economic base is too precarious, for it to undertake the role which would normally fall to it in the process. A mestizo class, ill-prepared for responsibility by temperament and background and an Indian majority singularly detached from the influences of Western civilization are dominant factors in an apparently hopeless combination of circumstances.

The classical example of mixed nations is Peru. An aristocracy that has deep roots in the land and which is predominantly European in blood, though with a considerable admixture of superior mestizos, dominates the country and its life by force of immemorial habit, the absence or ineptness of any challenge to its authority, and the possession of certain national gift of command. Aloft, and aloof, in the Andes there lies the vast and inarticulate body of the disinherited heirs of the Inca Empire. In a social limbo between the two, the mestizo masses of the population move uneasily and restlessly, a prey to their own inferiority complexes and to the appeals of messiahs who have never dared think through their social gospels to the logical conclusions of the premises. The Indian wishes only to keep on being an Indian. It may be a long time before he will consent to become a full-fledged Peruvian citizen with such privileges and responsibilities as may be inherent in that status. However, so long as he is content to remain a passive element in the population, he would not be an impediment to any movement for the social and political advancement of the nation. For the near future, any such program of amelioration depends on a fuller utilization of the energies and intelligence of the mestizo class, even though it may involve curtailment of the power of the oligarchy in national affairs.

As becomes a people so given to extremes, the Mexicans have settled by the violence of armed revolution one fundamental phase of the question about the form their social system is eventually to take. The old oligarchy of landholders and place-holders lost its traditional position of supremacy which has been taken over by the new mestizo lords of Mexico, who have the greatest opportunity to demonstrate their capacity that has fallen to their class in the New World. Although the Indian was originally heralded as the chief beneficiary released from the peonage of the hacienda régime, he still remains a class apart in Mexico. There are many of his folk and of many separate peoples—Aztec, Zapotec, Maya, Tarascan, Otomí, and the little tribes, like the Yaqui. He keeps to himself, at least inwardly, as much as possible, and guards his counsel. His final place in the Mexican scheme has not yet been determined.

The problem of Brazil's future is complicated by the necessity for reconciling both regional facets of culture and the ethnic variety of its inhabitants. Not only are the ways of the Bahiano different in many respect from those of the Paulista or the Mineiro, but there is every conceivable mixture of the white, red, and black races, including a dash of the yellow. In the more rigid social structure of the Spanish countries, this combination of circumstances would present an almost impossible barrier to the creation of a true national consciousness and a unified cultural pattern.

The tolerant spirit and deep humanity of the Brazilian people; the general attitude of live and let live, even though a passive sentiment, grounded in indifference; an extraordinary mellowness and warmth in the closer personal relationships; a general distaste for extreme solutions; the old tradition of an easygoing patriarchal régime in the back country—all these traits of national character ease the normal tensions of community living and provide (in the absence of active good will and neighborliness) a propitious setting for the building of the eventual Brazilian society. In the slow process of assimilating the ingredients of a composite civilization, there is a disposition to accept differences of outlook and opinion and not to insist on uniformity, so long as the essentials which distinguish Brazilians from other peoples are observed. In the *granfino* or Brazilian variety of aristocrat, there is little snobbishness, and in the *caboclo* (countryman) there is no servility, so that there exists a real social democracy to cushion the tensions which are incidental to the inevitable class distinctions of any complex society. In the meantime, as an essential concomitant of the evolutionary operation, miscegenation flourishes without impediment of law or custom.

The destiny of Latin America, and of its twenty component pieces, will depend, in part, on factors other than the successful assimilation of the ethnic ingredients in the population. Some of the ingredients, like the Peruvian Indians, are not highly soluble. There are vested grudges, as well as vested interests, that are committed to the continuation of things as they are. Though the common Hispanic heritage is an equalizing solvent in the equation, its intensity is unequal as between the various republics. In the long run, a few of the national societies may crystallize into something more Indian in essence than European, even though the civilization may be dressed in European clothes. For whatever form or direction the "soul" of the mixed peoples may eventually take, the nations are, by reason of their location and the circumstances of their immediate past, affiliates of Toynbee's West.

The trend of their future is conditioned by economic and political facts and habits. Some of these factors are fixed in nature itself so that there is a limit to their possibilities of development. They may have to live poorly, because they do not possess the natural resources to live otherwise. Some, like the Chileans, will probably overcome their handicap by superior character. Others are favored lands, with much bounty, both agricultural and mineral, for their people to draw on for a surplus of the things that make a "good life" and its cultural accessories.

In making the most of what they have, whether it be much or little, their governments will have to display more wisdom in economic policies than they have in the past. In a world whose parts are still interdependent, they will have to forgo their dreams of autarchy, unless they are resigned to the fabrication of hermetical poorhouses of countries that do not have the makings of self-sufficiency. They are too ready to yield to the cry for economic nationalism and state socialism to indulge in five-year plans for the industrialization of economies that are basically primitive and extractive, in a defiance of whatever economic laws are still in force and in the acrobatics of a premature welfare state. Their countries cannot afford an elaborate program of bonuses and favors to the populace without the risk of wrecking economies that have not yet accumulated reserves of capital for even elementary expansion. Only a few favored countries can allow themselves the luxury of these privileges of a mature and well-ordered society.

The progress of Latin America toward her well-deserved destination is still impeded by the survival of bad political habits. By its own high standards, as exemplified in the writings of its political philosophers and in the principles of its national constitutions, much of Latin America has not yet grown up politically. To arrive within sight of the goals set by its own ideals, it needs the extension of the kind of political democracy which prevails in Uruguay, and the end of a system that permits the capricious suppression of civil liberties, the Clodian demagoguery that is all too common nowadays, and the acceptance of the *cuartelazo*, or barrack revolt, as a normal device for changing governments.

If the Latin American peoples have many problems to solve before they can become what they would like to be, so, for our part, do we. Therefore, it would ill become us to be patronizing toward those who share with us in amity and a growing understanding the New World and its responsibilities for the future. Rather do we sincerely desire that those peoples shall realize in full measure the great promise that is in them.

INDEX

INDEX

Abipones, Indians of Argentina, 44

Acosta, José de, Jesuit priest, author of *The Natural and Moral History of the Indies,* comments on Chile, 6

Acuña, Cristóbal de, missionary-explorer in Amazon Valley, 17

Agassiz, J. L. and Elizabeth C., travellers in Amazon Valley, 17

Aguirre, Francisco de, conqueror of Chile, 114, 145-146, 285, 307

Aguirre, Lope de, renegade Spanish soldier, crimes, 116, 296

Aldana, Lorenzo de, conqueror of Peru, 113, 140

Aleijadinho (Antonio Francisco Lisboa), Brazilian architect-sculptor, 173, 367

Alencar, José de, Brazilian novelist, 62

Alessandri, Arturo, President of Chile, 230

Alamagro, Diego de, conqueror of Peru, civil war with the Pizarros, 9, 140; father of Almagro "el Niño," 64; execution, 113, 161; origin, 116; qualities of leadership, 118, 142; relations with Indians, 121; expedition into Chile, 139; city builder, 341

Alvarado, Alonso de, conqueror of Peru, 113, 139, 140

Alvarado, Diego de, conqueror of Peru, 113

Alvarado, Pedro de, lieutenant of Cortès and conqueror of Guatemala, origin, 116, 126; financing of conquests, 125; as military leader, 137; knightly personality, 141; marriages, 291; Indian mistress, 304

Amazon, river, 7, 16-25, 39, 66, 68, 229, 389; valley, 19-21, 139

amazons, Indian women warriors, 277, 278

Ambato, Ecuador, earthquake, 28

Anacaona, female chieftain of the Tainos, killed by the Spaniards, 293

anarchism, as an aberration of Spanish individualism, 94

Anchieta, José de, Jesuit missionary in early Brazil, 7, 163, 392

Andalusians, on Peruvian coast, 9, 85; character, 87-89; importance in conquest, 127

Andes, mountains, 7, 8-9, 25, 32

Animals, llama, 8; animals of the pampa, 12, 13, 39; animals of Amazon jungle, 22-24; in Brazilian folklore, 393

Anonymous Conqueror," "The, author of early work on Mexico, 5, 277

Apristas, member of political sect in Peru, 67

Aragón, and the Aragonese character, 86

Araucanians, Chilean Indians of the Tehualche race, tribal organization, 43; fighting qualities, 44, 51; adoption of Spanish military tactics, 45, 113; mixture with Spaniards, 63; leaders, 132

Arawak, Indian race in West Indies and northern South America, 37

architecture, 40, 42, 43, 48, 173, 366-370

Arequipa, Peru, 10, 26, 28

Argentina, the Gaucho and the Pampa, 11-14; expulsion of Indians from the pampa, 66; English invasions, 217; attitude towards foreigners, 232; cities, 358; rivalry of capital and provinces, 360; racial character, 376, 410 (see also "Buenos Aires")

Arica, Chile, earthquake, 29

Asturias, Spanish province, inhabitants, 8, 85, 87

Asuncion, Paraguay, original settlement, 63, 112, 298-299; secondary center of conquest, 143; early colonial society, 148; slowness of change in republican period, 354; population, 358

Atahualpa, Inca emperor, executed by Spaniards, 48, 123, 131

Atienza, Inéz de, murder by Lope de Aguirre, 295-296

Ayolas, Juan de, conqueror of Paraguay, 113

417

Rodríguez, Isabel, Spanish woman in conquest of Mexico, 288

Rogers, Woodes, English privateering captain, privateering voyage, 216; comments on Spanish priest, 262-263; capture of Guayaquil, 317

Rondón, Cándido Mariano da Silva, Brazilian explorer and head of the Indian Service, 17, 68

Roosevelt, Theodore, travels in interior of Brazil, 17

Saenz, Manuela, mistress of Simón Bolivar, 103, 321-323

Sahagún, Bernardino de, Spanish priest and writer on Indian culture of Mexico, 57, 281

Sandoval, Gonzalo de, lieutenant of Cortés in conquest of Mexico, 113, 137

San Salvador, 10

Santa Cruz de la Sierra, city in eastern Bolivia, 63, 354, 388

Santa Fé, Argentine city, 63

Santarem, town in the Amazon valley, 19

Santiago, Chile, 10, 31, 161, 203

Santo Domingo, revolt of slaves against French, 176

São Paulo, state and city, topography of state, 11; attitude of people towards Negroes, 175; architecture of city, 366, 367; character of city, 376-378; character of people (Paulistas), 396

Sarmiento, Domingo Faustino, Argentine president and writer, comments on: "barbarism" of the Pampa, 13, 234, 309, 360; slave-holding religious orders, 165

Schmidel, Ulrich, German soldier in conquest of River Plate region, 223, 300-302

schools, 57, 253, 256, 307

Scotch, colonies in Latin America, 227, 229, 230

Seneca, Lucius, Spanish-Roman philosopher of the Stoic school, 82

Serra, Junipero, Franciscan missionary in early California, 260

Sevilla, Andalusian city, 88, 162, 211, 287

siesta, custom in Latin America, 312-313

Siete Partidas, early Spanish legal code, 181

slavery, Indian, 54

slavery, Negro, 151, 161 ff, 362, 390

smoking, addiction of colonial Spanish women to, 313

Soto, Hernando de, Spanish conqueror and explorer, 110, 113, 118, 125, 140, 294

Spain, physical environment, 3-4, antipathy to life in Andes, 8, 9; Spanish settlers on Argentine Pampa, 13; aversion to living in jungle, 17-18; the Spanish character and influence on Latin American civilization, 78-103; heroism and fortitude of Spanish soldiers, 119; treatment of Indians, 120-122; Spanish attitude toward foreigners, 198-199; *Hispanidad,* 233; Spanish women in the conquest, 282-299; urban character of civilization, 339-340

Spanish Main, north coast of South America (Tierra Firme), 143, 177, 293

Spix, Johan Baptist von, and Carl Friedrich Philip von Martius, German scientists, author of work on Brazil, 17

Spratling, William, interest in development of Mexican handicrafts, 47

Squier, E. G., American writer on Peru, 349

Staden, Hans, German soldier in colonial Brazil, 7, 224

Stephens, John L., American traveller and author of works on Central America and southern Mexico, 264

Stevenson, William B., English resident in early 19th century Peru, 28, 178, 250, 314, 319

Suárez, Inés, mistress of Pedro de Valdivia, conqueror of Chile, 145, 285

suffrage, female, constitutional provisions regarding, 329-330

Swiss, colony in Argentina, 230

Tainos, West Indian branch of the Arawak race, 37, 44, 51, 54, 284, 293

Tarascans, Indians of western Mexico, 48

Tehuelches, Indians of Argentina and Chile, 14

Teixeira, Pedro, Portuguese explorer of the Amazon valley, 17, 388

Tenochtitlán. See Mexico City

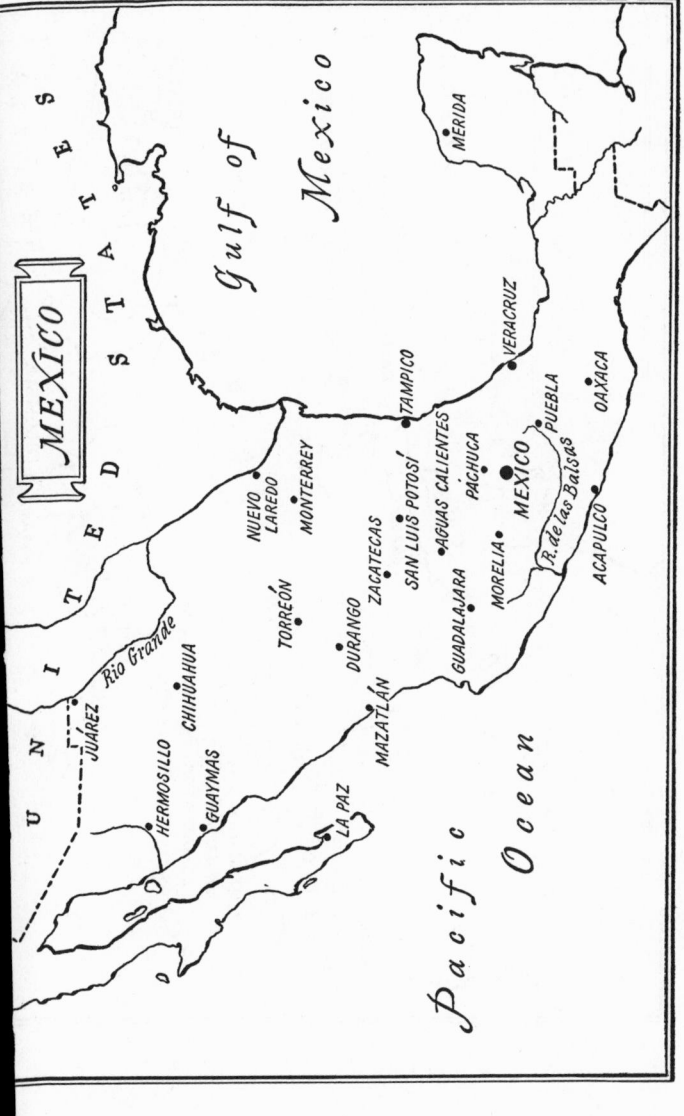

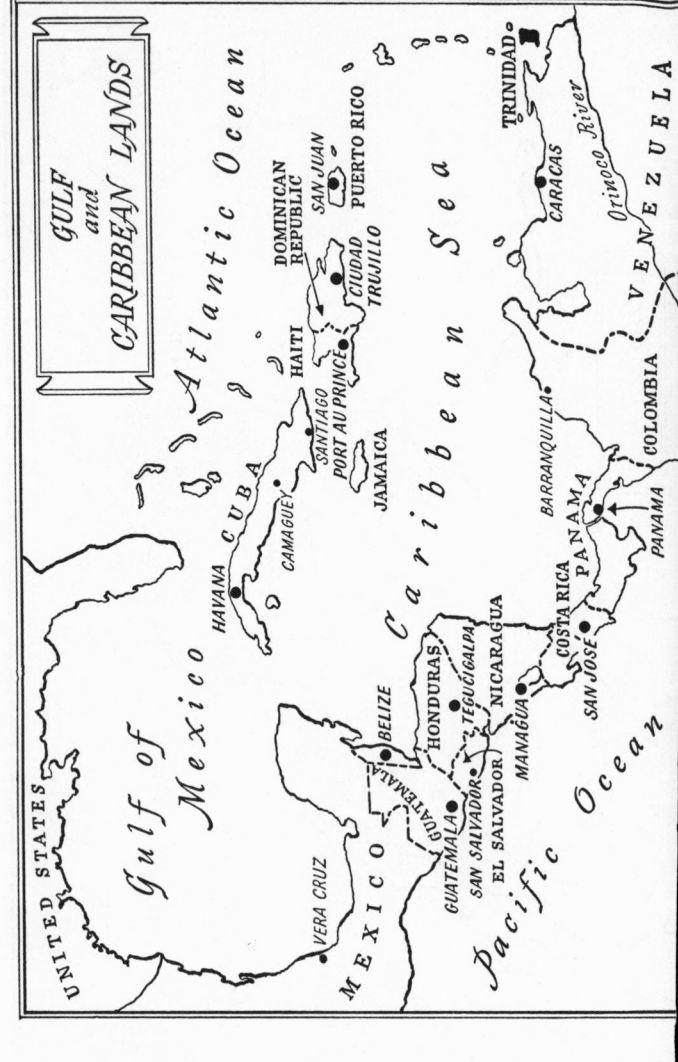

GULF
and
CARIBBEAN LANDS

NORTHWESTERN SOUTH AMERICA

BRAZIL

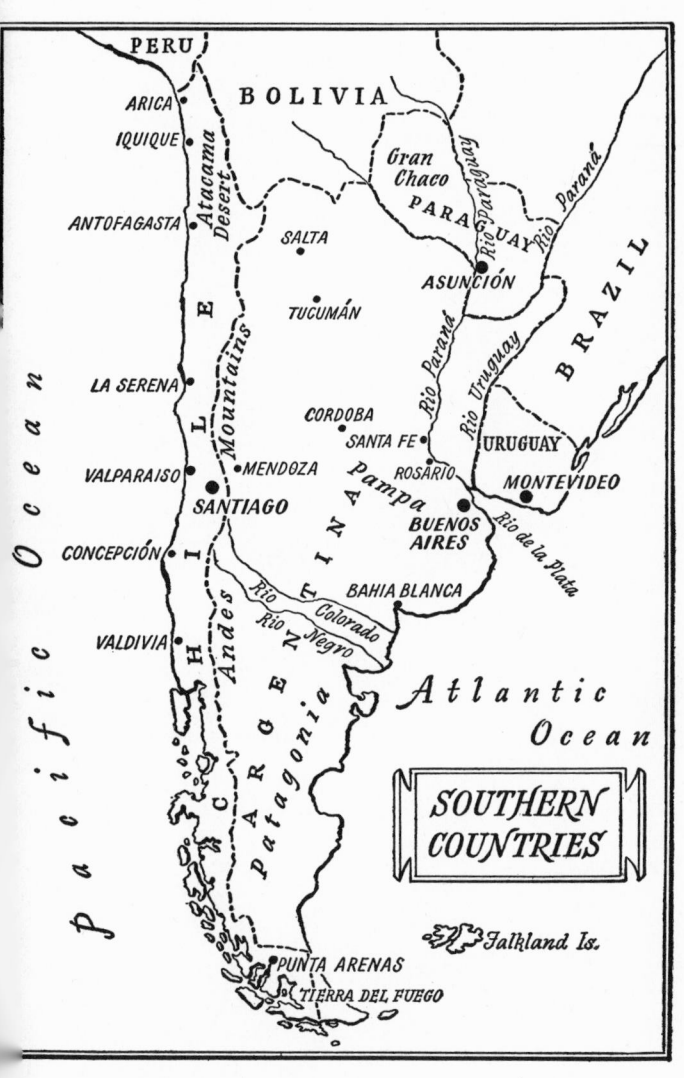

SOUTHERN COUNTRIES